MODAL LOGICS

CETTE COLLECTION EST DIVISÉE EN DEUX SÉRIES :

A. Monographies réunies par Mme P. Février (Paris).

B. Monographies réunies par R. Feys † et M. J. Dopp (Louvain).

Série A

I. *Les fondements logiques des mathématiques,* par M. E. W. Beth.

II. *Leçons de logique algébrique,* par M. Haskell B. Curry.

III. *Pages choisies d'analyse générale,* par M. M.Fréchet.

IV. *Les systèmes axiomatiques de la théorie des ensembles,* par MM. Hao Wang et Robert Mc Naughton.

V. *Applications scientifiques de la logique mathématique.* (Actes du 2e Colloque international de Logique Mathématique. Paris, août 1952).

VI. *Axiomatique intuitionniste sans négation de la géométrie projective,* par Melle N. Dequoy.

VII. *Deux esquisses de logique,* par M. J. Barkley Rosser.

VIII. *Théorie mathématique des idéaux,* par M. Abraham Robinson.

IX. *Les fondements des mathématiques. Intuitionisme. Théorie de la démonstration,* par M. A. Heyting.

X. *L'existence en mathématiques,* par M. E. W. Beth.

XI. *La structure algébrique des théories mathématiques,* par M. L. Henkin.

XII. *La crise de la raison et la logique,* par M. E. W. Beth.

XIII. *Initiation à la logique,* par le R.P. Dubarle.

XIV. *Logique mathématique appliquée,* par M. H. Freudenthal.

XV. *Les structures de commutation à* m *valeurs et les calculatrices numériques,* par M. J. Gazalé.

XVI. *Introduction à la logique,* par M. Alfred Tarski.

XVII. *Fonctions récursives,* par M. Andrej Grzegorczyk.

Série B

I. *Théorie des probabilités. Exposés sur les fondements et ses applications,* par MM. Gillis, von Mises, Ballieu, Van Dantzig, Coutrez, Bouckaert, Prigogine, Campus, Fauville, Fréchet, Hirsch.

II. *Les limitations internes des formalismes. Étude sur la signification du théorème de Gödel et des théorèmes apparentés dans la théorie des fondements des mathématiques,* par M. J. Ladrière.

III. *Logiques construites par une méthode de déduction naturelle,* par M. J. Dopp.

IV. *Modal Logics,* by Robert Feys. Edited with some complements by Joseph Dopp.

COLLECTION DE LOGIQUE MATHÉMATIQUE
SÉRIE B
MONOGRAPHIES RÉUNIES PAR M. J. DOPP (LOUVAIN)

IV

ROBERT FEYS

MODAL LOGICS

EDITED WITH SOME COMPLEMENTS BY

JOSEPH DOPP

PUBLISHED WITH SUPPORT OF THE FONDATION UNIVERSITAIRE DE BELGIQUE

LOUVAIN
E. NAUWELAERTS
ÉDITEUR
2, Place Cardinal Mercier, 2

PARIS
GAUTHIER-VILLARS
ÉDITEUR
55, Quai des Grands-Augustins, 55

1965

EDITOR'S FOREWORD

In 1948, on the occasion of the tenth International Congress of Philosophy at Amsterdam, Robert Feys proposed to his colleague and friend J. C. C. McKinsey the composition of a treatise of *Modal Logics*. The work was to comprise two parts, from which Feys was to draw up the first, McKinsey the second. The treatise was intended to be published under the names of both authors in the collection: *Studies in Logic and the Foundations of Mathematics* of the North-Holland Publishing Company.

The general idea was to consacrate the first part to a systematic exposition of the numerous modal systems elaborated in published writings, by ordering them around the systems of Lewis-Langford (which Feys considered in a certain sense as «classic» or «normal»). The exposition was to be limited to the formal aspects, to what Feys liked to call «the technique» of modal logic. The second part was to deal with metatheoretical questions and also with problems of interpretation and of philosophical plausibility. In Feys' mind, these last problems could only be approached after the first and in function of the formal results established previously.

We publish here the text of a manuscript note found among Feys's papers and which contains one of the first projects for the plan of the work. Here is the literal tenor of this document:

I. THE SYSTEMS (Feys making first draft).

§ 1. Short review of the notations, axioms, theses of the two-valued calculus.
§ 2. History of modality.
As a conclusion: notions, notations, chief problems raised.
§ 3. S 5. Axiomatic starting from the propositional calculus.
Possibility of representing by the class calculus.
Chief theses of strict-implication-propositional calculus (for demonstrations, see Lewis-Langford; heuristically one could refer to representation by class-calculus).
Hence the Lewis axiomatic for S 5.
§ 4. S 4. (Propositional calculus)
(and intermediary systems between S 4 and S 5 ?)
§ 5. S 3, S 2, S 1. (Propositional calculus)
The principal Parry reductions, with demonstration of $(\Box\Diamond)^2 p \leftrightarrow (\Box\Diamond)p$.
§ 6. Functional calculus (and possibility of class calculus).
§ 7. Identity, and Quine's paradox.

II. (Comparisons) REPRESENTATIONS AND INTERPRETATIONS (McKinsey making first draft).

§ 8. Representation by functional calculus and classes (summarily mentioned § 3). MacColl and older logical algebraists. Wajsberg.
§ 9. Matrices.
§ 10. Independence. — Decision problem and other analogous problems, v.g. completeness.
(The reduction theorems should be treated in part I).
§ 11. Gödel representation. (In § 9, or elsewhere, connection with Jaskowski).
§ 12. Topology.
§ 13. Modalities and polyvalent logics (Łukasiewicz, Moisil, Destouches).
§ 14. Possible syntactic interpretations.
§ 15. Conclusion. The Ghost of modality ?

In the course of the years 1948 to 1953 (year wherein occurred the death of McKinsey), Feys repeatedly reworked the part which had fallen to him, «McKinsey acting as advisor». One of these editions was even mimeographed and sent to several different colleagues, who referred to it at times in their writings under the title: FEYS-MCKINSEY, *Modal Logics I.*

As for the second part, which McKinsey was to do, only a few fragments seem to have been drawn up.

After the death of McKinsey, Feys had in mind several collaborators to complete the work begun, but no agreement was reached.

Little by little he came to the idea that the complete work was to comprise three volumes. And so, in May 1959, the general plan appeared to him as follows:

Volume I. — Theory

A. General introduction and comparison between the modal logics and the first order predicate logic.
B. The systems of Lewis-Langford's *Symbolic Logic* (whose modal part must be set «up to date».)
C. Logic of predicates and of identity.

Volume II. — Syntax and Algebra

A. The methods of natural deduction: Curry, Fitch and multiple special studies (Ridder and others).
B. Complete character of the systems and methods of decision.
C. Modal logics in their relations with intuitionism and topology (some notes would be able to be devoted to systems not mentioned in Volume I.)

Volume III. — Semantics and Interpretations

A. Semantics. Especially Carnap's study and Quine's objection to the possibility of a satisfactory semantic interpretation of the modalities.
B. Interpretations. This part was to resume the plan drawn up by von Wright. (*Essay*). Epistemic interpretations (attach to these that of Carnap).
Deontic interpretations.
Possibility of physical interpretations.

Later on, for lack of collaborators to draw up the other two volumes of this plan, Feys conceived the idea of publishing the first part independently. A few months before his death, he had begun a new revision of his manuscript, and was working to integrate with it certain expositions which, in the plan of 1959, were destined to form part of the second volume.

On the 13th of april 1961, this work was interrupted by death.

The work, which we publish here is substantially the manuscript left by Feys. The editor merely proceeded to a coordination of the references and to unessential stylistic modifications.

The editor, however, added to Feys's text a small number of new paragraphs relating to the studies which could be connected without too much contrivance to the plan of the work; some of these works were known by Feys, others were published after his death. All these passages, for which the editor bears sole responsibility, are signaled by the presence of an asterisk preceding the number of the paragraph.

Feys did not leave any bibliography intended to accompany his publication. The editor thought he might render some service to the world of logicians by composing a bibliography in the perspective of Feys' work.

This bibliography thus is centered on the formal aspects of the systems of modal logic, but it enlarges upon works of which Feys did not intend to speak, because he considered them as somewhat «aberrant» in relation with the «classical» systems of Lewis-Langford. More, the bibliography is brought up to the present moment.

It also mentions a few important works for the problems of interpretation or of acceptability, concerning among others the theory of entailment and of diverse forms of rigorous implications (other than the strict implication of Lewis), the intuitionist or plurivalent logics, the epistemic, the deontic, the physical interpretations.

The choice made among these last works is naturally rather arbitrary.

J. DOPP

CONTENTS

CHAPTER I

INTRODUCTION TO MODAL PROPOSITIONAL LOGIC

CHAPTER II

FORMAL SYSTEMS OF MODAL PROPOSITIONAL LOGIC

CHAPTER III

MODAL FUNCTIONAL LOGIC

* APPENDIX

CHAPTER I

INTRODUCTION TO MODAL PROPOSITIONAL LOGIC

SECTION 0 - HISTORICAL SKETCH

§ 01 - MODALITIES IN ARISTOTLE

In the sense in which the word is usually taken in this book a logic is *modal* and uses *modalities* if it does not only consider affirmations and negations but also what we might call strong affirmations or negations such as «This is necessarily true», «This is necessarily false», «This object necessarily possesses that quality», and weak affirmations and negations such as «This is possibly true», «This is possibly false», «This object possibly possesses that quality».

Modalities were introduced into logic by Aristotle, who regularly considers propositions of this kind. Although the interest of Aristotle in modal propositions was connected with his philosophical point of view, the treatment of modalities in Aristotle's works is purely logical, without admixture of philosophical presuppositions. Some rules of opposition and of deduction about modalities are given or used implicitely by him. It does not seem, however, that he uses all designations of modalities in a fixed technical sense; e.g. «possible» is interpreted rather variously, according to the various intuitive senses of the word, sometimes as «this is not necessarily false», more often as «this is neither necessarily true nor necessarily false» (in this sense «*p* is possible» would be the same as «non-*p* is possible»).

It must be remembered that Aristotle nowhere builds up a logic of propositions apart from his logic of classes; what he tries to settle is a table of oppositions and a syllogistic with modal universal and modal particular propositions. According to A. Becker he does not interpret such a modal proposition as a universal or a particular proposition affected by the modality «necessary» or «possibly» (as what has been termed later a «*modalis de dicto*»), but as something that so far has not been studied ex professo in modern logic, as a universal or particular proposition linking together «modal concepts», e.g. «that which has the property *a* necessarily has the property *b*», «that which is possibly an *a* possibly has the property *b*» (such propositions being nearly what medieval logic called «*modales de re*»). But Aristotle seems to have here also a somewhat fluctuating intuitive sense of his modal propositions.

§ 02 - MODALITIES IN TRADITIONAL LOGIC

02.1 - So far as we can ascertain from the fragments we have from them, Theophrastus and Eudemos (reflecting perhaps the later teaching of Aristotle himself) resume Aristotle's doctrine of modalities, with some tendency towards formalization, in this sense that their deductions are less based upon the usual and somewhat indeterminate sense of the words, and more upon a clearly defined terminology and upon rules of operations. «Possibility» is defined as «non-impossibility» and the modal propositions are considered as *modales de dicto* — which allows deduction conforming to the rule that «the conclusion has always the modality of the weakest premise».

02.2 - It is generally admitted that Stoics, consistently with their deterministic point of view, left no room for modalities in their logic. But modalities remained part of the «classical» logic, and they were usually presented just as Theophrastus and Eudemos did it. We may here leave aside the question to know how much some commentators on Aristotle remained faithful to his intuitive conceptions rather than to the «classical» point of view.

02.3 - Since our purpose is not historical and since the subject remains insufficiently explored, we shall not dwell at length upon the studies devoted by the Scholastics to modal logic.

02.4 - No use for the non-formalized concepts of modalities was found in the modern description of the physical world. Although the doctrine of modalities remained taught in modern classical logic, it remained there as a kind of *caput mortuum.*

§ 03 - LOGICAL ALGEBRA IN THE XIXth CENTURY

When a logical algebra was built up in the 19th Century, it would have been rather natural that the calculus of propositions be conceived in it as a modal one. For the starting-point of the whole construction was an algebra of classes, classes being, as wel known, properties of individuals, or, if taken extensively, sets of individuals to which a given property may be applied. The properties «non-*a*», «*a* and *b*», «*a* or *b*», were taken intuitively as the properties «not applicable to the individuals of the set *a*», «applicable to the individuals of the set *a* and (or) of the set *b*». The proposition «That which is *a* is *b*», meant that every individual of the set *a* is an individual of the set *b*.

The calculus of propositions, now, was formulated by means of analogy to this calculus of classes. Propositions were conceived as applicable to (verified in) various «cases», «circumstances», «moments of time», «states of affairs». From that point on, the analogy followed so closely that both calculi might be considered as two interpretations of one and the same algebra. Then propositions as «not-*p*», «*p* and *q*», «*p* or *q*» were to be conceived respectively as propositions applicable to those cases where *p* would not be verified, where *p* and (or) *q* would be verified. An implication was a proposition asserting that all cases in which *p* is verified are also cases in which *q* is verified.

But the lack of interest for modalities at that moment was such that this obvious *modal* interpretation, involving a *plurality* of cases, remained barely indicated. When these writers come to propositional calculus, then supplementary axioms are at once introduced to state at least the «two-valuedness» of the calculus, amounting to the supposition that there is but one case, the «real case», and that so only two possibilities are left open for a proposition; the set of cases to which it may be applied is either formed by the unique real case — and then the proposition is true — otherwise it is vacuous — and then the proposition is false.

The consideration of cases in which propositions are to be verified, leaving open the possibility of a plurality of such cases, will help us in the following §2 to build up heuristically a model of modal logic, but we shall not take 'model' as the older logical algebraists took it. For a logic of «classes of cases» — if it is not reduced by the supplementary axioms to a non-modal logic, — becomes something that has never been developed, namely a *purely modal logic*, a logic in which no propositions may be asserted except modal propositions. In our modal logic a purely assertoric proposition («*p* is true») will have sense as well as a modal one («*p* is necessary», «*p* is possible»).

§ 04 - THE LEWIS'S SYSTEMS

Except for studies by Mac Coll, modalities remained neglected untill the studies of Lewis, embodied in *A Survey of Symbolic Logic* (1917) and in *Symbolic Logic*, written in collaboration with Langford (1932). These may be said

1° to have formalized the system of classical modalities,

2° to have done so with some special purpose, viz. to build up a theory of «strict implication»,

3° to have originated the distinction between different systems of modal logic.

04.1 - The main features of the Lewis's calculi are modelled after those of the formalized logic of *Principia Mathematica*. Hence

(a) they start with a modal propositional calculus — in fact modal functional calculus is not treated, except for a rough sketch in the *Survey*;

(b) they are formulated with notations differing only typographically from those used in the present work;
(c) they are deduced axiomatically after the example of the *Principia.*

04.2 - It has to be stressed that Lewis had a particular purpose nowhere present in the works of earlier logicians. These, in so far as they had in mind to apply their theory, used modalities to express ontological concepts, to distinguish between necessary laws and contingent reality or factual data, to evoke a realm of possibility contrasted with that of factual reality, and so on; the idea of logical necessity is rather seldom mentioned here and there in Aristotle.

Lewis's idea is to distinguish between connectives endowed with logical necessity and other without necessity of that kind — especially to oppose to the «material implication» of the *Principia* a necessary or «strict» implication, whose logical laws would be better in accordance with the concept of «implication» as a relation justifiying deducibility.

That purpose had a technical consequence: as strict implication was meant to play the role material implication had played in the *Principia,* the axioms were analogues to these of the *Principia,* but with strict implication instead of material implication. That was a new way of building up a theory of modalities and it led to new results.

04.3 - We spoke of distinct Lewis's calculi. Lewis tried different axiomatizations, and that of the *Survey* (the system later named 'S3') was finally found stronger than that of *Symbolic Logic* (S2). One subsystem of S2 was distinguished as 'S1'; and the other systems were defined subsequently.

§ 05 - FURTHER DEVELOPMENTS

During the last 20 years there has been a lively activity in the field of modal logic, manifested by quite a number of monographs devoted to the subject. Let us leave aside for the moment the question of interpretation. The technical developments have been carried out in three directions.

05.1 - First quite a wealth of different modal systems were defined. We mentioned already S1, S2, S3 and subsystems.

But a new kind of research started when O. Becker tried to make clear by a formalism a fact known of old. Classical theory of modalities devotes all its attention to the modalities of truth, necessity, possibility and to their negations. But what of «superposed» modalities, as «necessarily-necessary», «necessarily-possible» or even superpositions of more than two modalities ? A formalized theory may not neglect them simply on the ground that, intuitively, they seem somewhat odd, but one may try to state axioms so as to «reduce» modalities to a certain number or to modalities of a certain kind.

If we state an axiom which reduces any complex modality to one of the six simplest modalities — which makes any superposed modality equivalent to a modality without superposition — we have the system that has been called 'S5'. But some weaker reductions can be devised; in the most obvious one, repeated necessity or repeated possibility is equivalent to simple necessity or possibility; this is the system called 'S4'.

Further research was stimulated by the proof (Mc Kinsey) that in S2 there is an infinity of non-equivalent superpositions of modalities and by the somewhat startling result of Parry that in the apparently harmless system S3 there are just 42 distinct simple or superposed modalities.

Between the main systems very numerous systems — at some points an infinity of them — may be intercalated; the implications and non-implications of modalities have been determined in them, and so on. Other extensions of the modal systems, e.g. specifying the non-emptiness of some classes of propositions, have been stated.

05.2 - The works of Lewis were devoted, as the *Principia* are, to the demonstration of a series of special theorems. Here as in other fields of logic interest has turned more recently to general problems. The decision problem has been solved, not only for the comparatively simple S5, but also for S2 and S4 (McKinsey). For the solution of this and related problems and of others a technique of matrices has been developed.

§ 06 - INTERPRETATION

Modal logic has thus become a highly developed branch of formalized logic. But the question of its interpretation remains open and comes to the foreground.

06.1 - The most obvious interpretation remains that intended by Lewis, identifying necessity with «logical necessity», which can be characterized syntactically. An extensive study by Carnap, using S5, tries to bring these notions together. Another syntactical interpretation, this time in S4 and starting with possibility, has been put forward (McKinsey). No interpretation of that kind has been reached for systems weaker than S4.

06.2 - A very interesting translation of intuitionistic logic by means of S4 has been biven by Gödel; here modality is shown to be helpfull to clarify some difficult logical concepts.

A topological interpretation of modality indicated by Tang Tsao-Cheng has been developed (McKinsey - Tarski); here modality might show its utility as a tool for mathematics.

06.3 - Another question might be the use of modalities for the description of the physical world. Recent lively discussions upon descriptions in modal logic have served rather to present some curious questions than to solve any problems. But, besides, modality might perhaps be used in the analysis of causality.

SECTION 1 - NOTATIONS. RECAPITULATION OF NON-MODAL CALCULUS

§ 10 NOTATIONS

10.1 - In a non-modal (or assertoric) propositional calculus (APC) we write '*p*', '*q*', '*r*', '*s*', for propositional variables, '$\sim$' for negation, '$\wedge$' for conjunction, '$\vee$' for alternation, '$\rightarrow$' for (material) implication, '$\leftrightarrow$' for (material) equivalence.

10.2 - In modal propositional calculus we write '$\Box$' for necessity, '$\Diamond$' for possibility, '$\Rightarrow$' for strict implication ,'$\Leftrightarrow$' for strict equivalence.

10.3 - In predicate-calculus or functional calculus, assertoric (AFC) or modal, we use '*x*', '*y*', '*z*', ... for individual variables, '**A***x*' to express «for all *x*», '**E***x*' to express «for some *x*».

10.4 - Well-formed expressions built up from the preceding symbols will be called «formulas». Instead of «well formed» we simply use «formula».

10.5 - The principal (or main) symbol of an expression will be the operational symbol (if any) containing all other symbols under its scope.

Formulas having '$\rightarrow$', '$\leftrightarrow$', '$\Rightarrow$' or '$\Leftrightarrow$' as their principal symbol will be called «hypotheticals».

10.6 - We write '*P*', '*Q*', '*R*', '*S*', as a syntactical denotation for a formula. We write '$\sim P$', '$P \vee Q$' as syntactical denotations for the negation of a formula, the alternative of two formulas, and similarly with other operational symbols.

10.7 - We use round brackets for parentheses, square brackets for stronger parentheses, and braces for even stronger parentheses.

10.8 - We write '$\sim\ \sim p$' instead of '$\sim(\sim p)$', '$\Diamond \sim p$' instead of '$\Diamond(\sim p)$', '$\Diamond p \wedge \sim q$' instead of '$(\Diamond p) \wedge (\sim q)$', and so on.

10.9 - We prefix '$\vdash$' to a formula valid in the system considered or to a schema of formula supposed to be valid in a rule of deduction.

§ 11 - CRITERION FOR VALIDITY OF FORMULAS IN APC

We admit the following well-known criterion of validity for formulas in APC.

11.1 - Formulas may just have two «truth-values», «true» and «false». They are true or false; they may not be true and false together.

Hence it is intuitively clear that there are $2^2=4$ combinations of values for a formula mentioning 2 different propositional variables, and in general 2^n combinations of values for a formula mentioning n different propositional variables.

11.2 - «Truth-functions» are formulas which have a determined truth value for each combination of truth-values of the propositional variables; «*p* is false» is a truth-function, because «*p* is false» has the value «true» whenever *p* is false and the value «false» whenever *p* is true. «I believe *p*» is not a truth-function, because the truth or falsity of the assertion «I believe *p*» is not settled by the fact that *p* is true or false.

11.3 - Only truth-functions are admitted in APC. In particular:
$\sim P$ is true when P is false and false when P is true;
$P \wedge Q$ is true when both P and Q are true, and false otherwise (i.e. when P is true and Q false, or P false and Q true, or P and Q both false);
$P \vee Q$ is false when P and Q are both false, and true otherwise;
$P \rightarrow Q$ is false when P is true and Q false and true otherwise (this amounts to interpret «$P \rightarrow Q$» as the affirmation that P is not true without Q being so);
$P \leftrightarrow Q$ is true when P and Q have the same value and false if not so.

If we write '1' for the value «true» and '0' for the value

«false», this may be summed up obviously in following «truth-tables» for negation ($\sim$), conjunction ($\wedge$), alternation ($\vee$), (material) implication ($\rightarrow$), (material) equivalence ($\leftrightarrow$):

P	$\sim P$
1	0
0	1

$\wedge$	1	0
1	1	0
0	0	0

$\vee$	1	0
1	1	1
0	1	0

$\rightarrow$	1	0
1	1	0
0	1	1

$\leftrightarrow$	1	0
1	1	0
0	0	1

11.4 - Using these tables, we may determine the value of any formula whatever of APC for all possible values of the variables.

Let us consider the formula $(p \rightarrow q) \leftrightarrow (\sim q \rightarrow \sim p)$. To build up this formula, we build up $p \rightarrow q$, $\sim q$, $\sim p$, then $\sim q \rightarrow \sim p$ by means of these last, finally the whole formula by means of $p \rightarrow q$ and of $\sim q \rightarrow \sim p$.

Clearly we have 4 combinations of values for p and q:

for p	1	1	0	0
for q	1	0	1	0

The corresponding values are:

for $p \rightarrow q$	1	0	1	1
for $\sim q$	0	1	0	1
for $\sim p$	0	0	1	1
for $\sim q \rightarrow \sim p$	1	0	1	1
for the whole formula ...	1	1	1	1

This may be summarized obviously in the following table:

$$
\begin{array}{ccccccccc}
(p & \rightarrow & q) & \leftrightarrow & (\sim & q & \rightarrow & \sim & p) \\
1 & 1 & 1 & 1 & 0 & 1 & 1 & 0 & 1 \\
1 & 0 & 0 & 1 & 1 & 0 & 0 & 0 & 1 \\
0 & 1 & 1 & 1 & 0 & 1 & 1 & 1 & 0 \\
0 & 1 & 0 & 1 & 1 & 0 & 1 & 1 & 0
\end{array}
$$

We give a table also for the formula $(p \wedge q) \leftrightarrow (\sim q \wedge \sim p)$:

$(p \wedge q)$	$\leftrightarrow$	$(\sim q \wedge \sim p)$
1 1 1	0	0 1 0 0 1
1 0 0	1	1 0 0 0 1
0 0 1	1	0 1 0 1 0
0 0 0	0	1 0 1 1 0

11.5 - We call a formula «valid» if and only if it has the value 1 (true) for each combination of the values of its propositional variables.

Hence the formula $(p \rightarrow q) \leftrightarrow (\sim q \rightarrow \sim p)$ is valid,
and the formula $(p \wedge q) \leftrightarrow (\sim q \wedge \sim p)$ is not valid.

§ 12 - LIST OF VALID FORMULAS IN APC

We call «**a**-formulas» ('**a**'standing for «assertoric propositional calculus» or «APC») all formulas valid in APC. We give here a list of the **a**-formulas which are most important for comparison with the theorems of modal propositional calculus; the validity of all these **a**-theorems can be checked by means of the criterion just given.

Formulas listed here in § 12 will be numbered '12.*x*' ('*x*' being the decimal part of the number) or more simply '**a***x*' ('**a**' is thus, in this case, short for '12.').

If a formula of the form $P \leftrightarrow Q$ is numbered '*y*', we number '*y*′' the formula $P \leftrightarrow Q$, and '*y*″' the formula $Q \rightarrow P$. (As will appear later in 14.32, if the formula *y* is valid, the formulas *y*′ and *y*″ are valid.)

Listed **a**-formulas may be divided into three groups, as follows: We call «*component*» of a formula a *proper part* of that formula which is also a formula.

In formulas of the first group (**a**0, **a**1, **a**2) no component is a hypothetical.

In formulas of the second group (**a**3, **a**4, **a**5) some components, but no component of a component, are hypotheticals.

In formulas of the third group (**a**6, **a**7) some components of components are hypotheticals.

Group 1

a0 - *Identity-principle and formulas about negation*

a00 - $\vdash$ $p \leftrightarrow p$ *Identity-principle*
a01 - $\vdash$ $\sim\sim p \leftrightarrow p$ *Negation of a negation*
a02 - $\vdash$ $\sim(p \wedge q) \leftrightarrow (\sim p \vee \sim q)$ *Negation of a conjunction*
a021 - $\vdash$ $(p \wedge q) \leftrightarrow \sim(\sim p \vee \sim q)$
a03 - $\vdash$ $\sim(p \vee q) \leftrightarrow (\sim p \wedge \sim q)$ *Negation of an alternation*
a031 - $\vdash$ $(p \vee q) \leftrightarrow \sim(\sim p \wedge \sim q)$
a05 - $\vdash$ $\sim(p \wedge \sim p)$ *Principium contradictionis*
a055 - $\vdash$ $(q \wedge \sim q) \rightarrow p$
a06 - $\vdash$ $p \vee \sim p$ *Tertium exclusum*
a065 - $\vdash$ $p \rightarrow (q \vee \sim q)$

a1 - *Theorems about conjunction*

a10 - $\vdash$ $(p \wedge q) \rightarrow p$
a101 - $\vdash$ $(p \wedge q) \rightarrow q$
a11 - $\vdash$ $(p \wedge q) \leftrightarrow (q \wedge p)$ *Commutativity of* $\wedge$
a12 - $\vdash$ $[p \wedge (q \wedge r)] \leftrightarrow [(p \wedge q) \wedge r]$ *Associativity of* $\vee$
We write '$p \vee q \vee r$' instead of '$[(p \vee q) \vee r]$'.
a13 - $\vdash$ $[p \wedge (q \vee r)] \leftrightarrow [(p \wedge q) \vee (p \wedge r)]$ *Distributivity of* $\wedge$ *with respect to* $\vee$
a14 - $\vdash$ $p \leftrightarrow (p \wedge p)$ *Idempotence of* $\wedge$
a15 - $\vdash$ $p \leftrightarrow [p \wedge (p \vee q)]$
a16 - $\vdash$ $p \leftrightarrow [p \wedge (q \vee \sim q)]$

a2 - *Theorems about alternation*

a20 - $\vdash$ $p \rightarrow (p \vee q)$
a201 - $\vdash$ $q \rightarrow (p \vee q)$
a21 - $\vdash$ $(p \vee q) \leftrightarrow (q \vee p)$ *Commutativity of* $\vee$
a22 - $\vdash$ $[p \vee (q \vee r)] \leftrightarrow [(p \vee q) \vee r]$ *Associativity of* $\vee$
We write '$p \vee q \vee r$' instead of '$[(p \vee q) \vee r]$'.
a23 - $\vdash$ $[p \vee (q \wedge r)] \leftrightarrow [(p \vee q) \wedge (p \vee r)]$ *Distributivity of* $\vee$ *with respect to* $\wedge$
a24 - $\vdash$ $p \leftrightarrow (p \vee p)$ *Idempotence of* $\vee$

a25 - $\vdash$ $p \leftrightarrow [p \vee (p \wedge q)]$
a26 - $\vdash$ $p \leftrightarrow [p \vee (q \wedge \sim q)]$

Group 2

a3 - *Theorems about implication*

a31 - $\vdash$ $(p \rightarrow q) \leftrightarrow (\sim q \rightarrow \sim p)$ *Contraposition*
a311 - $\vdash$ $(p \rightarrow \sim q) \leftrightarrow (q \rightarrow \sim p)$
a312 - $\vdash$ $(\sim p \rightarrow q) \leftrightarrow (\sim q \rightarrow p)$
a32 - $\vdash$ $[(p \wedge q) \rightarrow r] \leftrightarrow [(p \wedge \sim r) \rightarrow \sim q]$ *Antilogism*
a321 - $\vdash$ $[(p \wedge q) \rightarrow r] \leftrightarrow [(q \wedge \sim r) \rightarrow \sim p]$
a381 - $\vdash$ $(p \rightarrow q) \rightarrow [(r \wedge p) \rightarrow (r \wedge q)]$ *Factor-theorems*
a383 - $\vdash$ $(p \rightarrow q) \rightarrow [(r \vee p) \rightarrow (r \vee q)]$

a4 - *Theorems about equivalence*

a41 - $\vdash$ $(p \leftrightarrow q) \leftrightarrow (q \leftrightarrow p)$
a42 - $\vdash$ $(p \leftrightarrow q) \leftrightarrow (\sim p \leftrightarrow \sim q)$
a431 - $\vdash$ $(p \leftrightarrow q) \rightarrow (p \rightarrow q)$
a432 - $\vdash$ $(p \leftrightarrow q) \rightarrow (q \rightarrow p)$
a44 - $\vdash$ $(p \rightarrow q) \leftrightarrow [p \leftrightarrow (p \wedge q)]$
a441 - $\vdash$ $(p \rightarrow q) \leftrightarrow [p \rightarrow (p \wedge q)]$
a45 - $\vdash$ $(p \rightarrow q) \leftrightarrow [(p \vee q) \leftrightarrow q]$
a451 - $\vdash$ $(p \rightarrow q) \leftrightarrow [(p \vee q) \rightarrow q]$
a481 - $\vdash$ $(p \leftrightarrow q) \rightarrow [(p \wedge r) \leftrightarrow (q \wedge r)]$
a482 - $\vdash$ $(p \leftrightarrow q) \rightarrow [(p \vee r) \leftrightarrow (q \vee r)]$

a5 - *«Paradoxical» theorems about hypotheticals*

a501 - $\vdash$ $(p \rightarrow q) \leftrightarrow (\sim p \vee q)$
a502 - $\vdash$ $\sim (p \rightarrow q) \leftrightarrow (p \wedge \sim q)$
a503 - $\vdash$ $(p \rightarrow q) \leftrightarrow \sim (p \wedge \sim q)$
a511 - $\vdash$ $q \rightarrow (p \rightarrow q)$

a512 - $\vdash$ $\sim p \to (p \to q)$
a521 - $\vdash$ $(p \wedge q) \to (p \leftrightarrow q)$
a522 - $\vdash$ $(\sim p \wedge \sim q) \to (p \leftrightarrow q)$
a531 - $\vdash$ $p \leftrightarrow (\sim p \to p)$
a532 - $\vdash$ $\sim p \leftrightarrow (p \to \sim p)$
a541 - $\vdash$ $(p \to q) \vee (q \to p)$
a542 - $\vdash$ $(p \to q) \vee (p \to \sim q)$

Group 3

Here we may distinguish three subgroups:
A. (**a6**) One component is a conjunction or an alternative of propositions, one of which at least is a hypothetical.
B. (**a7**) One component is a hypothetical of propositions, one of which at least is a hypothetical.
C. (**a8**) One component is the negation of a hypothetical.

a6 - *Syllogism and composition*

Modus ponens and modus tollens.
a61 - $\vdash$ $[p \wedge (p \to q)] \to q$
a611 - $\vdash$ $[\sim q \wedge (p \to q)] \to \sim p$
a612 - $\vdash$ $\{p \wedge [(p \wedge r) \to q]\} \to (r \to q)$

Full syllogism.
a62 - $\vdash$ $[(p \to q) \wedge (q \to r)] \to (p \to r)$
a621 - $\vdash$ $[(q \to r) \wedge (p \to q)] \to (p \to r)$
a623 - $\vdash$ $[(p \leftrightarrow q) \wedge (q \leftrightarrow r)] \to (p \leftrightarrow r)$
a625 - $\vdash$ $\{(p \to q) \wedge [(q \wedge s) \to r]\} \to [(p \wedge s) \to r]$
a63 - $\vdash$ $[(p \to q) \wedge (q \to r) \wedge (r \to s)] \to (p \to s)$

Composition of a conjunction.
a651 - $\vdash$ $[(p \to q) \wedge (p \to s)] \leftrightarrow [(p \to (q \wedge s)]$
a655 - $\vdash$ $[(p \to q) \wedge (r \to q)] \leftrightarrow [(p \vee r) \to q]$
a661 - $\vdash$ $[(p \to q) \wedge (r \to s)] \leftrightarrow [(p \wedge r) \to (q \wedge s)]$
a665 - $\vdash$ $[(p \to q) \wedge (r \to s)] \leftrightarrow [(p \vee r) \to (q \vee s)]$

Composition of an alternative.

a67 - $\vdash$ $[(p \to q) \vee (p \to s)] \leftrightarrow [p \to (q \vee s)]$

a675 - $\vdash$ $[(p \to q) \vee (r \to q)] \leftrightarrow [(p \wedge r) \to q]$

Equivalence as a conjunction of implications.

a68 - $\vdash$ $[(p \to q) \wedge (q \to p)] \leftrightarrow (p \leftrightarrow q)$

Proof «ab absurdo» and dilemma.

a69 - $\vdash$ $[(p \to q) \wedge (p \to \sim q)] \leftrightarrow \sim p$

a695 - $\vdash$ $[(p \to q) \wedge (\sim p \to q)] \leftrightarrow q$

a696 - $\vdash$ $\{[(p \wedge q) \to r] \wedge [(p \wedge \sim q) \to r]\} \to (p \to r)$

a7 - *Exportation-importation theorems*

The principle.

a70 - $\vdash$ $[(p \wedge q) \to r] \leftrightarrow [p \to (q \to r)]$

a705 - $\vdash$ $[p \to (q \to r)] \leftrightarrow [q \to (p \to r)]$

«Exported» analogues of theorems **a6**.

All formulas **a6** of the form $(P \wedge Q) \to R$ have an *exported analogue* of the form $P \to [Q \to R]$.

The numbers of the exported analogues are the same as these of the corresponding formulas **a6**, except that their decimal part begins with '7'. So we have e.g.

a72 - $\vdash$ $(p \to q) \to [(q \to r) \to (p \to r)]$

a79 - $\vdash$ $(p \to q) \to [(p \to \sim q) \to \sim p]$

a8 - *Negations of conditionals*

a81 - $\vdash$ $\sim (p \to q) \leftrightarrow (p \wedge \sim q)$

a82 - $\vdash$ $\sim (p \to q) \to (p \to \sim q)$

a83 - $\vdash$ $\sim (p \leftrightarrow q) \leftrightarrow [(p \wedge \sim q) \vee (\sim p \wedge q)]$

a84 - $\vdash$ $\sim (p \leftrightarrow q) \leftrightarrow [(p \vee q) \wedge (\sim p \vee \sim q)]$

§ 13 - POSTULATES FOR APC

We mention for later references the axiom-system of Russell-Bernays for APC as appearing in Hilbert-Ackermann.

13.1 - *Axioms* (primitive propositions) are:
13.11 - $\vdash$ $(p \vee p) \rightarrow p$ (= **a24″**)
13.12 - $\vdash$ $p \rightarrow (p \vee q)$ (= **a20**)
13.13 - $\vdash$ $(p \vee q) \rightarrow (q \vee p)$ (= **a21′**)
13.14 - $\vdash$ $(p \rightarrow q) \rightarrow [(r \vee p) \rightarrow (r \vee q)]$ (= **a383**)

13.2 - According to the *rule of substitution,* a provable formula remains provable if a formula is substituted everywhere in it for a propositional variable.

Formulas are defined recursively as follows:
1⁰ - Propositional variables are formulas
2⁰ - if P, Q, are formulas, then $\sim P$, $P \wedge Q$, $P \vee Q$, $P \rightarrow Q$, $P \leftrightarrow Q$, are formulas.

13.3 - We have the *rule of detachment for* '$\rightarrow$':
If P is provable and if $P \rightarrow Q$ is provable then Q is provable. (As we abbreviate «P is provable» to «$\vdash P$», the rule becomes: If $\vdash P$ and if $\vdash P \rightarrow Q$, then $\vdash Q$.)

13.4 - The *definitions* will be:
13.41 - '$P \wedge Q$' for '$\sim(\sim P \vee \sim Q)$',
13.42 - '$P \rightarrow Q$' for '$\sim P \vee Q$',
13.43 - '$P \leftrightarrow Q$' for '$(P \rightarrow Q) \wedge (Q \rightarrow P)$'.

§ 14 - DERIVATIONS

All theorems listed in §12 and, in general, all theorems verifiable by means of the method of §11, can be derived from the set of postulates we have just stated. We do not give the derivation, which can be found in Hilbert-Ackermann. Our purpose was simply to state the postulates for further comparison, and now we still want to explain our notation of the proofs (according to which demonstrations will be carried out in §18) and to give a few derived rules — again for further comparison.

14.1 - When we carry out the proof of a theorem we shall proceed «step by step», each step being ordinarily mentioned on a different line.

Each step will start from a *theorem* (one of the axioms or a theorem proved and numbered before, or a lemma enunciated and numbered on a preceding line of the proof). If the theorem is not the one written on the preceding line, its number will be mentioned at the end of the line (ordinarily preceded by 'From').

Each step is made by virtue of a *rule* (primitive as in 14.2, derived as in 14.3) or of a *definition.*

The number of the rule or definition is indicated at the right of the line, or replaced by one of the abbreviations given below. When the rules used are obvious, their mention may be omitted or several «steps» may be compressed into one.

The last line is the theorem to be demonstrated; it is stated explicitly or abridged as 'Th'.

14.2 - The use of *primitive rules* or *definitions* will be mentioned as follows:

14.21 - The use of the rule of substitution might be mentioned 'By rule 13.2' —

So: (1) $\vdash\ (p\to q)\to[(\ r\vee p)\to(\ r\vee q)]$ 13.14

(2) $\vdash\ (p\to q)\to[(\sim r\vee p)\to(\sim r\vee q)]$ By rule 13.2

The use of this rule will ordinarily be left tacit or indicated only by «subst», written immediately after the number of the theorem in which the substitution is made. E.g.

$\vdash\ (p\to q)\to[(\sim r\vee p)\to(\sim r\vee q)]$ 13.14 subst.

14.22 - The use of the rule of detachment will be indicated 'By rule 13.3'.

Let us suppose we have proved **a**10 and **a**70′, and we want to prove $\vdash p\to(q\to p)$ from them.

(1) $\vdash\ [(p\wedge q)\to p]\to[p\to(q\to p)]$ **a**70′ subst

(2) $\vdash\ (p\wedge q)\to p$ **a**10

(3) $\vdash\ p\to(q\to p)$ From (1) and (2) by rule 13.3.

Ordinarily the use of 13.3 will be left tacit.

14.23 - The use of a definition numbered 'x' will be referred to by means of 'By df x'.

Let us prove $\vdash (p \to q) \to [(r \to p) \to (r \to q)]$.

(1) $\vdash (p \to q) \to [(\sim r \vee p) \to (\sim r \vee q)]$ 13.14 subst

(2) $\vdash$ Th By df 13.42

14.3 - Demonstrations might be carried out using only primitive rules (and definitions); to avoid trivial and tedious developments, use will be made of *derived rules,* some examples of which follow.

14.31 - Let us suppose we have demonstrated **a**06 $\vdash p \vee \sim p$. Almost instinctively it will be admitted that, «by virtue of 13.13», $\vdash (p \vee q) \leftrightarrow (q \vee p)$, we may conclude from **a**06 to $\vdash \sim p \vee p$.

If this is to be justified by primitive rules, we have:

(1) $\vdash p \vee \sim p$ **a**06

(2) $\vdash (p \vee \sim p) \to (\sim p \vee p)$ 13.13 subst

(3) $\vdash \sim p \vee p$ From (1) and (2) by rule 13.3

In general, if we have a theorem $\vdash R \to S$, let R', S' be expressions obtained by replacing all propositional variables in R and S by the corresponding capitals, then the derivation just given yields the same conclusion as a rule: «If $\vdash R'$, then $\vdash S'$».

If z is the number of the theorem $\vdash R \to S$, the use of such a rule will be indicated by the mention 'By z'.

And the demonstration given above will be abbreviated to:

(1) $\vdash p \vee \sim p$ **a**06

(2) $\vdash \sim p \vee p$ By 13.13

14.32 - In particular if a formula y of the form $P \leftrightarrow Q$ is valid, then, by **a**431, the formula y' is valid. And by **a**432, the formula y'' is valid. (For the notations 'y'' and 'y''', see § 12, p. 11).

14.4 - We may demonstrate other rules of deduction, the most general form of which is «If $\vdash$ ..., then $\vdash$ ...», following a pattern quite similar to that of §14.31.

Here our demonstration will start from the *hypothesis* of the rule of deduction or of the various hypotheses, introduced successively.

Intermediate steps will be «schemata» and will be justified by rules or definitions.

The conclusion will be the conclusion of the rule to be demonstrated.

Let us prove this way the rule:

If $\vdash P \rightarrow Q$ and if $\vdash R \rightarrow P$, then $\vdash R \rightarrow Q$.

(1)	$\vdash P \rightarrow Q$	14.23 (as a schema which may be indicated by '14.23 subst')
(2)	$\vdash (P \rightarrow Q) \rightarrow [(R \rightarrow P) \rightarrow (R \rightarrow Q)]$	By hp (= By hypothesis)
(3)	$\vdash (R \rightarrow P) \rightarrow (R \rightarrow Q)$	From (1) and (2) by rule 13.3
(4)	$\vdash R \rightarrow P$	By hp.
(5)	$\vdash R \rightarrow Q$	From (3) and (4) by rule 13.3

14.5 - In particular, from the set of postulates in §13, one can prove the rule of *replacement* (of material equivalents):

If P is provable and $Q \leftrightarrow R$ is provable, and if S results from P by replacing Q by R, or R by Q at one or more places, then S is provable.

§ 15 - MATRICES

15.1 - The method of verification explained in §11 may be stated in terms of what is called a *matrix*.

(a) The *values* of the matrix are 1 and 0.

(b) 1 is called the *designated value*.

(c) Negation and alternation are characterized by means of the *tables* given for them in §11.3.

(d) Then, by means of the definitions §13.4, tables of values can be derived for conjunction and equivalence, and these are the same as in §11.3.

15.2 - The criterion of validity worked out in §12 may be summed up as follows: A formula is valid if it has the designated value for every set of values of the propositional variables.

15.3 - The matrix described in §15.1 was only a very special example of a matrix. In general, to build up a matrix, it suffices:

(a) to determine a (finite or infinite) set of possible *values* of propositions;

(b) to take some of these as «designated values» for which a proposition is valid;

(c) to characterize fundamental functions of propositions (by means of which the other functions may be defined or constructed) by the table of their values for the possible sets of values of the variables.

Moreover, in the example 15.1, the values and functions had an intuitive sense, viz. «true», «negation», «alternation», which is usually attached to these terms in APC. But we may and frequently shall use matrices without any intuitive sense attached beforehand to their values and functions.

15.4 - In §15.2 we used a matrix to decide if, yes or no, a given formula was valid in a system (was derivable from a given set of axioms). To make the demonstration rigorous we should have had to demonstrate:

1°/ That every axiom and every formula derived from the axioms — here the axioms 13.1 and the propositions derived from them by 13.2 - 13.3 - 13.4 — satisfy the matrix.

2°/ That only the axioms or formulas derived from them satisfy the matrix.

In the future we shall not use matrices to show that a given formula is derivable from given axioms, but only that a given formula *cannot* be derived from given axioms. For that purpose it suffices to prove the 1° above and then to show that the given formula does not satisfy the matrix.

Let us e.g. show that the axiom 13.12 $\vdash p \rightarrow (p \vee q)$ cannot be derived from the other axioms of §13 (is independent of the other axioms).

We build up the following matrix:

(a) Values: 0, 1, 2, 3.
(b) Designated values: 0, 2.

(c)

P	$\sim P$
0	1
1	0
2	3
3	2

$\vee$	0	1	2	3
0	0	0	0	0
1	0	1	1	1
2	0	1	2	2
3	0	1	2	3

$\rightarrow$	0	1	2	3
0	0	1	1	1
1	0	0	0	0
2	0	1	2	3
3	0	1	2	2

It may be shown: 1°) that axioms 13.11-13-14 have always a designated value 0 or 2, 2°) that designated values are preserved in every formula derived according to rules 13.2-3 and to definitions 13.4.

Now if $p=2$ (if p has the value 2) and if $q=1$, then $p \rightarrow (p \vee q)$ has the value 1, not a designated value, therefore it cannot be derived from the other axioms.

15.5 - A proof of non-contradiction of a set of axioms is analogous to a proof of independence, because the set is non-contradictory if it is impossible to derive from it a formula P and its negation $\sim P$.

We show e.g. that the axiom-set of § 13 is non-contradictory, using the matrix 15.1.

It may be shown, as in 15.4 1°), that all axioms 13.1 have the designated value 1, 2°) that the designated values are preserved in all formulas derived according to 13.2-3-4.

Now if a formula P is valid, it has value 1, and then $\sim P$ has value 0, thus $\sim P$ is non-valid.

§ 16 - POSTULATES FOR THE ASSERTORIC FUNCTIONAL CALCULUS OF THE FIRST ORDER AF¹C

We consider here only the functional calculus of first order (i.e., the calculus of predicates of individuals). The theorems of this calculus may be derived from various sets of axioms;

for our purpose we find it best to use that of Quines' *Mathematical Logic* (with definitions 16.51-52 added) (1).

16.0 - We define «free» and «bound» as usual. We allow well-formed expressions such as '**AXEX** *P*', admitting that the quantifier '**AX**' applies to '**EX** *P*' in which '*X*' is a bound variable.

16.1 - The axioms, rules and definitions 13 of APC are also axioms, rules, definitions of AF^1C.

16.2 - *Rule of generalisation*: If $\vdash P$, then $\vdash$ **AX** *P*.

16.3 - *Proper axioms* (expressed as schemata):
16.31 - $\vdash$ **AX**$(P \to Q) \to ($**AX** $P \to$ **AX** $Q)$.
16.32 - If *X* is not free in *P*, then $\vdash P \to$ **AX** *P*.
16.33 - Let $(x/y)P$ be result of substituting '*Y*' for every free occurrence of '*X*' in '*P*', then if '*Y*' is not bound in '*P*' at a place where '*X*' is free, $\vdash$ **AX** $P \to (x/y)P$.
16.34 - $\vdash$ **AX** **AY** $P \to$ **AY** **AX** *P*,
or a rule dispensing with that axiom.

16.4 - Rules of substitution are not needed with axiom-schemata.

16.5 - *Definitions*:
16.51 - '**EX** *P*' for '$\sim$**AX**$\sim P$',
16.52 - '$P \underset{X}{\to} Q$' for '**AX**$(P \to Q)$',
16.53 - '$P \underset{X}{\leftrightarrow} Q$' for '**AX**$(P \leftrightarrow Q)$'.

---

(1) In §16 and §17 we consider AF^1C in its outmost generality. It will therefore be convenient not to state axioms or theorems, but schemata of axioms and theorems, where '*P*', '*Q*', '*R*' will be denominations for any kind of propositions, unless determined otherwise.

In §18 it will become opportune to deal with a special kind of «atomic» propositions, these containing '*x*' as a free variable; so in §18 '*p*', '*q*', '*r*' ... will be used only to represent propositions with '*x*' as free variable, and we shall generally state theorems, and not schemata of theorems.

§ 17 - PRINCIPAL THEOREMS AND DERIVED RULES PROPER TO AF¹C

These well-known theorems (written as schemata) and rules are here stated without demonstration.

17.0 - *Negation.*

17.01 - $\vdash$ $\sim \mathbf{AX}\, P \leftrightarrow \mathbf{EX} \sim P$

17.011 - $\vdash$ $\mathbf{AX}\, P \leftrightarrow \sim \mathbf{EX} \sim P$

17.02 - $\vdash$ $\sim \mathbf{EX}\, P \leftrightarrow \mathbf{AX} \sim P$

17.021 - $\vdash$ $\mathbf{EX}\, P \leftrightarrow \sim \mathbf{AX} \sim P$

17.1 - *Subordination* ('*Y*' not being bound in '*P*' at a place where '*X*' is free)

17.11 - $\vdash$ $\mathbf{AX}\, P \rightarrow (Y/X)P$ (= 16.33)

17.12 - $\vdash$ $(Y/X)\, P \rightarrow \mathbf{EX}\, P$

17.13 - $\vdash$ $\mathbf{AX}\, P \rightarrow \mathbf{EX}\, P$

17.2 - *Distribution of quantifiers with respect to* $\wedge$ *and* $\vee$.

17.21 - $\vdash$ $\mathbf{AX}(P \wedge Q) \leftrightarrow (\mathbf{AX}\, P \wedge \mathbf{AX}\, Q)$

17.22 - $\vdash$ $(\mathbf{AX}\, P \vee \mathbf{AX}\, Q) \rightarrow \mathbf{AX}(P \vee Q)$

17.23 - $\vdash$ $\mathbf{EX}(P \vee Q) \leftrightarrow (\mathbf{EX}\, P \vee \mathbf{EX}\, Q)$

17.24 - $\vdash$ $\mathbf{EX}(P \wedge Q) \rightarrow (\mathbf{EX}\, P \wedge \mathbf{EX}\, Q)$

17.241 - $\vdash$ $\mathbf{EX}(P \wedge Q) \rightarrow \mathbf{EX}\, P$

17.3 - *Distribution of quantifiers with respect to* $\rightarrow$ *and* $\leftrightarrow$.

17.31 - $\vdash$ $\mathbf{AX}(P \rightarrow Q) \rightarrow (\mathbf{AX}\, P \rightarrow \mathbf{AX}\, Q)$ (= 16.31)

17.315 - $\vdash$ $[\mathbf{AX}(P \rightarrow Q) \wedge \mathbf{AX}\, P] \rightarrow \mathbf{AX}\, Q$

17.32 - $\vdash$ $\mathbf{AX}(P \rightarrow Q) \rightarrow (\mathbf{EX}\, P \rightarrow \mathbf{EX}\, Q)$

17.325 - $\vdash$ $[\mathbf{AX}(P \rightarrow Q) \wedge \mathbf{EX}\, P] \rightarrow \mathbf{EX}\, Q$

17.33 - $\vdash$ $\mathbf{AX}(P \leftrightarrow Q) \rightarrow (\mathbf{AX}\, P \leftrightarrow \mathbf{AX}\, Q)$

17.34 - $\vdash$ $\mathbf{AX}(P \leftrightarrow Q) \rightarrow (\mathbf{EX}\, P \leftrightarrow \mathbf{EX}\, Q)$

17.4 - *Rules of deduction.*

17.41 - $\vdash$ If $\vdash \mathbf{AX}(P \rightarrow Q)$, then $\vdash \mathbf{AX}\, P \rightarrow \mathbf{AX}\, Q$.

17.42 - $\vdash$ If $\vdash \mathbf{AX}(P \rightarrow Q)$, then $\vdash \mathbf{EX}\, P \rightarrow \mathbf{EX}\, Q$.

17.43 - ⊢ If ⊢**A**X(*P*↔Q), then ⊢**A**X *P* ↔ **A**X Q.
17.44 - ⊢ If ⊢**A**X(*P*↔Q), then ⊢**E**X *P* ↔ **E**X Q.

§ **18** - REPLACEMENT OF MATERIAL BY FORMAL CONNECTIVES IN MONADIC AF¹C

18.0 - For our purpose it will be useful to consider a particular problem about a particular form of AF¹C.

18.00 - We shall consider only the *monadic* predicate-calculus, corresponding to ordinary class-calculus, and so, here in §18, we shall never have to use more than one free variable '*x*' for individuals.

18.01 - We consider no other atomic formulas than formulas where '*x*' is a free variable (formulas «about the variable '*x*'»).

18.02 - We put the question: Is it possible, in the formulas and rules stated before, to replace «material» connectives by «formal» ones, '$\underset{x}{\rightarrow}$' and '$\underset{x}{\leftrightarrow}$', and so to preserve validity ?

We say that the transformation may be carried out *fully* when a formula or rule preserves its validity when every '→' is replaced by '$\underset{x}{\rightarrow}$' and every '↔' by '$\underset{x}{\leftrightarrow}$', no other transformation being performed.

We shall mention also (in 18.1) the case where the *principal* symbol '→' or '↔' may be replaced by '$\underset{x}{\rightarrow}$' and '$\underset{x}{\leftrightarrow}$' (no other transformation being performed).

The transformation is, roughly speaking, that from a theorem of the logic of propositions to a theorem of first order functional logic with monadic predicates.

We shall give examples of the well-known methods which allow in general to carry out the transformations exactly (i.e. for all hypotheticals and without any other transformation). But in some cases the transformation will have to be strengthened (some quantifiers will have to be added) or weakened (not all hypotheticals will be transformed) or modified otherwise. In a few cases no transformation of a hypothetical will be allowed.

18.1 - As example for the *first group* let us take that of **a**01.

$\vdash$	$\sim\sim ax \leftrightarrow ax$	**a**01 subst
$\vdash$	$\mathbf{A}x(\sim\sim ax \leftrightarrow ax)$	By 16.2
$\vdash$	$\sim\sim ax \underset{x}{\leftrightarrow} ax$	By df 16.53

Such a transformation is always possible if the *principal* symbol is a hypothetical.

18.2 - As example for the *second group* let us consider **a**31.

$\vdash$	$(ax \rightarrow bx) \leftrightarrow (\sim bx \rightarrow \sim ax)$	**a**31 subst
$\vdash$	$\mathbf{A}x[(ax \rightarrow bx) \leftrightarrow (\sim bx \rightarrow \sim ax)]$	By 16.2
$\vdash$	$\mathbf{A}x(ax \rightarrow bx) \leftrightarrow \mathbf{A}x(\sim bx \rightarrow \sim ax)$	By 17.31

This is the transformation in its usual form, but it leaves the *principal* symbol untransformed. To transform it, we have to add the somewhat trivial following step:

$$\vdash \quad \mathbf{A}x[(ax \underset{x}{\rightarrow} bx) \leftrightarrow (\sim bx \underset{x}{\rightarrow} \sim ax)]$$
$$\vdash \quad (ax \underset{x}{\rightarrow} bx) \underset{x}{\leftrightarrow} (\sim bx \underset{x}{\rightarrow} \sim ax)$$

18.21 - It may however be underlined that this method may lead to «strengthened» transformations in some cases, as for **a**51:

$\vdash$	$bx \rightarrow (ax \rightarrow bx)$	**a**51 subst
$\vdash$	$\mathbf{A}x[bx \rightarrow (ax \rightarrow bx)]$	By 16.2
$\vdash$	$\mathbf{A}x\, bx \rightarrow \mathbf{A}x(ax \rightarrow bx)$	By 17.31
$\vdash$	$\mathbf{A}x\, bx \underset{x}{\rightarrow} (ax \underset{x}{\rightarrow} bx)$	(The last steps as above).

18.3 - For theorems of the *third group*.

The transformation is easy for expressions with a conjunction of hypotheticals.

$\vdash$	$[(ax \rightarrow bx) \wedge (bx \rightarrow cx)] \rightarrow (ax \rightarrow cx)$	**a**62 subst
$\vdash$	$\mathbf{A}x[(ax \rightarrow bx) \wedge (bx \rightarrow cx)] \underset{x}{\rightarrow} (ax \underset{x}{\rightarrow} cx)$	As in 18.2 above

$\vdash$ $[\mathbf{A}x(ax \rightarrow bx) \wedge \mathbf{A}x(bx \rightarrow cx)] \underset{x}{\rightarrow} (ax \underset{x}{\rightarrow} cx)$ By 17.21

$\vdash$ $[(ax \underset{x}{\rightarrow} bx) \wedge (bx \underset{x}{\rightarrow} cx)] \underset{x}{\rightarrow} (ax \underset{x}{\rightarrow} cx)$

18.31 - The transformation may involve weakenings and modifications in the subcases B and C (**a**7 and **a**8).

18.4 - An example of a theorem where no transformation is allowed.

$\vdash$ $(ax \rightarrow bx) \vee (bx \rightarrow ax)$ **a**541 subst

$\vdash$ $\mathbf{A}x[(ax \rightarrow bx) \vee (bx \rightarrow ax)]$ By 16.2

No further distribution of the quantifier '**A***x*' is possible.

18.5 - The theorems and rules of §17 may be transformed according the methods given above.

SECTION 2 - HEURISTICAL APPROACH TO MODAL PROPOSITIONAL LOGIC

§ 20 - IDEA OF THE AUXILIARY LOGIC M″PQ

20.1 - Modal propositional logic may be considered as an *extension* of APC, using the same variables '*p*', '*q*', '*r*', ..., and the same connectives of negation '∼', conjunction '∧', alternation '∨', material implication '→' ,material equivalence '↔', with the same axioms and rules as in APC, but admitting also the symbols «necessarily» ('□') and «possibly» ('◇').

20.2 - But we have to state postulates for the new symbols '□' and '◇'. To that effect we shall first formulate an auxiliary logic M″PQ ('M″PQ' may be translated «a modal logic interpreted by means of quantifiers»). We use 'M″' instead of 'M', because M″PQ is equivalent to the modal logic called 'M″' by von Wright, embodying an idea which, more or less distinctly, guided many logicians, that of considering a proposition of modal logic, not as being simply and categorically true or false, but as being true or false in a given case, in some cases, in all cases.

20.3 - A proposition of APC was the affirmation of a quite determined fact. To the contrary, modal logic considers some types of facts, some kinds of facts, which may be realized in various cases or circumstances.

We do not give the term «case» a precise meaning — we do not e.g. identify cases with moments of time or with possible worlds, at least in principle. Precise meanings might be introduced in applied modal logic, but we specify that difference of cases must not be identified with difference of individuals or of predicates. If '*t*' is a variable for cases, '*t*' is a variable of a special kind, not a variable for propositions, or for individuals, or for predicates.

For the «kinds of facts» or «contents of facts» to be realized in the cases, we shall use special roman variables 'p', 'q', 'r', distinct from the (italic) variables '*p*', '*q*', '*r*', to be used in §22 and from section 3 on.

'p happens in the case *t*' will be translated by 'p*t*'. 'p*t*' may be compared with a proposition '*ax*' applying a monadic predicate to an individual.

20.4 - 'p happens necessarily' may be expressed in our auxiliary language as '**A***t* p*t*' (for all *t*, p is realized in the case *t*) and similarly 'p happens possibly' will be '**E***t* p*t*' (for some *t*, p is realized in the case *t*).

We call our auxiliary language 'M″PQ' because symbols of necessity or possibility are replaced in it by quantifiers.

20.5 - But what of the proposition affirmed without modality and which is usually expressed by '*p*' ? We express it by 'p*t*'.
20.51 - One might be tempted to interpret the modal 'p' as meaning «p is true in reality», as affirming that p is true in some constant case, in «the real case».

But let us remember that 'p' is not a propositional constant, but a propositional variable, and that a variable denotes ambiguously all values it can assume. In assertoric logic, '*p*' is ambiguous because it denotes (let us say) all conceivable facts. In modal logic, there may be various contents of facts in various cases, hence the '*p*' of later modal logic will have to denote ambiguously «any content of fact in any case».
20.52 - We confine ourselves here to pure calculus and we leave aside what might be called *applied* modal calculus.

Applied assertoric calculus can mention some constant facts, applied modal calculus might mention constant contents of facts and constant cases. But only in such an applied calculus would the possibility arise
(1) of a variable content of fact in a constant case, e.g. in the «real case»;
(2) of a constant content of fact in a variable case, e.g. as in the statement «It rains», if the circumstances in which it rains are left ambiguous;
(3) of a constant content of fact in a constant case.

20.6 - Expressions of M″PQ might mention various «circumstantial» variables, but one variable '*t*' suffices for the translation of the usual modal logic, in which circumstantial variables remain unexpressed and which is not fit to express any difference of cases.

§ 21 - THE CALCULUS M″PQ

21.1 - We call 'M″PQ' the calculus we have just outlined; M″PQ is a modal propositional calculus in which modality is expressed by quantifiers .

21.2 - As will be explained in detail, M″PQ is just parallel to a «strictly monadic» calculus as defined in §18.01, which is a sub-calculus of the AF¹C of §§ 16 and 17.

21.3 - *Formation rules* of M″PQ.

An infinite list of variables 'p', 'q', 'r', 's', 'p′', 'q′' ... . The variables of this list will be designated by 'P', 'Q', ... A variable '*t*', which may be designated by '*T*'.

21.32 - A proposition of M″PQ will be designated by '*M*', '*N*', ...

Propositions of M″PQ may be defined recursively as follows: Expressions of the form P*T* are expressions of propositions; thus 'p*t*', 'q*t*', 'r*t*' are propositions (but not 'p', nor 'q').

If *M* and *N* are propositions, $\sim M$, $M \wedge N$, $M \vee N$, $M \rightarrow N$, $M \leftrightarrow N$, are propositions.

If *M* is a proposition, **A***T M* and **E***T M* are propositions.

21.4 - We could formulate postulates for M″PQ parallel to those of AF¹C. The «parallelism» calls however for some remarks:

21.41 - A formation rule would have to be framed, stating that '**Q′T Q***T PT* ('**Q**' and '**Q**′', being '**A**' or '**E**') is well-formed. In '**Q′***T* **Q***T* P*T*', the last '*T*' is bound by the innermost quantifier '**Q***T*'.

21.42 - The rule of generalization parallel to 16.2 is essential to our interpretation. This rule will later be found valid in the systems S5, S4 and S2′.

21.43 - By virtue of the analogue of 16.33, '**Q**′*T* **Q***T PT*' will be proved to reduce to (to be strictly equivalent to) '**Q***T* P*T*'.
21.44 - There is no analogue to axiom 16.34.

21.5 - Let us call «*corresponding*» propositions, theorems, rules, definitions of M″PQ and AFC, respectively, the propositions, theorems, rules, definitions obtained by the replacement
of p, q, r, s, p′ ... P, Q, ... *t*, **A***t*, **E***t*,
by *a*, *b*, *c*, *d*, *a*′ ... *A*, *B*, ... *x*, **A***x*, **E***x*.

21.6 - If an expression of AFC is well-formed, it is then seen that the corresponding expression (if any) of M″PQ is well-formed.

21.7 - And if a proposition of AFC is valid, the corresponding proposition of M″PQ is valid. According to this rule we may derive propositions of M″PQ according to an intuitive correspondence to monadic AF^1C. And a proof in M″PQ may be parallelled by a proof in AF^1C.
E.G. **A***x*[*ax*→(*bx*∨*ax*)] is valid in AF^1C; hence **A***t*[p*t*→(q*t*∨p*t*)] is valid in M″PQ.

21.8 - And we shall admit in M″PQ the definitions and rules corresponding to those of AF^1C.
E.g. we shall define 'p*t*$\underset{t}{\rightarrow}$q*t*' as short for '**A***t*(p*t*→q*t*)',
'p*t*$\underset{t}{\leftrightarrow}$q*t*' as short for '**A***t*(p*t*↔q*t*)'.

§ 22 - THE LOGIC M″PQC

From now on (except in chapter III), we shall no longer make use of the explicit calculus M″PQ, but of a calculus which will be called 'M″PQC', because it is deductively equivalent to M″PQ, while using the notations of usual modal propositional logic, which will be called 'M″PC'.

22.1 - We form an expression of M″PQ from an expression of M″PQ by replacement of p*t*, q*t*, r*t*, ... **A***t*, **E***t*, $\underset{t}{\rightarrow}$, $\underset{t}{\leftrightarrow}$,
by *p*, *q*, *r*, ... □, ◇, ⇒, ⇔.

22.2 - The replacement is such as to secure a one-one correspondence and to preserve validity.

22.3 - From the above correspondence, it results that definitions 23.5 below are to be admitted in M″PQC.

§ 23 - POSTULATES SUGGESTED BY THE HEURISTICAL CORRESPONDENCE (¹)

23.1 - All Principles of APC are valid in M″PQC:
23.11 - The axioms 13.1 of APC;
23.12 - The rule of substitution 13.2;
23.13 - The rule of detachment 13.3;
23.14 - The definitions 13.4 (of '∧', '→' and '↔') (²).

(¹) We might now state forthwith the theorems (and rules) of M″PQ. corresponding to those of §§ 16, 17, 18, by virtue of the correspondence 21.5.

But let us mention first a development of some interest, which is easy to obtain. By virtue of the correspondence, we are to state the validity of theorems (and rules) of M″PQC, but we are not able to *demonstrate* these theorems (and rules) in M″PQC; we can only demonstrate the corresponding theorem or rule in the associated calculus, and then apply the correspondence.

We have however only to apply the correspondence to the set of postulates of §16 to get valid propositions and rules in M″PC (this system of postulates will even be somewhat simpler than that of AF¹C, stated in §16, as M″PCQ corresponds only to a strictly monadic calculus, thus to a subsystem of AF¹C).

We shall then, in the following numbers, have two possibilities before us: 1° to state simply the theorems by means of the correspondence; 2° to demonstrate them in M″PC, using the axiomatic we are going to state, and having demonstrations just parallel to those that were given, or might have been given in §§ 16, 17, 18.

(²) As a consequence of 22.1, all formulas valid in APC (thus all **a**-formulas) are theorems of M″PCQ.

23.2 - The *rule*: If $\vdash P$, then $\vdash \Box P$.

23.3 - *Proper axioms* for modality:
23.31 - $\vdash \quad \Box(p \rightarrow q) \rightarrow (\Box p \rightarrow \Box q)$;
23.32 - If 'P' is a proper modality (see 30.6), then $\vdash P \rightarrow \Box P$;
23.33 - $\vdash \quad \Box p \rightarrow p$;
(An analogue of 16.34 is not needed).

23.4 - If 'P' is a formula in APC, 'P' is a formula (in M″PQC);
If 'P', 'Q' are formulas; '$\sim P$', '$P \vee Q$', '$\Box P$' are formulas.

23.5 - *Definitions*:
23.51 - '$\Diamond P$' for '$\sim \Box \sim P$',
23.52 - '$P \Rightarrow Q$' for '$\Box(P \rightarrow Q)$',
23.53 - '$P \Leftrightarrow Q$' for '$\Box(P \leftrightarrow Q)$'.

§ 24 - PRINCIPAL THEOREMS AND RULES ABOUT MODALITIES IN M″PQC

We state here the formulas and rules coresponding to those of § 17 according to correspondence 21.5. (We have applied definitions 23.51-52 wherever it was possible). These formulas and rules are thus valid in M″PQC, and might be derived from the axioms 22.
Instead of writing '24.*x*', we shall designate them as '**m***x*'.

24.0 - (**m0**) *Negation*.
m01 - $\vdash \quad \sim \Box p \leftrightarrow \Diamond \sim p$
m011 - $\vdash \quad \Box p \leftrightarrow \sim \Diamond \sim p$
m02 - $\vdash \quad \sim \Diamond p \leftrightarrow \Box \sim p$
m021 - $\vdash \quad \Diamond p \leftrightarrow \sim \Box \sim p$

24.1 - (**m1**) *Subordination*.
m11 - $\vdash \quad \Box p \rightarrow p$
m12 - $\vdash \quad p \rightarrow \Diamond p$
m13 - $\vdash \quad \Box p \rightarrow \Diamond p$

24.2 - (**m2**) *Distribution of modalities with respect to* $\wedge$ *and* $\vee$.

m21 - $\vdash \Box(p\wedge q) \leftrightarrow (\Box p \wedge \Box q)$
m22 - $\vdash (\Box p \vee \Box q) \rightarrow \Box(p\vee q)$
m23 - $\vdash \Diamond(p\vee q) \leftrightarrow (\Diamond p \vee \Diamond q)$
m24 - $\vdash \Diamond(p\wedge q) \rightarrow (\Diamond p \wedge \Diamond q)$
m241 - $\vdash \Diamond(p\wedge q) \rightarrow \Diamond p$

24.3 - (**m3**) *Distribution of modalities with respect to hypothetical connectives.*

m31 - $\vdash (p\Rightarrow q) \rightarrow (\Box p \rightarrow \Box q)$
m315 - $\vdash [(p\Rightarrow q)\wedge \Box p] \rightarrow \Box q$
m32 - $\vdash (p\Rightarrow q) \rightarrow (\Diamond p \rightarrow \Diamond q)$
m325 - $\vdash [(p\Rightarrow q)\wedge \Diamond p] \rightarrow \Diamond q$
m33 - $\vdash (p\Leftrightarrow q) \rightarrow (\Box p \leftrightarrow \Box q)$
m34 - $\vdash (p\Leftrightarrow q) \rightarrow (\Diamond p \leftrightarrow \Diamond q)$

24.4 - (**m4**) *Rules of deduction.*

m41 - If $\vdash P\Rightarrow Q$, then $\vdash \Box P \rightarrow \Box Q$
m42 - If $\vdash P\Rightarrow Q$, then $\vdash \Diamond P \rightarrow \Diamond Q$
m43 - If $\vdash P\Leftrightarrow Q$, then $\vdash \Box P \leftrightarrow \Box Q$
m44 - If $\vdash P\Leftrightarrow Q$, then $\vdash \Diamond P \leftrightarrow \Diamond Q$

§ 25 - DESIGNATIONS OF FORMULAS AND RULES

For the purpose of reference and comparison, we shall use the following designations (we state at once the whole terminology).

25.0 - (Designations already introduced in §§ 12 and 24.)

An **a**-formula is a formula valid in APC (a tautology of APC). Some **a**-formulas are listed in §12 and designated there by '**a**' followed by a number.

An **m**-formula or **m**-rule is a formula or rule listed in §24. It is designated by '**m**' followed by a number.

If '**a***x*' or '**m***x*' designate a formula '$P\leftrightarrow Q$', then '**a***x*′' or '**m***x*′' designate '$P\rightarrow Q$', and '**a***x*″' or '**m***x*″' designate '$Q\rightarrow P$'.

25.1 - The following designations will be used from §26 on:

25.11 - The **S**-*transformation* of a formula or rule is the result of the replacement of each '$\rightarrow$' or '$\leftrightarrow$' in it by a '$\Rightarrow$' or '$\Leftrightarrow$'. If there is no '$\rightarrow$' or '$\leftrightarrow$' in the original formula, then the transformation is trivially impossible.
25.12 - The **s**-*transformation* of a formula is the result of the replacement of its *principal* symbol '$\rightarrow$' or '$\leftrightarrow$' by '$\Rightarrow$' 'or '$\Leftrightarrow$'. If there is no principal symbol '$\rightarrow$' or '$\leftrightarrow$' in the original formula, then the transformation is trivially impossible.
25.13 - Transformations which are not **S**- nor **s**-transformations will be designated

- as **S′**-*transformations* (or strenghtened transformations), if some modality-signs are added;
- as **S″**-*transformations* (or weakened transformations), if a part only of the non-principal hypotheticals are replaced by strict ones;
- as **S‴**-*transformations* in other cases.

25.14 - The formulas resulting from **s**-, **S**-, **S′**-, **S″**-, **S‴**-transformations of a formula designated by '*d*' will be called the **s**-formula **s***d*, the **S**-formula **S***d*, the **S′**-formula **S′***d*, the **S″**-formula **S″***d*, the **S‴**-formula **S‴***d*. And similarly for rules having undergone the same transformation. E.g. the **S**-transformation of **a**62 is **Sa**62.

§ 26 - REPLACEMENT OF MATERIAL CONNECTIVES BY STRICT CONNECTIVES IN M″PQC

26.0 - To get a preliminary idea of the general physionomy of modal propositional logic, it is interesting to see how far material (hypothetical) connectives may be replaced by strict ones in the theorems of APC. It was indeed the purpose of the Lewis's calculi to build up a «strict» calculus which might perform the functions of the usual propositional calculus, but in which so-called «paradoxical» theorems (such as those of **a**5) would not be valid. Now the M″PQ has in most cases very simple methods at hand to prove the transformations in question. These methods are exactly parallel to those of §18; and they make use of the same language as the Lewis's MPC if account is taken of the rules of correspondence of §22.

26.01 - We call '⇒' and '⇔' *strict hypothetical connectives* (strict hypotheticals), the material hypothetical connectives being '→' and '↔'.

26.02 - In the terminology of 24.1, the question of replaceability of material by strict connectives becomes: How far can **S**-transformations be carried out in M″PQC ? How far are **S**′-, **S**″-, **S**‴-transformations only available ? In which cases is any transformation of hypotheticals impossible ?

Let us consider the different groups of **a**-theorems, as in §19.

26.1 - In the theorems of the *first group,* the transformation can be carried out if there is exactly one hypothetical, which is the principal symbol. Rule 23.2 and, of course, definitions have only to be used.

In the case of **a**01:

⊢	$\sim\sim p \leftrightarrow p$	**a**01
⊢	$\Box(\sim\sim p \leftrightarrow p)$	By 23.2
⊢	$\sim\sim p \Leftrightarrow p$	Df 23.53

26.11 - If no hypothetical occurs in the **a**-formula, then the transformation considered is trivially impossible.

If 23.2 is applied to **a**05 and **a**06, the result is respectively ⊢ $\Box\sim(p\wedge\sim p)$ and ⊢ $\Box(p\vee\sim p)$, to be compared with the **S**′-theorems of 26.21.

26.12 - The use of 23.2 enables us to perform the **S**-transformation upon any theorem.

26.2 - For most of the theorems of the *second group,* the full **S**-transformation can be performed, according to the method used in following example, to transform **a**31.

⊢	$(p\rightarrow q) \leftrightarrow (\sim q\rightarrow\sim p)$	**a**31
⊢	$\Box[(p\rightarrow q) \leftrightarrow (\sim q\rightarrow\sim p)]$	By 23.2
⊢	$\Box\ (p\rightarrow q) \leftrightarrow \Box(\sim q\rightarrow\sim p)$	By 23.31
⊢	$(p\Rightarrow q) \leftrightarrow (\sim q\Rightarrow\sim p)$	By 23.52
⊢	$\Box[(p\Rightarrow q) \leftrightarrow (\sim q\Rightarrow\sim p)]$	By 23.2
⊢	$(p\Rightarrow q) \Leftrightarrow (\sim q\Rightarrow\sim p)$	By 23.52

This will justify an **S**-transformation of a hypothetical of *two* hypotheticals.

26.21 - But let us try the same method with **a511**.

$\vdash$	$q \rightarrow (p \rightarrow q)$	**a511**
$\vdash$	$\Box q \rightarrow (p \Rightarrow q)$	By 23.2 and 23.31 and def 23.52
$\vdash$	$\Box q \Rightarrow (p \Rightarrow q)$	By 23.2 again, and by def 23.52

Here we get an **S′**-transformation only, and this will be the case each time we have to do with an implication or alternative between two propositions one of which is *not* a hypothetical.

26.3 - There is no difficulty in general with subgroup A(**a6**), if we have to do with conjunctions of hypotheticals.

$\vdash$	$[(p \rightarrow q) \wedge (q \rightarrow r)] \rightarrow (p \rightarrow r)$	**a62**
$\vdash$	$\Box[(p \rightarrow q) \wedge (q \rightarrow r)] \Rightarrow (p \Rightarrow r)$	By the method of 26.2
$\vdash$	$[(p \Rightarrow q) \wedge (q \Rightarrow r)] \Rightarrow (p \Rightarrow r)$	By 17.21 and 23.52

26.4 - For subgroup B (**a7**) we have no **S**-transformation of the theorems **a70**, **a705** of importation-exportation, but we may get (not by a method similar to the preceding ones) special kinds of **S′**- or **S″**-transformations.

It is possible to justify the **S**-transformation of theorems of the form $P \rightarrow (Q \rightarrow M)$, where P, Q, M are hypotheticals. The method involves a use of 23.2.

$\vdash$	$P \rightarrow (Q \rightarrow M)$	By hypothesis
$\vdash$	$\Box P \rightarrow \Box(Q \rightarrow M)$	By 23.2 and 23.31
$\vdash$	$\Box\Box P \rightarrow \Box\Box(Q \rightarrow M)$	By 23.2 and 23.31 again
$\vdash$	$\Box P \rightarrow \Box\Box(Q \rightarrow M)$	By 23.32
$\vdash$	$\Box P \rightarrow \Box(\Box Q \rightarrow \Box M)$	By 23.31
$\vdash$	$\Box P \rightarrow (\Box Q \Rightarrow \Box M)$	By 23.52
$\vdash$	$\Box P \Rightarrow (\Box Q \Rightarrow \Box M)$	By 23.2 and 23.52

This method allows us to pass

from $\vdash$ $(p \rightarrow q) \rightarrow [(q \rightarrow r) \rightarrow (p \rightarrow r)]$ (**a72**),

to $\vdash$ $(p \Rightarrow q) \Rightarrow [(q \Rightarrow r) \Rightarrow (p \Rightarrow r)]$ (**Sa72**).

26.5 - In subgroup C(**a**8) we have only **S**‴-transformations, because the modality '◇' has to be introduced.

Even a **S**‴-transformation of **a**82 is impossible; **a**82 says that $(p \wedge \sim q) \rightarrow (p \rightarrow \sim q)$, but the negation of $p \Rightarrow q$ is $\Diamond(p \wedge \sim q)$, and we have not $\Diamond(p \wedge \sim q) \Rightarrow \Box(p \rightarrow \sim q)$.

26.6 - Transformations of the types explained are impossible with alternatives of hypotheticals, because there is no theorem like **m**21 allowing the distribution of '□' towards '∨'.

§ 27 - TRANSFORMATIONS OF APC THEOREMS VALID IN M″PQC

The theorems are the strongest provable in M″PQC. We do not mention the **a**-theorems, and we do not mention the **sa**-theorems if **Sa**-, **S′a**-, **S″a**-theorems are valid. Since M″PQC may be shown equivalent to the strongest modal system S5, the following table gives an idea of the principal theorems to be reached at the end of the developments of M″PC.

The denomination chosen for a theorem is the weakest possible; if a theorem may be called a **sa**- or (trivially) a **Sa**-theorem, we use the denomination '**sa**'.

Subgroup **a** 0

sa00 - $\vdash \quad p \Leftrightarrow p$
sa01 - $\vdash \quad \sim\sim p \Leftrightarrow p$
sa02 - $\vdash \quad \sim(p \wedge q) \Leftrightarrow (\sim p \vee \sim q)$
sa021 - $\vdash \quad (p \wedge q) \Leftrightarrow \sim(\sim p \vee \sim q)$
sa03 - $\vdash \quad \sim(p \vee q) \Leftrightarrow (\sim p \wedge \sim q)$
sa031 - $\vdash \quad (p \vee q) \Leftrightarrow \sim(\sim p \wedge \sim q)$
sa055 - $\vdash \quad (q \wedge \sim q) \Rightarrow p$
sa065 - $\vdash \quad p \Rightarrow (q \vee \sim q)$

Subgroup **a** 1

sa10 - $\vdash (p \wedge q) \Rightarrow p$
sa101 - $\vdash (p \wedge q) \Rightarrow q$
sa11 - $\vdash (p \wedge q) \Leftrightarrow (q \wedge p)$
sa12 - $\vdash [p \wedge (q \wedge r)] \Leftrightarrow [(p \wedge q) \wedge r]$
sa13 - $\vdash [p \wedge (q \vee \mathrm{r})] \Leftrightarrow [(p \wedge q) \vee (p \wedge r)]$
sa14 - $\vdash p \Leftrightarrow (p \wedge p)$
sa15 - $\vdash p \Leftrightarrow [p \wedge (p \vee q)]$
sa16 - $\vdash p \Leftrightarrow [p \wedge (q \vee \sim q)]$

Subgroup **a** 2

sa20 - $\vdash p \Rightarrow (p \vee q)$
sa201 - $\vdash q \Rightarrow (p \vee q)$
sa21 - $\vdash (p \vee q) \Leftrightarrow (q \vee p)$
sa22 - $\vdash [p \vee (q \vee r)] \Leftrightarrow [(p \vee q) \vee r]$
sa23 - $\vdash [p \vee (p \wedge r)] \Leftrightarrow [(p \vee q) \wedge (p \vee r)]$
sa24 - $\vdash p \Leftrightarrow (p \vee p)$
sa25 - $\vdash p \Leftrightarrow [p \vee (p \wedge q)]$
sa26 - $\vdash p \Leftrightarrow [p \vee (q \wedge \sim q)]$

Subgroup **a** 3

Sa31 - $\vdash (p \Rightarrow q) \Leftrightarrow (\sim q \Rightarrow \sim p)$
Sa311 - $\vdash (p \Rightarrow \sim q) \Leftrightarrow (q \Rightarrow \sim p)$
Sa312 - $\vdash (\sim p \Rightarrow q) \Leftrightarrow (\sim q \Rightarrow p)$
Sa32 - $\vdash [(p \wedge q) \Rightarrow r] \Leftrightarrow [(p \wedge \sim r) \Rightarrow \sim q]$
Sa321 - $\vdash [(p \wedge q) \Rightarrow r] \Leftrightarrow [(q \wedge \sim r) \Rightarrow \sim p]$
Sa381 - $\vdash (p \Rightarrow q) \Rightarrow [(r \wedge p) \Rightarrow (r \wedge q)]$
Sa383 - $\vdash (p \Rightarrow q) \Rightarrow [(r \vee p) \Rightarrow (r \vee q)]$

Subgroup **a** 4

Sa41 - $\vdash (p \Leftrightarrow q) \Leftrightarrow (q \Leftrightarrow p)$
Sa42 - $\vdash (p \Leftrightarrow q) \Leftrightarrow (\sim p \Leftrightarrow \sim q)$
Sa431 - $\vdash (p \Leftrightarrow q) \Rightarrow (p \Rightarrow q)$
Sa432 - $\vdash (p \Leftrightarrow q) \Rightarrow (q \Rightarrow p)$
Sa44 - $\vdash (p \Rightarrow q) \Leftrightarrow [p \Leftrightarrow (p \wedge q)]$
Sa441 - $\vdash (p \Rightarrow q) \Leftrightarrow [p \Rightarrow (p \wedge q)]$
Sa45 - $\vdash (p \Rightarrow q) \Leftrightarrow [(p \vee q) \Leftrightarrow q]$

Sa451 - $\vdash$ $(p \Rightarrow q) \Leftrightarrow [(p \vee q) \Rightarrow q]$
Sa481 - $\vdash$ $(p \Leftrightarrow q) \Rightarrow [(p \wedge r) \Leftrightarrow (q \wedge r)]$
Sa482 - $\vdash$ $(p \Leftrightarrow q) \Rightarrow [(p \vee r) \Leftrightarrow (q \vee r)]$

Subgroup **a** 5

S'a501 - $\vdash$ $(p \Rightarrow q) \Leftrightarrow \Box(\sim p \vee q)$
S'a502 - $\vdash$ $\sim (p \Rightarrow q) \Leftrightarrow \Diamond(p \wedge \sim q)$
S'a503 - $\vdash$ $(p \Rightarrow q) \Leftrightarrow \Box \sim (p \wedge \sim q)$
S'a511 - $\vdash$ $\Box q \Rightarrow (p \Rightarrow q)$
S'a512 - $\vdash$ $\Box \sim p \Rightarrow (p \Rightarrow q)$
S'a521 - $\vdash$ $\Box(p \wedge q) \Rightarrow (p \Leftrightarrow q)$
S'a522 - $\vdash$ $\Box(\sim p \wedge \sim q) \Rightarrow (p \Leftrightarrow q)$
S'a531 - $\vdash$ $\Box p \Leftrightarrow (\sim p \Rightarrow p)$
S'a532 - $\vdash$ $\Box \sim p \Leftrightarrow (p \Rightarrow \sim p)$
S'a541 - $\vdash$ $\Diamond(p \Rightarrow q) \vee \Box(q \Rightarrow p)$
S'''a542 - $\vdash$ $\Diamond(p \rightarrow q) \vee (p \Rightarrow \sim q)$
and $\vdash$ $(p \Rightarrow q) \vee \Diamond(p \rightarrow \sim q)$

Subgroup **a** 6

Sa61 - $\vdash$ $[p \wedge (p \Rightarrow q)] \Rightarrow q$
Sa611 - $\vdash$ $[\sim q \wedge (p \Rightarrow q)] \Rightarrow \sim p$
S'a612- $\vdash$ $\{\Box p \wedge [(p \wedge r) \Rightarrow q]\} \Rightarrow (r \Rightarrow q)$
Sa62 - $\vdash$ $[(p \Rightarrow q) \wedge (q \Rightarrow r)] \Rightarrow (p \Rightarrow r)$
Sa621 - $\vdash$ $[(q \Rightarrow r) \wedge (p \Rightarrow q)] \Rightarrow (p \Rightarrow r)$
Sa623 - $\vdash$ $[(p \Leftrightarrow q) \wedge (q \Leftrightarrow r)] \Leftrightarrow (p \Leftrightarrow r)$
Sa625 - $\vdash$ $\{(p \Rightarrow q) \wedge [(q \wedge s) \Rightarrow r]\} \Rightarrow [(p \wedge s) \Rightarrow r]$
Sa63 - $\vdash$ $[(p \Rightarrow q) \wedge (q \Rightarrow r) \wedge (r \Rightarrow s)] \Rightarrow (p \Rightarrow s)$
Sa651 - $\vdash$ $[(p \Rightarrow q) \wedge (p \Rightarrow s)] \Leftrightarrow [p \Rightarrow (q \wedge s)]$
Sa655 - $\vdash$ $[(p \Rightarrow q) \wedge (r \Rightarrow q)] \Leftrightarrow [(p \vee r) \Rightarrow q]$
Sa661 - $\vdash$ $[(p \Rightarrow q) \wedge (r \Rightarrow s)] \Leftrightarrow [(p \wedge r) \Rightarrow (q \wedge s)]$
Sa665 - $\vdash$ $[(p \Rightarrow q) \wedge (r \Rightarrow s)] \Leftrightarrow [(p \vee r) \Rightarrow (q \vee s)]$
S'a67 - $\vdash$ $\Box((p \Rightarrow q) \vee (p \Rightarrow s)) \Leftrightarrow (p \Rightarrow (q \vee s))$
S'a675- $\vdash$ $\Box((p \Rightarrow q) \vee (r \Rightarrow q)) \Leftrightarrow ((p \vee r) \Rightarrow q)$
Sa68 - $\vdash$ $[(p \Rightarrow q) \wedge (q \Rightarrow p)] \Leftrightarrow (p \Leftrightarrow q)$
S'a69 - $\vdash$ $[(p \Rightarrow q) \wedge (p \Rightarrow \sim q)] \Leftrightarrow \Box \sim p$
S'a695- $\vdash$ $[(p \Rightarrow q) \wedge (\sim p \Rightarrow q)] \Leftrightarrow \Box q$
but $\vdash$ $[(p \Rightarrow q) \wedge (\sim p \Rightarrow q)] \Rightarrow q$
Sa696 - $\vdash$ $\{[(p \wedge q) \Rightarrow r] \wedge [(p \wedge \sim q) \Rightarrow r]\} \Rightarrow (p \Rightarrow r)$

Subgroup **a** 7

S″a70 - $\vdash$ $[(p\wedge q)\Rightarrow r] \Leftrightarrow [p\Rightarrow(q\rightarrow r)]$
S′a70 - $\vdash$ $[(\Box p\wedge \Box q)\Rightarrow \Box r] \Leftrightarrow [\Box q\Rightarrow(\Box p\Rightarrow \Box r)]$
S″a705- $\vdash$ $[p\Rightarrow(q\rightarrow r)] \Leftrightarrow [q\Rightarrow(p\rightarrow r)]$
S′a705- $\vdash$ $[\Box p\Rightarrow(\Box q\Rightarrow \Box r)] \Leftrightarrow [\Box p\Rightarrow(\Box q\Rightarrow \Box r)]$
Sa72 - $\vdash$ $(p\Rightarrow q) \Rightarrow [(q\Rightarrow r)\Rightarrow(p\Rightarrow r)]$
Sa721 - $\vdash$ $(q\Rightarrow r) \Rightarrow [(p\Rightarrow q)\Rightarrow(p\Rightarrow r)]$
Sa723 - $\vdash$ $(p\Leftrightarrow q) \Rightarrow [(q\Leftrightarrow r)\Rightarrow(p\Leftrightarrow r)]$
Sa725 - $\vdash$ $(p\Rightarrow q) \Rightarrow \{[(q\wedge s)\Rightarrow r]\Rightarrow[(p\wedge s)\Rightarrow r]\}$
Sa73 - $\vdash$ $(p\Rightarrow q) \Rightarrow \{[(q\Rightarrow r)\wedge(r\Rightarrow s)]\Rightarrow(p\Rightarrow s)\}$
Sa796 - $\vdash$ $[(p\wedge q)\Rightarrow r] \Rightarrow \{[(p\wedge \sim q)\Rightarrow r]\Rightarrow(p\Rightarrow r)\}$

Subgroup **a** 8

S‴a81- $\vdash$ $\sim(p\Rightarrow q) \Leftrightarrow \Diamond(p\wedge \sim q)$
S‴a82- $\vdash$ $\sim\Diamond(p\rightarrow q) \Rightarrow (p\Rightarrow \sim q)$
or $\vdash$ $\sim(p\Rightarrow q) \Rightarrow \Diamond(p\rightarrow \sim q)$
S‴a83- $\vdash$ $\sim(p\Leftrightarrow q) \Leftrightarrow [\Diamond(p\wedge \sim q)\vee\Diamond(\sim p\wedge q)]$
S‴a84- $\vdash$ $\sim\Diamond(p\leftrightarrow q) \Leftrightarrow [\Box(p\vee q) \wedge \Box(\sim p\vee \sim q)]$
or $\vdash$ $\sim(p\Leftrightarrow q) \Leftrightarrow \Diamond[(p\vee q) \wedge (\sim p\vee \sim q)]$

§ **28** - TRANSFORMATIONS OF THEOREMS AND RULES ABOUT MODALITIES

For further comparison we state here the **s**- and **S**-transforms of the theorems and rules about (explicit) modalities in §24.

28.0 - *Negation.*
sm01 - $\vdash$ $\sim\Box p \Leftrightarrow \Diamond\sim p$
sm011 - $\vdash$ $\Box p \Leftrightarrow \sim\Diamond\sim p$
sm02 - $\vdash$ $\sim\Diamond p \Leftrightarrow \Box\sim p$
sm021 - $\vdash$ $\Diamond p \Leftrightarrow \sim\Box\sim p$

28.1 - *Subordination.*
sm11 - $\vdash$ $\Box p \Rightarrow p$
sm12 - $\vdash$ $p \Rightarrow \Diamond p$
sm13 - $\vdash$ $\Box p \Rightarrow \Diamond p$

28.2 - *Distribution of modalities with respect to* $\wedge$ *and* $\vee$.

Sm21 - $\vdash \Box(p\wedge q) \Leftrightarrow (\Box p\wedge\Box q)$

Sm22 - $\vdash (\Box p\vee\Box q) \Rightarrow \Box(p\vee q)$

Sm23 - $\vdash \Diamond(p\vee q) \Leftrightarrow (\Diamond p\vee\Diamond q)$

Sm24 - $\vdash \Diamond(p\wedge q) \Rightarrow (\Diamond p\wedge\Diamond q)$

Sm241 - $\vdash \Diamond(p \wedge q) \Rightarrow \Diamond p$

28.3 - *Distribution of modalities with respect to* $\Rightarrow$ *and* $\Leftrightarrow$.

Sm31 - $\vdash (p\Rightarrow q) \Rightarrow (\Box p\Rightarrow\Box q)$

Sm315 - $\vdash [(p\Rightarrow q)\wedge\Box p] \Rightarrow \Box q$

Sm32 - $\vdash (p\Rightarrow q) \Rightarrow (\Diamond p\Rightarrow\Diamond q)$

Sm325 - $\vdash [(p\Rightarrow q)\wedge\Diamond p] \Rightarrow \Diamond q$

Sm33 - $\vdash (p\Leftrightarrow q) \Rightarrow (\Box p\Leftrightarrow\Box q)$

Sm34 - $\vdash (p\Leftrightarrow q) \Rightarrow (\Diamond p\Leftrightarrow\Diamond q)$

28.4 - *Rules of deduction.*

Sm41 - If $\vdash P\Rightarrow Q$, then $\vdash \Box P\Rightarrow\Box Q$.

Sm42 - If $\vdash P\Rightarrow Q$, then $\vdash \Diamond P\Rightarrow\Diamond Q$.

Sm43 - If $\vdash P\Leftrightarrow Q$, then $\vdash \Box P\Leftrightarrow\Box Q$.

Sm44 - If $\vdash P\Leftrightarrow Q$, then $\vdash \Diamond P\Leftrightarrow\Diamond Q$.

§ 29 - TRANSITION FROM M″PQC TO OTHER SETS OF POSTULATES

29.1 - M″PQC is advantageous as an heuristical starting point, in view of the simple correspondence between it and monadic AF^1C. But, because of its strength, M″PQC is a somewhat trivial system and it will be interesting to study «weaker» systems, in which modality and the strict connectives will be characterized less narrowly.

The obvious way to reach such systems will be to replace some axioms by weaker ones, provided, what we take here for granted, that the axioms transformed or omitted be independent of the others.

29.2 - One of our postulates of §23 can obviously be weakened, namely 23.32: «If P is a proper modality, then $\vdash P\rightarrow\Box P$».

29.21 - This postulate was nowhere used in § 26 as enunciated, and it would not be necessary for the proof of the transforms of §28; it would lead to the system to be called later 'S5'.

29.22 - For all demonstrations of §26, including those of 26.4, it suffices to accept the weaker postulate $\vdash \Box p \rightarrow \Box\Box p$. This will lead to a weaker system called 'S4'.
29.23 - Even if 23.32 is simply omitted, the proofs of §26 remain valid except 26.4. This would lead us to the system to be called later 'S2'' (see p. 123).

29.3 - But for our M''PQC-deductions it is essential to have the rule 23.2: «If $\vdash P$, then $\vdash \Box P$». Now it will be shown that this rule is not valid in the systems to be called later 'S3', 'S2', 'S1'.

29.4 - Another way was taken by Lewis and his followers, and this way proved fruitful. Instead of accepting rule 23.2 — which raises at once all APC theorems to transforms of them in **s**-theorems (and which even indefinitely passes from any logical affirmation to a logical necessary affirmation) — one would start, more modestly, from a set of axioms equivalent to the **S**-transforms of the axioms 13.1 of APC.

This set of axioms, roughly said, would suffice to the proof of most **S**-transforms listed in §27, but would prove only a rather small part of the theorems and rules of §28.

29.5 - The Lewis's school discovered a series of independent axioms, whose addition to the fundamental set of axioms would allow a gradual derivation of the transforms of §28.

If we add as axiom **Sm**12 $\vdash p \Rightarrow \Diamond p$, we may derive the system to be called 'S1'.

If we add as axiom **Sm**23 $\vdash \Diamond(p \vee q) \Leftrightarrow (\Diamond p \vee \Diamond q)$, then we may derive the system to be called 'S2'.

If we add **Sm**32 $\vdash (p \Rightarrow q) \Rightarrow (\Diamond p \Rightarrow \Diamond q)$, then we get the system to be called 'S3'.

If we add the axiom mentioned in 29.22, we get S4.

If we add the axiom 23.32, or an axiom equivalent to it, we get S5.

Using this method we shall now proceed to study the system derived from 29.4, which we shall call 'S1°', and then the systems S1 to S5 and their possible extensions.

CHAPTER II

NORMAL SYSTEMS OF MODAL PROPOSITIONAL LOGIC

SECTION 3 - SYSTEMS 1⁰ AND 1

From this point on, no demonstration will use a statement of the three preceding introductory sections, unless it has been stated or demonstrated anew. The terminology of these preceding chapters however will remain in force and the number of a theorem or rule in M″PQC will be quoted for reference only.

§ 30 - POSTULATES FOR SYSTEM 1^0

We call '*System 1^0*' (or 'S1^0') the system with the following postulates. (System 1 will be defined in § 36.)

30.1 - *Proper axioms* (primitive propositions):

30.11 - $\vdash \quad p \wedge q \Rightarrow p;$

30.12 - $\vdash \quad p \wedge q \Rightarrow q \wedge p;$

30.13 - $\vdash \quad [(p \wedge q) \wedge r] \Rightarrow [p \wedge (q \wedge r)];$

30.14 - $\vdash \quad p \Rightarrow p \wedge p;$

30.15 - $\vdash \quad [(p \Rightarrow q) \wedge (q \Rightarrow r)] \Rightarrow (p \Rightarrow r).$

30.2 - *Primitive rules*:

30.20 - *Formation rules.*

A propositional variable is a formula;

If 'P' and 'Q' are formulas, '$\sim P$', '$\Diamond P$', '$P \wedge Q$' are formulas.

30.21 - *Rule of substitution.*

A valid proposition remains valid if a formula is substituted everywhere in it for a propositional variable.

30.22 - *Rule of adjunction.*
If $\vdash P$ and if $\vdash Q$, then $\vdash P \wedge Q$.
30.23 - *Rule of detachment for '$\Rightarrow$'.*
If $\vdash P$ and if $\vdash P \Rightarrow Q$, then $\vdash Q$.
30.24 - *Rule of replacement of strict equivalents.*
If $\vdash P \Leftrightarrow Q$, then a valid formula remains valid if 'Q' is replaced somewhere in it by 'P'.

30.3 - *Definitions.*
30.31 - '$P \vee Q$' for '$\sim(\sim P \wedge \sim Q)$',
30.32 - '$P \rightarrow Q$' for '$\sim(P \wedge \sim Q)$',
30.33 - '$P \leftrightarrow Q$' for '$(P \rightarrow Q) \wedge (Q \rightarrow P)$',
30.34 - '$P \Rightarrow Q$' for '$\sim \Diamond (P \wedge \sim Q)$',
30.35 - '$P \Leftrightarrow Q$' for '$(P \Rightarrow Q) \wedge (Q \Rightarrow P)$',
30.36 - '$\Box P$' for '$\sim \Diamond \sim P$'.

30.4 - *Remarks about the postulates.*
30.41 - *Axioms.* The axioms may be compared with those of §13. The first differences are that the present axioms are **sa**-axioms, stating *strict* implications, and that they are axioms about conjunction instead of axioms about alternation.

Axiom 30.13 corresponds to an axiom of the *Principia,* shown provable in APC. Lewis-Langford adds an axiom **sa**01'': $\vdash p \Rightarrow \sim\sim p$. This has been shown provable (see 31.32) by McKinsey.

Axiom 30.15 is the only axiom stating a strict implication between strict implications (more precisely: between a conjunction of strict implications and a strict implication). A syllogism of the form **Sa**72 (strict implication implying strictly a strict implication of strict implications) would express something much stronger than 30.15, and something not even provable in S1°.

The use of 30.15 as axiom has notable consequences. As a conjunction occurs in the axiom, it becomes necessary to have axioms about conjunction; hence the rule of adjunction 30.22 becomes necessary.

New methods of syllogistic inferences will become usual (32.3 and 33.4).

30.42 - *Rules*.

Rule 30.21 (of substitution) calls for no comment.

Rule 30.22 (of adjunction) is necessary for deductions by 30.15.

Rule 30.23 (of detachment) is in itself stricter than the usual rule of detachment 13.3; but this higher strictness is only apparent, as the rule of detachment with material implication can be derived in the system (32.211).

Rule 30.24 (of replacement of strict equivalents) is indeed stricter than the rule of replacement with material equivalents in APC; but this rule is used very frequently, helping, so to say, to supplement the strictness of the axioms.

It seems that the four rules are independent from the axioms.

30.43 - *Definitions*.

The definitions of material connectives call for no comment. It has to be underlined that, although the axioms are axioms about strict implication (at such a point that no modality is mentioned explicitly in the axioms), strict implication is a *defined* notion, whose properties depend somewhat trivially upon the properties of (material) conjunction.

The strict equivalence defined in 30.35 is not exactly the same as $\Box(p \leftrightarrow q)$; the strict equivalence between '$p \Leftrightarrow q$' and '$\Box(p \leftrightarrow q)$' can only be proved in a system stronger than 1° (namely S2°, see 45.1).

We have kept '$\Diamond$' as a primitive notion, as in Lewis-Langford, and we have defined '$\Box$'; '$\Box$' would do as well as '$\Diamond$' as a primitive notion.

30.5 - *Consistency of System 1°*.

To prove the consistency of a system, it suffices to have a matrix in which, if *P* is provable in the system, *P* has designated values and $\sim P$ has not designated values.

This is the case with following matrix (being Group V of Lewis-Langford) for S1°:

Values: 1, 2, 3, 4. Designated values: 1, 2.

p	$\sim p$
1	4
2	3
3	2
4	1

p	$\Diamond p$
1	1
2	2
3	1
4	3

$\wedge$	1	2	3	4
1	1	2	3	4
2	2	2	4	4
3	3	4	3	4
4	4	4	4	4

And, according to the definitions,

p	$\sim\Diamond p$	$\Box p$
1	4	2
2	3	4
3	4	4
4	2	4

$\vee$	1	2	3	4
1	1	1	1	1
2	1	2	1	2
3	1	1	3	3
4	1	2	3	4

$\Rightarrow$	1	2	3	4
1	2	4	3	4
2	2	2	3	3
3	2	4	2	4
4	2	2	2	2

$\Leftrightarrow$	1	2	3	4
1	2	4	4	4
2	4	2	4	4
3	4	4	2	4
4	4	4	4	2

A provable formula P has a designated value, and then $\sim P$ has the values 4 or 3, which are not designated. So, system 1° is consistent.

30.6 - *Terminology.*

We shall use, from this paragraph on, terms used by Parry in closely related senses.

A «*modal*» expression will be defined:

1° A propositional variable is a modal expression (a modal proposition);

2° If 'P' and 'Q' are modal propositions, so are '$\sim P$', '$P \wedge Q$', '$\Diamond Q$';

3° Each expression equivalent by definition to a modal proposition is a modal proposition.

A «*modality*» is a sequence of symbols '$\sim$', '$\Diamond$', or any expression which may be substituted by virtue of a definition to such a sequence.

When there is no danger of ambiguity, we shall use the word «modality» also for such a sequence followed by a propositional expression.

The «*degree*» of a modality equals the number of diamonds

(symbols '◇') contained in a modality formed only by '∼' and '◇' and equivalent by definition to the modality in question.

A «*proper modality*» is a modality of degree higher than zero.

An «*affirmative modality*» is a modality in which the number of symbols of negation is zero or even, a «*negative*» is one in which the number of negation symbols is odd.

We call '◇', a «*possibility-sign*» and '□', a «*necessity-sign*».

§ 31 - THEOREMS AND DERIVED RULES (MATERIAL CONNECTIVES)

31.0 - *Derived rules.*

To avoid a needless multiplication of deduction steps, we shall formulate derived rules and adopt special designations for them. The use of the substitution rule 30.21, which will occur in most of the deductions, will frequently be left tacit, or barely indicated by 'subst'.

31.01 - Let 'P'' and 'Q'' be obtained from 'P' and 'Q' by a same substitution according to rule 30.21; then: if $\vdash P \Rightarrow Q$ and if $\vdash P'$, then $\vdash Q'$.

(1)	$\vdash$	$P \Rightarrow Q$	By hp
(2)	$\vdash$	$P' \Rightarrow Q'$	By rule 30.21
(3)	$\vdash$	P'	By hp
(4)	$\vdash$	Q'	By rule 30.23

This derived rule amounts to a particular application of the rule of detachment 30.23.

If $\vdash P \Rightarrow Q$ is numbered '*a*' and if $\vdash P'$ is numbered '*b*', the use of this rule is mentioned as 'From *b* by *a*'.

If $\vdash P$ is written on the preceding line, we simply write 'By *a*'.

31.02 - If $\vdash (P \wedge Q) \Rightarrow R$, if $\vdash P$ and if $\vdash Q$, then $\vdash$R.

(1)	$\vdash$	$(P \wedge Q) \Rightarrow R$	By hp
(2)	$\vdash$	P	By hp
(3)	$\vdash$	Q	By hp
(4)	$\vdash$	$(P \wedge Q)$	By rule 30.22
(5)	$\vdash$	R	From (1) and (4) by rule 30.23.

'*a*' being the number of $\vdash (P \wedge Q) \Rightarrow R$, 'b' the number of $\vdash P$, '*c*' the number of $\vdash Q$, we write simply 'By *a* from *b* and *c*'.

This rule involves an application of the rule of adjunction 30.22 and of the rule of detachment 30.23.

31.021 - With the notation 'By 30.15' we mean an application of the rule: «If $\vdash P \Rightarrow Q$ and if $\vdash Q \Rightarrow R$, then $\vdash P \Rightarrow R$».

31.022 - If $\vdash P \Rightarrow Q$ and if $\vdash Q \Rightarrow P$, then $\vdash P \Leftrightarrow Q$.

(1)	$\vdash$	$P \Rightarrow Q$	By hp
(2)	$\vdash$	$Q \Rightarrow P$	By hp
(3)	$\vdash$	$(P \Rightarrow Q) \wedge (Q \Rightarrow P)$	By rule 30.22
(4)	$\vdash$	$(P \Leftrightarrow Q)$	By df 30.35

'*a*' being the number of $\vdash (P \Rightarrow Q)$, '*b*' the number of $\vdash (Q \Rightarrow P)$, we write 'From *a* and *b* by df 30.35'.

31.03 - According to the rule 30.24 of replacement of strict equivalents, if we have $\vdash P \Leftrightarrow Q$, we may replace '*P*' by 'Q' and inversely. If the theorem $\vdash P \Leftrightarrow Q$ is numbered '*a*', the application of the rule will be mentioned by 'Rp by *a*'.

31.04 - Replacements by virtue of a definition numbered '*a*' will be denoted 'By df *a*'.

31.1 - *Identity principle.*

31.11 - $\vdash$ $p \Rightarrow p$ (=**sa**00′)

(1)	$\vdash$	$p \Rightarrow (p \wedge p)$	30.14
(2)	$\vdash$	$(p \wedge p) \Rightarrow p$	30.11 subst
(3)	$\vdash$	Th	From (1) and (2) by 30.15

31.12 - $\vdash$ $p \Leftrightarrow p$ (=**sa**00)

From 31.11 stated twice, by df 30.35.

31.15 - If '*P*' for 'Q', then $\vdash P \Leftrightarrow Q$.

(1) $\vdash$ $P \Leftrightarrow P$ 31.12

(2) $\vdash$ $P \Leftrightarrow Q$ Subst by the supposed definition «'*P*' for 'Q'».

31.16 - If $\vdash P \Leftrightarrow Q$, then $\vdash P \Rightarrow Q$.

(1)	$\vdash$	$P \Leftrightarrow Q$	By hp
(2)	$\vdash$	$P \Rightarrow P$	31.11
(3)	$\vdash$	Th	Rp by (1)

The same method of proof may be used for the other rules of 31.1.

(1) and (3) as in 31.16.

(2) being the consequence to be proved, putting '*P*' instead of 'Q', the result being some form of 31.11 subst or 31.12 subst.

31.161 - If $\vdash P \Leftrightarrow Q$, then $\vdash Q \Rightarrow P$,
31.17 - If $\vdash P \Leftrightarrow Q$, then $\vdash Q \Leftrightarrow P$,
31.18 - If $\vdash P \Leftrightarrow Q$, then $\vdash \sim P \Leftrightarrow \sim Q$,
31.181 - If $\vdash P \Leftrightarrow Q$, then $\vdash (R \wedge P) \Leftrightarrow (R \wedge Q)$,
31.182 - If $\vdash P \Leftrightarrow Q$, then $\vdash (R \vee P) \Leftrightarrow (R \vee Q)$,
31.19 - If $\vdash P \Leftrightarrow Q$, then $\vdash \Box P \Leftrightarrow \Box Q$, **(Sm43)**
31.191 - If $\vdash P \Leftrightarrow Q$, then $\vdash \Diamond P \Leftrightarrow \Diamond Q$, **(Sm44)**
31.192 - If $\vdash P \Leftrightarrow Q$, then $\vdash \sim \Diamond P \Leftrightarrow \sim \Diamond Q$.

The remaining part of §31 is devoted to the proof of the **sa**-theorems. Except for the purpose of reference, we prove only those **sa**-theorems which are necessary to establish the meta-theorem 33.4, according to which all **sa**-theorems are valid.

For the proof of the **sa**-theorems, it will be necessary to prove first a few **Sa**-theorems: the identity-principle and various forms of the conversion of strict implication (31.6 is only mentioned for the purpose of reference).

31.2 - *Conjunction.*

In this §31.2, the axioms 30.12-13-14 will be transformed into strict equivalences (31.23 is a corollary).

31.21 -	$\vdash$	$(p \wedge q) \Leftrightarrow (q \wedge p)$	(=**sa**11)
(1)	$\vdash$	$(p \wedge q) \Rightarrow (q \wedge p)$	30.12
(2)	$\vdash$	$(q \wedge p) \Rightarrow (p \wedge q)$	30.12 subst
(3)	$\vdash$	Th	From (1) and (2); by df 30.35
31.22 -	$\vdash$	$p \Leftrightarrow (p \wedge p)$	(=**sa**14)
(1)	$\vdash$	$p \Rightarrow (p \wedge p)$	30.14
(2)	$\vdash$	$(p \wedge p) \Rightarrow p$	30.11 subst
(3)	$\vdash$	Th	From (1) and (2) by df 30.35
31.23 -	$\vdash$	$(p \wedge q) \Rightarrow q$	(=**sa**101)
(1)	$\vdash$	$(q \wedge p) \Rightarrow q$	30.11 subst
(2)	$\vdash$	Th	Rp by 31.21
31.24 -	$\vdash$	$[p \wedge (q \wedge r)] \Leftrightarrow [(p \wedge q) \wedge r]$	(=**sa**12)
(1)	$\vdash$	$[(p \wedge q) \wedge r] \Rightarrow [p \wedge (q \wedge r)]$	30.13
(2)	$\vdash$	$[p \wedge (q \wedge r)] \Leftrightarrow [p \wedge (r \wedge q)]$	From 31.12 Rp by 31.21
(3)	$\vdash$	$[p \wedge (q \wedge r)] \Leftrightarrow [(r \wedge q) \wedge p)]$	Rp by 31.21
(4)	$\vdash$	$[(r \wedge q) \wedge p] \Rightarrow [r \wedge (q \wedge p)]$	From 30.13 subst, Rp by 31.21
(5)	$\vdash$	$[(r \wedge q) \wedge p] \Rightarrow [r \wedge (p \wedge q)]$	Rp by 31.21

(6)	$\vdash$	$[(r\wedge q)\wedge p] \Rightarrow [(p\wedge q)\wedge r]$	Rp by 31.21
(7)	$\vdash$	$[(q\wedge r)\wedge p] \Rightarrow [(p\wedge q)\wedge r]$	Rp by 31.21
(8)	$\vdash$	$[p\wedge (q\wedge r)] \Rightarrow [(p\wedge q)\wedge r]$	Rp by (3)
(9)	$\vdash$	Th	From (1) and (8) by df 30.35

31.241 - We write: '$p\wedge q\wedge r$' for '$(p\wedge q)\wedge r$'.

31.3 - *Negation.*

31.31 -	$\vdash$	$(\sim p\Rightarrow q) \Leftrightarrow (\sim q\Rightarrow p)$	(=**Sa**312)
(1)	$\vdash$	$(\sim p\wedge \sim q) \Leftrightarrow (\sim q\wedge \sim p)$	31.21 subst
(2)	$\vdash$	$\sim\Diamond(\sim p\wedge \sim q) \Leftrightarrow \sim\Diamond(\sim q\wedge \sim p)$	By rule 31.192
(3)	$\vdash$	Th	By df 30.34

It may be stressed that 31.31 (from which 31.34 and 31.341 follow by 31.32) is simply a consequence of 31.21 (commutativity of conjunction) by virtue of the definition 30.34 of strict implication.

31.32 -	$\vdash$	$\sim\sim p\Leftrightarrow p$	(=**sa**01)
(1)	$\vdash$	$\sim p \Rightarrow \sim p$	31.11 subst
(2)	$\vdash$	$\sim\sim p \Rightarrow p$	By 31.31
(3)	$\vdash$	$\sim\sim\sim\sim p \Rightarrow \sim\sim p$	Subst in (2)
(4)	$\vdash$	$\sim\sim\sim\sim p \Rightarrow p$	From (3) and (2) by 30.15
(5)	$\vdash$	$\sim p \Rightarrow \sim\sim\sim p$	Rp by 31.31
(6)	$\vdash$	$\sim\sim\sim p \Rightarrow \sim p$	(2) Subst
(7)	$\vdash$	$\sim\sim\sim p \Leftrightarrow \sim p$	From (5) and (6) by df
(8)	$\vdash$	$\sim\Diamond(p\wedge \sim p)$	From 31.11 by df 30.34
(9)	$\vdash$	$\sim\Diamond(p\wedge \sim\sim\sim p)$	Rp by (7)
(10)	$\vdash$	$p \Rightarrow \sim\sim p$	By df 30.34
(11)	$\vdash$	Th	From (2) and (10) by df 30.35
31.34 -	$\vdash$	$(p\Rightarrow q) \Leftrightarrow (\sim q\Rightarrow \sim p)$	(=**Sa**31)
(1)	$\vdash$	$(\sim\sim p\Rightarrow q) \Leftrightarrow (\sim q\Rightarrow \sim p)$	31.31 subst
(2)	$\vdash$	Th	Rp by 31.32
31.341 -	$\vdash$	$(p\Rightarrow \sim q) \Leftrightarrow (q\Rightarrow \sim p)$	(=**Sa**311)
(1)	$\vdash$	$(p\Rightarrow \sim q) \Leftrightarrow (\sim\sim q\Rightarrow \sim p)$	31.34 subst
(2)	$\vdash$	Th	Rp by 31.32
31.35 -	$\vdash$	$(p\vee q) \Leftrightarrow \sim(\sim p\wedge \sim q)$	(=**sa**031) From df 30.31 by rule 31.15
31.351 -	$\vdash$	$\sim(p\vee q) \Leftrightarrow (\sim p\wedge \sim q)$	(=**sa**03)
(1)	$\vdash$	$\sim(p\vee q) \Leftrightarrow \sim\sim(\sim p\wedge \sim q)$	From 31.35 by rule 31.18
(2)	$\vdash$	Th	Rp by 31.32
31.36 -	$\vdash$	$\sim(p\wedge q) \Leftrightarrow (\sim p\vee \sim q)$	(=**sa**02)

(1)	$\vdash$	$(\sim p \vee \sim q) \Leftrightarrow \sim(\sim\sim p \wedge \sim\sim q)$	31.35 subst
(2)	$\vdash$	$(\sim p \vee \sim q) \Leftrightarrow \sim(p \wedge q)$	From 31.32 by rule 31.03
(3)	$\vdash$	Th	By 31.17
31.361 -	$\vdash$	$(p \wedge q) \Leftrightarrow \sim(\sim p \vee \sim q)$	(=**sa**021)
(1)	$\vdash$	$\sim(\sim p \vee \sim q) \Leftrightarrow (\sim\sim p \wedge \sim\sim q)$	31.351 subst
(2)	$\vdash$	$\sim(\sim p \vee \sim q) \Leftrightarrow (p \wedge q)$	From 31.32 by rule 31.03
(3)	$\vdash$	Th	By 31.17

31.4 - *Alternation.*

Theorems about alternation are now simply consequences of definition 30.31.

31.41 -	$\vdash$	$(p \vee q) \Leftrightarrow (q \vee p)$	(=**sa**21)
(1)	$\vdash$	$(\sim p \wedge \sim q) \Leftrightarrow (\sim q \wedge \sim p)$	31.21 subst
(2)	$\vdash$	$\sim(\sim p \wedge \sim q) \Leftrightarrow \sim(\sim q \wedge \sim p)$	By rule 31.18
(3)	$\vdash$	Th	By df 30.31
31.42 -	$\vdash$	$p \Leftrightarrow (p \vee p)$	(=**sa**24) similarly
31.43 -	$\vdash$	$p \Rightarrow (p \vee q)$	(=**sa**20)
(1)	$\vdash$	$(\sim p \wedge \sim q) \Rightarrow \sim p$	31.11 subst
(2)	$\vdash$	$\sim\sim p \Rightarrow \sim(\sim p \wedge \sim q)$	By 31.24
(3)	$\vdash$	Th	By df 30.31 and subst by 31.32
31.44 -	$\vdash$	$[p \vee (q \vee r)] \Leftrightarrow [(p \vee q) \vee r]$	(=**sa**22)

Proof as for 31.41.

31.441 - We write: '$p \vee q \vee r$' for '$(p \vee q) \vee r$'.

31.5 - *Material implication.*

Theorems mentioning material implication may be derived by means of df 30.32. A few examples:

31.51 -	$\vdash$	$\sim(p \rightarrow q) \Leftrightarrow (p \wedge \sim q)$	(=**sa**502)
(1)	$\vdash$	$(p \rightarrow q) \Leftrightarrow \sim(p \wedge \sim q)$	From df 30.32 by rule 31.15
(2)	$\vdash$	$\sim(p \rightarrow q) \Leftrightarrow \sim\sim(p \wedge \sim q)$	By rule 31.18
(3)	$\vdash$	Th	Rp by 31.32
31.52 -	$\vdash$	$(p \rightarrow q) \Leftrightarrow (\sim p \vee q)$	(=**sa**501)
(1)	$\vdash$	$(p \rightarrow q) \Leftrightarrow \sim(p \wedge \sim q)$	From df 30.32 by rule 31.15
(2)	$\vdash$	$(p \rightarrow q) \Leftrightarrow (\sim p \vee \sim\sim q)$	By 31.361
(3)	$\vdash$	Th	By 31.32
31.53 -	$\vdash$	$p \Leftrightarrow (\sim p \rightarrow p)$	(=**sa**531)
(1)	$\vdash$	$p \Leftrightarrow (p \vee p)$	31.42
(2)	$\vdash$	$p \Leftrightarrow (\sim\sim p \vee p)$	By 31.32

(3) ⊢ Th By 31.52

31.54 - ⊢ $\sim p \Leftrightarrow (p \rightarrow \sim p)$ (=**sa**532) similarly

31.6 - *Strict equivalence.*

The following theorems (not to be used in § 34) are direct consequences of definition 30.35 and 31.34.

31.61 - ⊢ $(p \Leftrightarrow q) \Leftrightarrow (q \Leftrightarrow p)$ (=**Sa**41)

(1) ⊢ $[(p \Rightarrow q) \wedge (q \Rightarrow p)] \Leftrightarrow [(q \Leftrightarrow p) \wedge (p \Leftrightarrow q)]$ 21 subst

(2) ⊢ Th By df 30.35

31.62 - ⊢ $(p \Leftrightarrow q) \Leftrightarrow (\sim p \Leftrightarrow \sim q)$ (=**Sa**42)

(1) ⊢ $[(p \Rightarrow q) \wedge (q \Rightarrow p)] \Leftrightarrow [(q \Rightarrow p) \wedge (p \Rightarrow q)]$ 31.21 subst

(2) ⊢ $[(p \Rightarrow q) \wedge (q \Rightarrow p)] \Leftrightarrow [(\sim p \Rightarrow \sim q) \wedge (\sim q \Rightarrow \sim p)]$ Rp by 31.34

(3) ⊢ Th By df 30.35

31.631 - ⊢ $(p \Leftrightarrow q) \Rightarrow (p \Rightarrow q)$ (=**Sa**431)

(1) ⊢ $[(p \Rightarrow q) \wedge (q \Rightarrow p)] \Rightarrow (p \Rightarrow q)$ 30.11 subst

(2) ⊢ Th By df 30.35

31.632 - ⊢ $(p \Leftrightarrow q) \Rightarrow (q \Rightarrow p)$ (=**Sa**432)

(1) ⊢ $[(p \Rightarrow q) \wedge (q \Rightarrow p)] \Rightarrow (q \Rightarrow p)$ 31.23 subst

(2) ⊢ Th By df 30.35

§ 32 - DERIVATIONS IN SYSTEM 1° (STRICT IMPLICATION)

This new series of derived theorems may be divided in two. We give first theorems about strict implication and complex inferences using strict implications (theorem 32.4 may be added to this part). Then, in § 33, these theorems will be used to derive theorems about explicit modalities.

32.0 - *Strict implication.*

32.01 - ⊢ $(p \Rightarrow q) \Leftrightarrow \Box \sim (p \wedge \sim q)$ (=**S′a**503)

(1) ⊢ $(p \Rightarrow q) \Leftrightarrow \sim \Diamond (p \wedge \sim q)$ From 30.32 by rule 31.15

(2) ⊢ $(p \Rightarrow q) \Leftrightarrow \sim \Diamond \sim \sim (p \wedge \sim q)$ Rp by 31.32

(3) ⊢ Th By df 30.36

32.02 - ⊢ $(p \Rightarrow q) \Leftrightarrow \Box (p \rightarrow q)$ From 32.01 by df 30.32

The use of this equivalence will be frequent.

32.03 - ⊢ $(p \Rightarrow q) \Leftrightarrow \Box (\sim p \vee q)$ (=**S′a**501)

(1) ⊢ $(p \rightarrow q) \Leftrightarrow (\sim p \vee q)$ 31.52

(2) ⊢ $\Box(p\rightarrow q) \Leftrightarrow \Box(\sim p \vee q)$ By rule 31.19
(3) ⊢ Th Rp by 32.02

32.1 - *Antilogism — Importation-exportation.*

32.11 - ⊢ $[(p\wedge q)\Rightarrow r] \Leftrightarrow [(p\wedge \sim r)\Rightarrow \sim q]$ (=**Sa**32)
(1) ⊢ $(q\wedge \sim r) \Leftrightarrow (\sim r\wedge q)$ 31.21 subst
(2) ⊢ $[p\wedge(q\wedge \sim r)] \Leftrightarrow [p\wedge(\sim r\wedge q)]$ By rule 31.181
(3) ⊢ $[(p\wedge q)\wedge \sim r] \Leftrightarrow [(p\wedge \sim r)\wedge q]$ By 31.24
(4) ⊢ $[(p\wedge q) \wedge \sim r) \Leftrightarrow [(p\wedge \sim r) \wedge \sim\sim q]$ By 31.32
(5) ⊢ $\sim\Diamond[(p\wedge q)\wedge \sim r] \Leftrightarrow \sim\Diamond[(p\wedge \sim r) \wedge \sim\sim q]$ By rule 31.192
(6) ⊢ Th By df 30.34

This theorem will be used in the proof of 32.21.

32.111 - ⊢ $[(p\wedge q)\Rightarrow r] \Leftrightarrow [(q\wedge \sim r)\Rightarrow \sim p]$ (=**Sa**321)
(1) ⊢ $[(p\wedge q)\wedge \sim r] \Leftrightarrow [p\wedge(q\wedge \sim r)]$ From 31.24 subst by rule 16
(2) ⊢ $[(p\wedge q)\wedge \sim r] \Leftrightarrow [(q\wedge \sim r)\wedge p]$ By 31.21
(3) ⊢ $[(p\wedge q)\wedge \sim r] \Leftrightarrow [(q\wedge \sim r)\wedge \sim\sim p]$ By 31.32
(4) ⊢ $\sim\Diamond[(p\wedge q)\wedge \sim r] \Leftrightarrow \sim\Diamond[(q\wedge \sim r)\wedge \sim\sim p]$ By rule 31.192
(5) ⊢ Th By df 30.34

32.12 - ⊢ $[(p\wedge q)\Rightarrow r] \Leftrightarrow [p\Rightarrow(q\rightarrow r)]$ (=**S″a**70)
(1) ⊢ $[(p\wedge q)\wedge \sim r] \Leftrightarrow [p\wedge(q\wedge \sim r)]$ From 31.24 subst by rule 31.161
(2) ⊢ $[(p\wedge q)\wedge \sim r] \Leftrightarrow [p\wedge \sim(q\rightarrow r)]$ Rp by 31.51
(3) ⊢ $\sim\Diamond[(p\wedge q)\wedge \sim r] \Leftrightarrow \sim\Diamond[p\wedge \sim(q\rightarrow r)]$ By rule 31.192
(4) ⊢ Th By df 30.34

32.121 - ⊢ $[(p\wedge \sim r)\Rightarrow \sim q] \Leftrightarrow [p\Rightarrow(q\rightarrow r)]$ From 32.12 rp by 32.11

32.13 - ⊢ $[p\Rightarrow(q\rightarrow r)] \Leftrightarrow [q\Rightarrow(p\rightarrow r)]$ (=**S″a**705)
(1) ⊢ $[p\Rightarrow(q\rightarrow r)] \Leftrightarrow [(p\wedge \sim r)\Rightarrow \sim q]$ From 32.121 by rule 31.17
(2) ⊢ $[p\Rightarrow(q\rightarrow r)] \Leftrightarrow [q\sim \sim(p\wedge \sim r)]$ By 31.341
(3) ⊢ Th By df 30.32

32.2 - *Modus ponens with material implication.*

32.21 - ⊢ $[p\wedge(p\rightarrow q)] \Rightarrow q$ (=**sa**61)
(1) ⊢ $(p\wedge \sim q) \Rightarrow (p\wedge \sim q)$ 31.12 subst
(2) ⊢ $[p\wedge \sim(p\wedge \sim q)] \Rightarrow \sim\sim q$ By 32.11
(3) ⊢ $[p\wedge(p\rightarrow q)] \Rightarrow \sim\sim q$ By df 30.32
(4) ⊢ Th By 31.32

32.211 - If ⊢ $P\rightarrow Q$ and if ⊢ P, then ⊢ Q.

(1)	$\vdash$	$P \rightarrow Q$	By hp
(2)	$\vdash$	P	By hp
(3)	$\vdash$	$P \wedge (P \rightarrow Q)$	By rule 30.22
(4)	$\vdash$	$[P \wedge (P \rightarrow Q)] \Rightarrow Q$	32.21
(5)	$\vdash$	Th	By rule 30.23
32.22 -	$\vdash$	$[\sim q \wedge (p \rightarrow q)] \Rightarrow \sim p$	(=**sa**611)
(1)	$\vdash$	$[p \wedge (p \rightarrow q)] \Rightarrow q$	32.21
(2)	$\vdash$	$[(p \rightarrow q) \wedge \sim q] \Rightarrow \sim p$	By 32.111
(3)	$\vdash$	Th	By 31.21

32.3 - *Complex syllogistic inferences.*

32.31 - $\vdash$ $\{(p \Rightarrow q) \wedge [(q \wedge s) \Rightarrow r]\} \Rightarrow [(p \wedge s) \Rightarrow r]$ (=**Sa**625)

(1) $\vdash$ $\{[(s \wedge \sim r) \Rightarrow \sim q)] \wedge (\sim q \Rightarrow \sim p)\} \Rightarrow [(s \wedge \sim r) \Rightarrow \sim p]$
30.15 subst

(2) $\vdash$ $\{[(q \wedge s) \Rightarrow r] \wedge (\sim q \Rightarrow \sim p)]\} \Rightarrow [(p \wedge s) \Rightarrow r]$
By 32.111 used twice

(3) $\vdash$ $[(q \wedge s \Rightarrow r) \wedge (p \Rightarrow q)] \Rightarrow (p \wedge s \Rightarrow r)$ By 31.34

(4) $\vdash$ Th By 31.21

This theorem will be used in the proofs of 33.32 and 33.35.

32.311 - If $\vdash P \Rightarrow Q$ and if $\vdash (Q \wedge S) \Rightarrow R$, then $\vdash (P \wedge S) \Rightarrow R$
From: 32.31 by rule 31.02

32.32 - $\vdash$ $[(p \Rightarrow q) \wedge (q \Rightarrow r) \wedge (r \Rightarrow s)] \Rightarrow (p \Rightarrow s)$ (=**Sa**63)

(1) $\vdash$ $[(q \Rightarrow r) \wedge (r \Rightarrow s)] \Rightarrow (q \Rightarrow s)$ 30.15 subst

(2) $\vdash$ $[(q \Rightarrow s) \wedge (p \Rightarrow q)] \Rightarrow (p \Rightarrow s)$ From 30.15 by 31.21

(3) $\vdash$ $[(q \Rightarrow r) \wedge (r \Rightarrow s) \wedge (p \Rightarrow q)] \Rightarrow (p \Rightarrow s)$
By rule 32.311, (1) being $P \Rightarrow Q$ and (2) being $(Q \wedge S) \Rightarrow R$

(4) $\vdash$ Th By 31.21 (and 31.241)

This theorem will be used in the proof of 33.31.

32.4 - $\vdash$ $(p \rightarrow q) \Rightarrow [(r \vee p) \rightarrow (r \vee q)]$ (=**sa**382)

(1) $\vdash$ $[\sim q \wedge (p \rightarrow q)] \Rightarrow \sim p$ 32.22

(2) $\vdash$ $(\sim q \wedge \sim r) \Rightarrow (\sim r \wedge \sim p)$ 31.12 subst

(3) $\vdash$ $[\sim q \wedge (p \rightarrow q) \wedge \sim r] \Rightarrow (\sim r \wedge \sim p)$ By rule 32.311
(1) being $P \Rightarrow Q$ and (2) being $(Q \wedge S) \Rightarrow R$.

(4) $\vdash$ $[(p \rightarrow q) \wedge \sim r \wedge \sim q] \Rightarrow (\sim r \wedge \sim p)$ By 31.21 and 31.24

(5) $\vdash$ $[(p \rightarrow q) \wedge \sim (r \vee q)] \Rightarrow \sim (r \vee p)$ Rp by 31.351

(6) $\vdash$ Th By 32.121

This theorem will be used in 34.114.

§ 33 - EXPLICIT MODALITIES IN SYSTEM 1°

Since in S1° there are no axioms with explicit modalities appearing in them, but only axioms with strict implications, we have first to state strict equivalences between explicit modalities and strict implications (33.1); these will allow us to derive the theorems 33.3.

Theorems about negation of modalities (33.2) are direct consequences of definition 30.36.

33.1 - *Strict implications equivalent to modalities.*

33.11 -	$\vdash$	$\Box p \Leftrightarrow (\sim p \Rightarrow p)$	(=**S'a**531)
(1)	$\vdash$	$p \Leftrightarrow (p \vee p)$	31.42
(2)	$\vdash$	$p \Leftrightarrow (\sim\sim p \vee p)$	By 31.32
(3)	$\vdash$	$\Box p \Leftrightarrow \Box(\sim\sim p \vee p)$	By 31.19
(4)	$\vdash$	Th	Rp by 32.02
33.12 -	$\vdash$	$\Box \sim p \Leftrightarrow (p \Rightarrow \sim p)$	(=**S'a**532)
(1)	$\vdash$	$\sim p \Leftrightarrow (\sim p \vee \sim p)$	31.42 subst
(2)	$\vdash$	$\Box \sim p \Leftrightarrow \Box(\sim p \vee \sim p)$	By 31.19
(3)	$\vdash$	Th	Rp by 32.03

33.2 - *Negations of modalities.*

33.21 -	$\vdash$	$\sim\Diamond\sim p \Leftrightarrow \Box p$	(=**sm**011)	From df. 30.36 by 31.15
33.211 -	$\vdash$	$\Diamond\sim p \Leftrightarrow \sim\Box p$	(=**sm**01)	
(1)	$\vdash$	$\vdash \sim\sim\Diamond\sim p \Leftrightarrow \sim\Box p$		From 33.21 by 31.18
(2)	$\vdash$	Th		Rp by 31.32
33.22 -	$\vdash$	$\sim\Box\sim p \Leftrightarrow \Diamond p$		(=**sm**021)
(1)	$\vdash$	$\sim\Box\sim p \Leftrightarrow \Diamond\sim\sim p$		33.211 subst
(2)	$\vdash$	Th		Rp by 31.32
33.23 -	$\vdash$	$\sim\Diamond p \Leftrightarrow \Box\sim p$		(=**sm**02)
(1)	$\vdash$	$\sim\Diamond p \Leftrightarrow \sim\sim\Box\sim p$		From 33.22 by 31.18
(2)	$\vdash$	Th		Rp by 31.32

33.3 - *Modus ponens with modal affirmations.*

33.31 -	$\vdash$	$[(p \Rightarrow q) \wedge \Box p] \Rightarrow \Box q$	(=**Sm**315)
(1)	$\vdash$	$[(\sim q \Rightarrow \sim p) \wedge (\sim p \Rightarrow p) \wedge (p \Rightarrow q)] \Rightarrow (\sim q \Rightarrow q)$	32.32 subst
(2)	$\vdash$	$[(p \Rightarrow q) \wedge (\sim q \Rightarrow \sim p) \wedge (\sim p \Rightarrow p)] \Rightarrow (\sim q \Rightarrow q)$	By 31.21
(3)	$\vdash$	$[(p \Rightarrow q) \wedge (\sim p \Rightarrow p)] \Rightarrow (\sim q \Rightarrow q)$	Rp by 31.34 and 31.22
(4)	$\vdash$	Th	Rp by 33.11

33.311 -	$\vdash$	$(p\Rightarrow q) \Rightarrow (\Box p\rightarrow\Box q)$ (=**Sm**31)	From 33.31 by 32.12
33.32 -	$\vdash$	$[(p\Rightarrow q)\wedge\Diamond p] \Rightarrow \Diamond q$	(=**Sm**325)
(1)	$\vdash$	$[(\sim q\Rightarrow\sim p)\wedge\Box\sim q] \Rightarrow \Box\sim p$	33.31 subst
(2)	$\vdash$	$[(p\Rightarrow q)\wedge\Box\sim q] \Rightarrow \Box\sim p$	Rp by 32.12
(3)	$\vdash$	$[(p\Rightarrow q)\wedge\sim\Box\sim p] \Rightarrow \sim\Box\sim q$	By 32.11
(4)	$\vdash$	Th	Rp by 33.22
33.321 -	$\vdash$	$(p\Rightarrow q) \Rightarrow (\Diamond p\rightarrow\Diamond q)$ (=**Sm**32)	From 33.32 by 32.12

33.4 -	$\vdash$	$\{[(p\wedge r)\Rightarrow q]\wedge\Box p\} \Rightarrow (r\Rightarrow q)$	
(1)	$\vdash$	$\{[p\Rightarrow(r\rightarrow q)]\wedge\Box p\} \Rightarrow \Box(r\rightarrow q)$	33.31 subst
(2)	$\vdash$	$\{(p\wedge r\Rightarrow q)\wedge\Box p\} \Rightarrow \Box(r\rightarrow q)$	Rp by 32.12
(3)	$\vdash$	Th	Rp by 32.02

33.5 - Notwithstanding their elementary character, it may be worth to give rules for the *negation of modalities*. By repeated use of 32.63 and 32.64 and possibly of 31.32, it is clear that:
33.51 - If *Mp* is a proper modality, then $\vdash \sim Mp\Leftrightarrow M'\sim p$, where '*M*' and '*M'*' are obtained from each other by exchanging the signs '$\Box$' and '$\Diamond$'.
33.52 - If *Mp* is an affirmative proper modality, there exists an (affirmative) modality M'*p* strictly equivalent to *Mp*, in which 'M'' does not contain any sign of negation.
33.53 - If *Mp* is a proper negative modality, there exists an affirmative modality *M'p*, in which '*M'*' does not contain any sign of negation, and such that $\vdash Mp\Leftrightarrow M'\sim p$.
33.54 - If *Mp* is a proper negative modality, there exists an affirmative modality *M''p*, in which '*M''*' does not contain any sign of negation, and such that $\vdash Mp\Rightarrow\sim M''p$.

33.6 - To eliminate tedious repetitions of demonstrations, we may extend to System 1° the usual methods of proof by *duality*.
33.61 - We shall define the dual X* of a formula X as the negation of the formula obtained by substituting '$\sim p$', '$\sim q$', '$\sim r$' ... for '*p*', '*q*', '*r*', in it. We might write:

'X*' for '$\sim[\sim p/p,\ \sim q/q,\ \sim r/r]$ X'.

33.62 - If X is a propositional variable *P*, X* is $\sim\sim P$, hence X* is X.

33.63 - According to the definitory rule 33.61 and to several theorems about negation:

$\vdash \quad (\sim P)^* \Leftrightarrow \sim (P^*)$

$\vdash \quad (P \wedge Q)^* \Leftrightarrow (P^* \vee Q^*)$

$\vdash \quad (P \vee Q)^* \Leftrightarrow (P^* \wedge Q^*)$

$\vdash \quad (P \rightarrow Q)^* \Leftrightarrow \sim (Q^* \rightarrow P^*)$

$\vdash \quad (P \leftrightarrow Q)^* \Leftrightarrow \sim (P^* \leftrightarrow Q^*)$

$\vdash \quad (\ \Box P)^* \Leftrightarrow \Diamond (P^*)$

$\vdash \quad (\ \Diamond P)^* \Leftrightarrow \Box (P^*)$

$\vdash \quad (P \Rightarrow Q)^* \Leftrightarrow \sim (Q^* \Rightarrow P^*)$ (1)

$\vdash \quad (P \Leftrightarrow Q)^* \Leftrightarrow \sim (P^* \Leftrightarrow Q^*)$

33.64 - We may state the rules:

$\vdash \quad (P \Rightarrow Q)^* \Leftrightarrow \sim (Q^* \Rightarrow P^*)$ (1)

If $\vdash P$, then $\vdash \sim P^*$. By virtue of rule 30.21 and of 33.61.

Hence by 33.63:

If $\vdash P \rightarrow Q$, then $\vdash Q^* \rightarrow P^*$,

If $\vdash P \leftrightarrow Q$, then $\vdash P^* \leftrightarrow Q^*$,

If $\vdash P \Rightarrow Q$, then $\vdash Q^* \Rightarrow P^*$,

If $\vdash P \Leftrightarrow Q$, then $\vdash P^* \Leftrightarrow Q^*$.

33.65 - We shall in the future derive some theorems by duality and write simply: 'From... by duality'; so we might have had e.g.

(31.41) $\vdash \quad (p \vee q) \Leftrightarrow (q \vee p)$ From 31.21 by duality

(31.43) $\vdash \quad p \Rightarrow (p \vee q)$ From 31.23 by duality

33.66 - The formulas we shall derive «by duality» will be generally of the form $Q^* \Rightarrow P^*$ or $P^* \Leftrightarrow Q^*$. In this case the derivation by duality may be proved as done in 33.63, i.e.:

(1) stating the original theorem $P \Rightarrow Q$ or $P \Leftrightarrow Q$, substituting '$\sim p$', '$\sim q$', '$\sim r$' ... for 'p', 'q', 'r', in it;

(2) then using 31.18 or 31.34;

(3) then applying theorems about negation, such as 31.32-35-36 and 31.32-61-62.

---

(1) We might define 'P **O** Q' for '$\Diamond (P \wedge Q)$'; then $\vdash (P \Rightarrow Q)^* \Leftrightarrow (\sim P)^*$**O**$Q^*$.

§ 34 - GENERAL METATHEOREMS FOR SYSTEM 1°

34.1 - If P is valid in APC, then $\vdash \Box P$ (i.e. $\Box P$ is valid in system 1°).

The demonstration proceeds as follows:

34.11 - If P is an axiom in §13, then $\vdash \Box P$.

We prove this for the four axioms 13.1.

34.111 - $\vdash$ $\Box[(p \vee p) \rightarrow p]$

(1)	$\vdash$	$p \Leftrightarrow (p \vee p)$	31.42
(2)	$\vdash$	$(p \vee p) \Rightarrow p$	By rule 31.161
(3)	$\vdash$	Th	Rp by 32.02

34.112 - $\vdash$ $\Box[p \rightarrow (p \vee q)]$

(1)	$\vdash$	$p \Rightarrow (p \vee q)$	31.43
(2)	$\vdash$	Th	Rp by 32.02

34.113 - $\vdash$ $\Box[(p \vee q) \rightarrow (q \vee p)]$

(1)	$\vdash$	$(p \vee q) \Leftrightarrow (q \vee p)$	31.41
(2)	$\vdash$	$(p \vee q) \Rightarrow (q \vee p)$	By rule 31.16
(3)	$\vdash$	Th	Rp by 32.02

34.114 - $\vdash$ $\Box\{(p \rightarrow q) \rightarrow [(r \vee p) \rightarrow (r \vee q)]\}$

(1)	$\vdash$	$(p \rightarrow q) \Rightarrow [(r \vee p) \rightarrow (r \vee q)]$	32.4
(2)	$\vdash$	Th	By 32.02

34.12 - If $\vdash Q$ is derived from $\vdash P$ by the rule of substitution 13.2, then $\vdash \Box Q$ from $\vdash \Box P$, by the rule of substitution 30.21.

34.13 - If $\vdash Q$ is derived from $\vdash P \rightarrow Q$ and $\vdash P$ by the rule of detachment 13.3, then $\vdash \Box Q$ from $\vdash \Box(P \rightarrow Q)$ and $\vdash \Box P$.

(1)	$\vdash$	$\Box(P \rightarrow Q)$	By hp
(2)	$\vdash$	$P \Rightarrow Q$	By 32.02
(3)	$\vdash$	$\Box P$	By hp
(4)	$\vdash$	$(P \Rightarrow Q) \wedge \Box P$	By rule 30.22
(5)	$\vdash$	$\Box Q$	By 33.31

34.14 - *If* $\vdash Q$ is derived from $\vdash P$ by substitution according to the definitions 13.4, then $\vdash \Box Q$ from $\vdash \Box P$.

34.141 - For definition 13.41 of $\wedge$.

(1)	$\vdash$	$\Box P$	By hp
(2)	$\vdash$	$P \Leftrightarrow Q$	By 31.36
(3)	$\vdash$	$\Box P \Leftrightarrow \Box Q$	By rule 31.19
(4)	$\vdash$	$\Box Q$	By rule 30.24

34.142 - For definition 13.42 of '$\rightarrow$'.
Similarly, $\vdash P \Leftrightarrow Q$ being proved by 31.52.
34.143 - For definition 13.43 of '$\leftrightarrow$'.
Similarly, $\vdash P \Leftrightarrow Q$ being proved by df 30.33 and rule 31.15.
34.15 - And so if P is an **a**-formula (valid and thus provable) in APC, $\vdash \Box P$ is valid (in system 1°).

34.2 - If $\vdash \Box P$, then $\vdash P$ (P is valid in system 1°)

(1)	$\vdash$	$\Box P$	By hp
(2)	$\vdash$	$\sim P \Rightarrow P$	Rp by 33.11
(3)	$\vdash$	$(\Box P \vee \sim P) \Rightarrow \sim P$	31.23 subst
(4)	$\vdash$	$(\Box P \wedge \sim P) \Rightarrow P$	From (3) and (2) by 30.15
(5)	$\vdash$	$\Box P \Rightarrow (\sim P \rightarrow P)$	By 32.12
(6)	$\vdash$	$\Box P \Rightarrow P$	Rp by 31.53
(7)	$\vdash$	P	By rule 30.23 [1]

34.3 - All **a**-formulas are valid.
(1) If P is an **a**-formula, then $\Box P$ is valid, by 34.15.
(2) If $\Box P$ is valid, then P is valid by 34.2.
Hence in the future we may assert any **a**-formula without demonstration, writing simply 'From APC' or 'From APC, by 34.3'.

34.4 - All **sa**-formulas are valid.
Three cases are to be considered:
A. There is no main symbol '$\rightarrow$' or '$\leftrightarrow$' in the **a**-formula. Then the **sa**-formula is the same as the **a**-formula, which is valid, as just stated.
B. The main symbol of the **a**-formula is '$\rightarrow$'; then the **a**-formula is of the form $P \rightarrow Q$, and the **sa**-formula is $P \Rightarrow Q$.
34.41 - If $P \rightarrow Q$ is valid in APC, then $\vdash P \Rightarrow Q$.

(1)	$\vdash$	$\Box(P \rightarrow Q)$	By 34.15
(2)	$\vdash$	$P \Rightarrow Q$	By 32.02

C. The main symbol of the **a**-formula is '$\leftrightarrow$', then the **a**-formula is of the form $P \leftrightarrow Q$, and the **sa**-formula is $P \Leftrightarrow Q$.

---

[1] It may be stressed that the (6) in this proof is not the same as «$\Box p \Rightarrow p$», which is not provable in system 1°.
The (6) says that *if* $\Box P$ is valid, *then* $\vdash \Box P \Rightarrow P$.

34.42 - If $P \leftrightarrow Q$ is valid in APC, then $\vdash P \Leftrightarrow Q$.

We have first in APC:

(1)	$P \leftrightarrow Q$ is valid	By hp
(2)	$(P \to Q) \wedge (Q \to P)$ is valid	By df 13.43
(3)	$P \to Q$ is valid	By **a**431
(4)	$Q \to P$ is valid	By **a**432

Then we have in the system 1°:

(5)	$\vdash \Box(P \to Q)$	From (3) by 34.15
(6)	$\vdash P \Rightarrow Q$	By 32.02
(7)	$\vdash \Box(Q \to P)$	From (4) by 34.15
(8)	$\vdash Q \Rightarrow P$	By 32.02
(9)	$\vdash (P \Rightarrow Q) \wedge (Q \Rightarrow P)$	By rule 30.22
(10)	$\vdash P \Leftrightarrow Q$	By df 30.35

We shall frequently in the future state **sa**-formulas without demonstration, mentioning only 'From APC, by 34.4'.

Theorem 34.421 is a corollary of 34.42 and 34.422 an example of a theorem provable by 34.421.

34.421 - If $P \leftrightarrow Q$ is valid in APC, then $\vdash \Box P \Leftrightarrow \Box Q$;

(1)	$\vdash P \Leftrightarrow Q$	From the hp by 34.4
(2)	$\vdash \Box P \Leftrightarrow \Box Q$	By rule 31.19

34.422 - $\vdash (p \Rightarrow q) \Leftrightarrow [p \Rightarrow (p \wedge q)]$

(1)	$\vdash (p \to q) \Leftrightarrow [p \to (p \wedge q)]$	By APC
(2)	$\vdash \Box(p \to q) \Leftrightarrow \Box[(p \to p) \wedge q]$	By 34.421
(3)	$\vdash$ Th	By 32.02

***34**.5 - Thomas (1963) has shown that the following rule is valid in S1°:

***34**.51 - If $\vdash \Diamond p \Rightarrow \Box q$, then $\vdash p \Rightarrow q$.

One has also the following weakened rules:

***34**.52 - If $\vdash \Diamond p \to \Box q$, then $\vdash p \to q$, and

***34**.53 - If $\vdash \Diamond p \Rightarrow \Box q$, then $\vdash p \to q$.

But one cannot prove, in S1°, the corresponding formulas:

$(\Diamond p \Rightarrow \Box q) \to (p \Rightarrow q)$ (provable in S2°),
$(\Diamond p \to \Box q) \to (p \to q)$ (provable in S2),
$(\Diamond p \Rightarrow \Box q) \to (p \to q)$ (provable in S1),
$(\Diamond p \Rightarrow \Box q) \Rightarrow (p \Rightarrow q)$ (provable in S2°),
$(\Diamond p \to \Box q) \Rightarrow (p \to q)$ (provable in S2), nor
$(\Diamond p \Rightarrow \Box q) \Rightarrow (p \to q)$ (provable in S1).

§ 35 - T-THEOREMS IN SYSTEM 1°

35.0 - A «T-theorem» may be characterized as follows:

a. It is a formula of the form $(T \wedge P) \Rightarrow Q$;

b. 'T' designates a determined valid formula, but not an **a**-formula;

c. The formula $(T \wedge P) \Rightarrow Q$ is valid in System 1°;

d. The formula $P \Rightarrow Q$ is not valid in the same system, or at least no proof of it is known.

The reason why T may not be an **a**-formula is this: by 34.1, $\Box T$ would then be valid, and by 33.4, $\vdash P \Rightarrow Q$ might be deduced.

Examples of T-theorems:

$\vdash \quad \{[(p \wedge q) \Rightarrow p] \wedge \Diamond(p \wedge q)\} \Rightarrow \Diamond p$ (35.32)

$\vdash \quad \{[(q \wedge r) \Rightarrow (q \wedge r)] \wedge (p \Rightarrow q)\} \Rightarrow [(r \wedge p) \Rightarrow (r \wedge q)]$ (35.21)

In 35.32 the 'T' designates the valid formula '$(p \wedge q) \Rightarrow p$'.
In 35.21 the 'T' designates the valid formula '$(q \wedge r) \Rightarrow (q \wedge r)$'.
If '*d*' is the reference sign of the theorem without 'T', we write 'T*d*' for the theorem with 'T'. So the two preceding theorems are respectively T**sm**241 and T**Sa**381, because the theorems without 'T' would be **sm**241 and **Sa**381.

35.1 - *What can be deduced from* T-*theorems ?*

35.11 - If $\vdash (T \wedge P) \Rightarrow Q$ and if $\vdash P$, then $\vdash Q$.

(1)	$\vdash$	T	(T is valid)
(2)	$\vdash$	P	By hp
(3)	$\vdash$	$T \wedge P$	By rule 30.22
(4)	$\vdash$	$(T \wedge P) \Rightarrow Q$	By hp
(5)	$\vdash$	Q	From (3) and (4) by rule 30.23

35.111 - Hence we may deduce a consequence «by a T-theorem», just as well as by the theorem without T, in 31.01.

35.12 - If $\vdash (T \wedge P) \Rightarrow Q$, then $\vdash P \rightarrow Q$.

(1)	$\vdash$	$(T \wedge P) \Rightarrow Q$	By hp
(2)	$\vdash$	$T \Rightarrow (P \rightarrow Q)$	Subst by 32.12
(3)	$\vdash$	T	(T is valid)
(4)	$\vdash$	$P \rightarrow Q$	From (2) and (3) by rule 30.23

35.121 - By virtue of 32.211, we might justify 35.111 from the fact that $\vdash P \rightarrow Q$.

35.13 - What is the case when we have a T-theorem «both sides», i.e. when we have $\vdash (T \wedge P) \Rightarrow Q$ and $\vdash (T' \wedge Q) \Rightarrow P$, 'T' and 'T'' not being necessarily the same ?

35.131 - By virtue of 34.11, we have «If $\vdash P$, then $\vdash Q$» and «If $\vdash Q$, then $\vdash P$». (P and Q are deductively equivalent.) It might also be proved (taking $T'' = T \wedge T'$) that $\vdash (T'' \wedge P) \leftrightarrow (T' \wedge P)$.

35.132 - But $\vdash (T \wedge P) \Rightarrow Q$ and $\vdash (T' \wedge Q) \Rightarrow))P$ do not allow us to conclude $\vdash P \Leftrightarrow Q$, and so a «T-theorem both sides» does not allow the use of rule 30.24 of replacement of strict equivalents.

35.14 - By virtue of 35.12, if we have $\vdash (T \wedge P) \Rightarrow Q$ and $(T' \wedge Q) \Rightarrow P$, then $\vdash P \rightarrow Q$ and $\vdash Q \rightarrow P$, thus $\vdash P \leftrightarrow Q$.

35.141 - But this *material* equivalence between P and Q does not allow the use of the rule 30.24; the replacement is possible only for *strict* equivalents.

35.2 - *«Factor-theorems» and composition-theorems.*

35.21 - $\vdash$ $[T \wedge (p \Rightarrow q)] \Rightarrow [(r \wedge p) \Rightarrow (r \wedge q)]$ (=**TSa**381)
$T = [(q \wedge r) \Rightarrow (q \wedge r)]$ (31.12)
(1) $\vdash$ $\{[(p \Rightarrow q) \wedge [(q \wedge r) \Rightarrow (q \wedge r)]\} \Rightarrow [(p \wedge r) \Rightarrow (q \wedge r)]$ 32.31 subs
(2) $\vdash$ Th By 31.21

35.211 - $\vdash$ $[T \wedge (p \Rightarrow q)] \Rightarrow [(r \vee p) \Rightarrow (r \vee q)]$ (=**TSa**383)
$T = (p \vee r) \Rightarrow (p \vee r)$ (31.12)
(1) $\vdash$ $\{[(\sim p \wedge \sim r) \Rightarrow (\sim p \wedge \sim r)] \wedge (\sim q \Rightarrow \sim p)\} \Rightarrow [(\sim r \wedge \sim q) \Rightarrow (\sim r \wedge \sim p)]$ 34.21 subst
(2) $\vdash$ Th By 31.34 and 31.3.

35.22 - $\vdash$ $[T \wedge (p \Rightarrow q) \wedge (p \Rightarrow s)] \Rightarrow [p \Rightarrow (q \wedge s)]$ (=**TSa**651′)
$T = [(q \wedge s) \Rightarrow (q \wedge s)]$
(1) $\vdash$ $\{(p \Rightarrow q) \wedge [(q \wedge s) \Rightarrow (q \wedge s)]\} \Rightarrow [(p \wedge s) \Rightarrow (q \wedge s)]$ (31.12)
(2) $\vdash$ $\{(p \Rightarrow s) \wedge [(s \wedge p) \Rightarrow (q \wedge s)]\} \Rightarrow [(p \wedge p) \Rightarrow (q \wedge s)]$ 32.31 subst
(3) $\vdash$ $\{[(p \wedge s) \Rightarrow (q \wedge s)] \wedge (p \Rightarrow s)\} \Rightarrow [p \Rightarrow (q \wedge s)]$ 32.31 subst
(4) $\vdash$ $\{(p \Rightarrow q) \wedge [(q \wedge s) \Rightarrow (q \wedge s)] \wedge (p \Rightarrow s)\} \Rightarrow [(p \Rightarrow q) \wedge s]$
By 31.21 and 31.2
From (1) and (3) by rule 3.2311
(5) $\vdash$ Th By 31.21 and 31.2

35.221 - $\vdash$ $\{T \wedge [p \Rightarrow (q \wedge s)]\} \Rightarrow [(p \Rightarrow q) \wedge (p \Rightarrow s)]$ (=**TSa**651″)
$T = [\{[(q \wedge s) \Rightarrow q] \wedge (q \wedge s)\} \Rightarrow s]$ (31.12)
From 35.22 as 35.211 from 35.21

35.23 - $\vdash$ $[T \wedge (p \Rightarrow q) \wedge (r \Rightarrow q)] \Rightarrow [(p \vee r) \Rightarrow q]$ (=**TSa**655′)
$T = [(\sim p \wedge \sim r) \Rightarrow (\sim p \wedge \sim r)]$

(1) ⊢ $\{[(\sim p\wedge\sim r)\Rightarrow(\sim p\wedge\sim r)]\wedge[(\sim q\Rightarrow\sim p)\wedge(\sim q\Rightarrow\sim r)]\}$
$\Rightarrow[\sim q\Rightarrow(\sim p\wedge\sim r)]$ 35.21 subst $p/\sim q,\ q/\sim p,\ s/\sim r$

(2) ⊢ $\{[(\sim p\wedge\sim r)\Rightarrow(\sim p\wedge\sim r)]\wedge(p\Rightarrow q)\wedge(r\Rightarrow q)\}$
$\Rightarrow[(p\vee r)\Rightarrow q]$ By 31.34 and 31.35

(3) ⊢ Th

35.231 - ⊢ $\{T\wedge[(p\vee r)\Rightarrow q]\}\Rightarrow[(p\Rightarrow q)\wedge(r\Rightarrow q)]$ (=**TSa**655″)
$T=\{[p\Rightarrow(p\vee r)]\wedge[r\Rightarrow(p\vee r)]\}$ (31.23)
From 35.25; proof as 35.211 from 35.21

35.3 - *Distribution of modalities.*

35.31 - ⊢ $[T\wedge\Box(p\wedge q)]\Rightarrow\Box p$
'T' for '$(p\wedge q)\Rightarrow p$' (31.231)
32.71 subst

35.32 - ⊢ $[T\wedge\Diamond(p\wedge q)]\Rightarrow\Diamond q$ (=**TSm**241)
'T' for '$(p\wedge q)\Rightarrow p$'
32.72 subst

35.33 - ⊢ $[T\wedge\Box p]\Rightarrow\Box(p\vee q)$
'T' for '$p\Rightarrow(p\vee q)$' (31.43)
32.71 subst

35.34 - ⊢ $[T\wedge\Diamond p]\Rightarrow\Diamond(p\vee q)$
'T' for '$p\Rightarrow(p\vee q)$' (31.43)
32.72 subst

35.4 - TS′-theorems.

35.41 - ⊢ $[T\wedge\Box q]\Rightarrow(p\Rightarrow q)$ (=**TS′a**511)
'T' for '$q\Rightarrow(p\Rightarrow q)$' (**a**511)

(1) ⊢ $\{[q\Rightarrow(p\rightarrow q)]\wedge\Box q\}\Rightarrow\Box(p\rightarrow q)$ 33.31 subst

(2) ⊢ Th Rp by 32.02

35.42 - ⊢ $(T\wedge\Box\sim p)\Rightarrow(p\Rightarrow q)$ (=**TS′a**512)
'T' for '$\sim p\Rightarrow(p\rightarrow q)$' (**a**512)

(1) ⊢ $\{[\sim p\Rightarrow(p\rightarrow q)]\wedge\Box\sim p\}\Rightarrow\Box(p\rightarrow q)$ 32.71 subst

(2) ⊢ Th Rp by 32.02

35.5 - For most theorems 35.2-3-4 it is possible to show that they are *not provable without* 'T' in system 1° (or in system 1). And so with matrix 30.4 the following formulas have value 4:

35.21 for $p=1,\ q=3,\ r=4$,
35.211 for $p=1,\ q=3,\ r=1$,
35.23 for $p=1,\ q=1,\ r=3$,

35.31 for $p=1$, $q=3$,
35.32 for $p=2$, $q=4$,
35.33 for $p=3$, $q=1$,
35.34 for $p=1$, $q=3$,
35.41 for $p=3$, $q=3$,
35.42 for $p=1$, $q=3$.
We have not found a matrix to show that 35.22 without 'T' fails.

§ 36 - THE SYSTEM 1

We call *System 1* (or S1) the system derived from System 1° together with postulate 36.0:

36.0 - $\vdash \quad p \Rightarrow \Diamond p$.

36.1 - Axiom 36.0 is *independent* of the postulates of S1°.
This can be shown by means of the following matrix (Group IV of Lewis-Langford).

Values: 1, 2, 3, 4 Designated values: 1, 2

p	$\sim p$	$\Diamond p$
1	4	2
2	3	2
3	2	2
4	1	4

$\wedge$	1	2	3	4
1	1	2	3	4
2	2	2	4	4
3	3	4	3	4
4	4	4	4	4

And, according to the definitions :

p	$\sim\Diamond p$	$\Box p$
1	3	1
2	3	3
3	3	3
4	1	3

$\vee$	1	2	3	4
1	1	1	1	1
2	1	2	1	2
3	1	1	3	3
4	1	2	3	4

$\Rightarrow$	1	2	3	4
1	1	3	3	3
2	1	1	3	3
3	1	3	1	3
4	1	1	1	1

$\Leftrightarrow$	1	2	3	4
1	1	3	3	3
2	3	1	3	3
3	3	3	1	3
4	3	3	3	1

All axioms of S1° have designated values, and designated values are preserved by the use of the rules. But 36.0 has values 3 for $p=1$ or for $p=3$.

36.2 - System 1 is *consistent*. This is shown by the same matrix as system 1° (30.5).

§ 37 - THEOREMS PROPER TO SYSTEM 1

37.0 - As was stated in 30.4, System 1 is the system derived from the postulates of system 1°, together with the supplementary axiom: 36.0 $\vdash p \Rightarrow \Diamond p$.

37.1 - As immediate consequences we have

37.11 -	$\vdash$	$\sim \Diamond p \Rightarrow \sim p$	From 36.0 by 31.34
37.12 -	$\vdash$	$\Box p \Rightarrow p$	(= **sm** 12)
(1)	$\vdash$	$\sim \Diamond p \Rightarrow \sim \sim p$	37.11 subst
(2)	$\vdash$	Th	Rp by 31.32 and df 30.36
37.121 -	$\vdash$	$\Box \Box p \Rightarrow p$	From 37.12 subst and 35.12 by 30.15
37.13 -	$\vdash$	$\Box p \Rightarrow \Diamond p$	From 37.12 and 36.1 by 30.15
37.15 -	If $\vdash P \Rightarrow \Box Q$, then $\vdash P \Rightarrow Q$		
(1)	$\vdash$	$P \Rightarrow \Box Q$	By hp
(2)	$\vdash$	$\Box Q \Rightarrow Q$	Rp by 37.12
(3)	$\vdash$	$P \Rightarrow Q$	From (1) and (2) by 30.15

37.2 -	$\vdash$	$(p \Rightarrow q) \Rightarrow (p \rightarrow q)$	
(1)	$\vdash$	$\Box(p \rightarrow q) \Rightarrow (p \rightarrow q)$	37.12 subst
(2)	$\vdash$	Th	Rp by 32.12

37.3 -	$\vdash$	$[p \wedge (p \Rightarrow q)] \Rightarrow q$	(=**Sa**61)
(1)	$\vdash$	$[(p \Rightarrow q) \wedge p] \Rightarrow q$	From 37.2 by 32.12
(2)	$\vdash$	Th	Rp by 31.21
37.31 -	$\vdash$	$[\sim q \wedge (p \Rightarrow q)] \Rightarrow \sim p$	(=**Sa**611)
(1)	$\vdash$	$[(p \Rightarrow q) \wedge \sim q] \Rightarrow \sim p$	From 37.2 Rp by 32.121
(2)	$\vdash$	Th	Rp by 31.21 (1)

---

(1) Our axiom 36.0 might be derived from 37.3 as follows:

(1)	$\vdash$	$[(p \Rightarrow \sim p) \wedge p] \Rightarrow \sim p$	37.3 subst
(2)	$\vdash$	$(p \Rightarrow \sim p) \Rightarrow (p \rightarrow \sim p)$	Rp 37.12
(3)	$\vdash$	$\Box \sim p \Rightarrow \sim p$	Rp by 33.12 and 31.54
(4)	$\vdash$	$\sim \sim p \Rightarrow \sim \Box \sim p$	By 31.34
(5)	$\vdash$	$p \Rightarrow \Diamond p$	Rp by 31.32 and 33.22

As 36.0 and 37.3 are deductively equivalent (may be derived from each other), 37,3 might be assumed as axiom instead of 36.0.

37.4 - Rule 34.2, «If $\vdash \Box P$, then $\vdash P$», may be applied to 37.12 - 12 - 121 - 13, 37.2, 37.3 - 31.

E.g. $\vdash \Box p \rightarrow p$ (=**m**11) From 37.12

37.41 - If $\vdash \Box P$, then $\vdash \Diamond P$

(1) $\vdash$ $\Box P$ By hp

(2) $\vdash$ $\Box P \Rightarrow \Diamond P$ By 37.13

(3) $\vdash$ Th By rule 30.23

This would allow us to derive from each theorem $\vdash \Box P$ a theorem $\vdash \Diamond P$.

37.5 - Very few **Sa**-theorems (in fact only **Sa**61-611) are derived in System 1. The interest of 36.0 is elsewhere: it is to state strict implications between modalities. Without these implications we would not be able, in §5 and later, to establish reduction theorems (by strict equivalence) or subordination theorems (by strict implication) between modalities.

§ 38 - NO FINITE CHARACTERISTIC MATRIX FOR SYSTEM 1

Matrices have hitherto repeatedly been used to prove the independence of axioms. Is it possible to construct a characteristic matrix for System 1 (i.e. a matrix giving a designated value for a formula if and only if the formula is provable in the system) ?

It can be proved (Dugundji) that there is no finite characteristic matrix for S1. (The proof is also valid for System 2, 3, 4, 5.)

As remarked by Parry, the result for S1 (and S2) follows from the matrix stated below in Section 49 and 50.01.

§ *39 - ALTERNATIVE SET OF POSTULATES FOR SYSTEM 1

***39.0** - Lemmon (1957) formulated a modal system, which he called 'P1' and he has shown that it is equivalent to S1.

The postulates of P1 are the following:

***39.1** - The *theorems* of the APC.

***39.2** - *Rules:*

***39**.20 - Substitution for propositional variables;

***39**.21 - If $\vdash P$ is a tautology of APC or an axiom of P1, then $\vdash \Box P$;

***39**.22 - Strict equivalent propositions are intersubstitutable.

***39.3** - *Axioms*:

***39**.31 - $\vdash \quad \Box p \rightarrow p$;

***39**.32 - $\vdash \quad [\Box(p \rightarrow q) \wedge \Box(q \rightarrow r)] \rightarrow \Box(p \rightarrow r)$.

SECTION 4 - SYSTEMS 2⁰ AND 2

§ 40 - POSTULATES FOR THE SYSTEMS 2⁰ AND 2

40.0 - We call '*System 2⁰*' (or 'S2⁰') the system derived from the postulates of system 1⁰ plus postulate 40.1.

We call '*System 2*' (or 'S2') the system derived from the postulates of system 1 plus postulate 40.1.

40.1 - $\vdash \quad \Diamond(p \wedge q) \Rightarrow \Diamond p.$

40.2 - Systems 2⁰ and 2 are *consistent.*

Their consistency results from matrix 50.1 below. With this matrix, a provable P has a designated value 1 or 2, and $\sim P$ has one of the values 8 or 7, which are not designated.

40.3 - Axiom 40.1 is *independent* of the axioms 30.1 of S1⁰ and of axiom 36.0 of S1.

With the matrix 30.5, all axioms 30.1 and axiom 40.1 have designated values for each value of their variables. And if formulas have designated values, then all formulas derived from them according to the rules 30.2 have designated values. But 40.1 has value 4 for $p=2$ and $q=4$.

Theorems provable in System 2⁰ — hence also in System 2 — may be divided in two sets. The first one (41 to 44) consists of the theorems about the distribution of modalities with respect to $\wedge$ and $\vee$, and about the composition of strict implications — together with the so-called factor-theorems. These two kinds of theorems have to be treated together, since some theorems about modalities (those in §44) depend on theorems about composition.

Another set of theorems (45 and 46) depend on theorem 45.21, by virtue of which a strict implication becomes strictly equivalent to a strict equivalence. This result leads to *Becker's rules,* which may be considered as rules for distribution of modalities with respect to the strict connectives.

§ 41 - DISTRIBUTION OF MODALITIES (FIRST SET: IMPLICATIONS)

41.1 - $\vdash$ $\Diamond(p \wedge q) \Rightarrow \Diamond p$ (=Axiom 40.1)
41.11 - $\vdash$ $\Box p \Rightarrow \Box(p \vee q)$ From 41.1 by duality

41.2 - $\vdash$ $\Diamond p \Rightarrow \Diamond(p \vee q)$
(1) $\vdash$ $\Diamond[(p \vee q) \wedge p] \Rightarrow \Diamond(p \vee q)$ 41.1 subst
(2) $\vdash$ $[(p \vee q) \wedge p] \Leftrightarrow p$ From APC by 34.42
(3) $\vdash$ Th Rp by (2)
41.21 - $\vdash$ $\Box(p \wedge q) \Rightarrow \Box p$ From 41.2 by duality

41.3 - $\vdash$ $\Diamond(p \wedge q) \Rightarrow (\Diamond p \wedge \Diamond q)$
(1) $\vdash$ $\Diamond(p \wedge q) \Rightarrow \Diamond p$ 41.1
(2) $\vdash$ $\Diamond(q \wedge p) \Rightarrow \Diamond q$ 41.1 subst
(3) $\vdash$ $\Diamond(p \wedge q) \Rightarrow \Diamond q$ Rp by 31.21
(4) $\vdash$ Th — From (1) and (3) by 35.22 according to 35.111
41.31 - $\vdash$ $(\Box p \vee \Box q) \Rightarrow \Box(p \vee q)$ From 41.3 by duality

41.4 - $\vdash$ $\Box(p \wedge q) \Rightarrow (\Box p \wedge \Box q)$ Proof similar to the one of 41.3
41.41 - $\vdash$ $(\Diamond p \vee \Diamond q) \Rightarrow \Diamond(p \vee q)$ From 41.4 by duality

§ 42 - FACTOR- AND DECOMPOSITION-THEOREMS

42.1 - *Factor-theorems.*
42.11 - $\vdash$ $(p \Rightarrow q) \Rightarrow [(r \wedge p) \Rightarrow (r \wedge q)]$ (=**Sa**381)
(1) $\vdash$ $\Diamond(r \wedge p \wedge \sim q) \Rightarrow \Diamond(p \wedge \sim q)$ From 41.1 subst by 31.24
(2) $\vdash$ $\sim\Diamond(r \wedge \sim q) \Rightarrow \sim\Diamond(r \wedge p \wedge \sim q)$ By 31.34
(3) $\vdash$ $(r \wedge p \wedge \sim q) \Leftrightarrow [(r \wedge p) \wedge \sim(r \wedge q)]$ From APC by 34.42
(4) $\vdash$ $\sim\Diamond(p \wedge \sim q) \Rightarrow \sim\Diamond[(r \wedge p) \wedge (r \wedge q)]$ Rp in (2) by (3)
(5) $\vdash$ Th Rp by df 30.34
42.12 - $\vdash$ $(p \Rightarrow q) \Rightarrow [(r \vee p) \Rightarrow (r \vee q)]$ (=**Sa**383)
(1) $\vdash$ $(\sim q \Rightarrow \sim p) \Rightarrow [(\sim r \wedge \sim q) \Rightarrow (\sim r \wedge \sim p)]$ 42.11 subst
(2) $\vdash$ $(p \Rightarrow q) \Rightarrow [\sim(\sim r \wedge \sim p) \Rightarrow \sim(\sim r \wedge \sim q)]$ By 31.34
(3) $\vdash$ Th By df 30.34

42.2 - *Composition-theorems.*

42.21 - $\vdash$ $[(p \Rightarrow q) \wedge (p \Rightarrow s)] \Rightarrow [p \Rightarrow (q \wedge s)]$ (=**Sa**651′)

(1) $\vdash$ $(p \Rightarrow q) \Rightarrow [(p \wedge s) \Rightarrow (q \wedge s)]$ From 42.11 subst by 31.2

(2) $\vdash$ $\{[(p \wedge s) \Rightarrow (q \wedge s)] \wedge [p \Rightarrow (p \wedge s)]\} \Rightarrow [p \Rightarrow (q \wedge s)]$
From 30.15 by 31.2

(3) $\vdash$ $\{(p \Rightarrow q) \wedge [p \Rightarrow (p \wedge s)]\} \Rightarrow [p \Rightarrow (q \wedge s)]$
From (1) and (2) by rule 32.311

(4) $\vdash$ Th Rp by 34.422

42.22 - $\vdash$ $[(p \Rightarrow q) \wedge (r \Rightarrow q) \Rightarrow [(p \vee r) \Rightarrow q]$ (=**Sa**655′)

(1) $\vdash$ $[(\sim q \Rightarrow \sim p) \wedge (\sim q \Rightarrow \sim r)] \Rightarrow [\sim q \Rightarrow (\sim p \wedge \sim r)]$ 42.22 subst

(2) $\vdash$ $[(p \Rightarrow q) \wedge (r \Rightarrow q)] \Rightarrow [\sim (\sim p \wedge \sim r) \Rightarrow \sim \sim q]$ By 31.34

(3) $\vdash$ Th Rp by 31.35 and 31.

42.23 - $\vdash$ $[p \Rightarrow (q \wedge s)] \Rightarrow [(p \Rightarrow q) \wedge (p \Rightarrow s)]$ (=**Sa**651″)

(1) $\vdash$ $\Box[(p \rightarrow q) \wedge (p \rightarrow s)] \Rightarrow [\Box(p \rightarrow q) \wedge \Box(p \rightarrow s)]$ 41.14 subst

(2) $\vdash$ $[(p \rightarrow q) \wedge (p \rightarrow s)] \Leftrightarrow [p \rightarrow (q \wedge s)]$ From APC by 34.

(3) $\vdash$ $\Box[p \rightarrow (q \wedge s)] \Rightarrow [\Box(p \rightarrow q) \wedge \Box(p \rightarrow s)]$ Rp in (1) by (2)

(4) $\vdash$ Th By 32.02

42.3 - *Double composition.*

42.31 - $\vdash$ $[(p \Rightarrow q) \wedge (r \Rightarrow s)] \Rightarrow [(p \wedge r) \Rightarrow (q \wedge s)]$ (=**Sa**661

(1) $\vdash$ $(p \Rightarrow q) \Rightarrow [(r \wedge p) \Rightarrow (r \wedge q)]$ 41.21

(2) $\vdash$ $(p \Rightarrow q) \Rightarrow [(p \wedge r) \Rightarrow (r \wedge q)]$ By 31.21

(3) $\vdash$ $(r \Rightarrow s) \Rightarrow [(p \wedge q) \Rightarrow (q \wedge s)]$ By 30.15

(4) $\vdash$ $[(p \Rightarrow q) \wedge (r \Rightarrow s)] \Rightarrow$
$\{[(p \wedge r) \Rightarrow (r \wedge q)] \wedge [(r \wedge q) \Rightarrow (q \wedge s)]\}$ By 42.21

(5) $\vdash$ Th By 30.15

42.32 - $\vdash$ $[(p \Rightarrow q) \wedge (r \Rightarrow s)] \Rightarrow [(p \vee r) \Rightarrow (q \vee s)]$ (=**Sa**665
Proof from 42.31 as in 42.22

A corollary is:

42.33 - $\vdash$ $[(p \Leftrightarrow q) \wedge (q \Leftrightarrow r)] \Rightarrow (p \Leftrightarrow r)$ (=**Sa**623

(1) $\vdash$ $[(p \Rightarrow q) \wedge (q \Rightarrow r)] \Rightarrow (p \Rightarrow r)$ 30.15

(2) $\vdash$ $[(r \Rightarrow q) \wedge (q \Rightarrow p)] \Rightarrow (r \Rightarrow p)$ 30.15 sub

(3) $\vdash$ $[(p \Rightarrow q) \wedge (q \Rightarrow r) \wedge (r \Rightarrow q) \wedge (q \Rightarrow p)] \Rightarrow$
$[(p \Rightarrow r) \wedge (r \Rightarrow p)]$ By 42.31

(4) $\vdash$ $[(p \Rightarrow q) \wedge (q \Rightarrow p) \wedge (q \Rightarrow r) \wedge (r \Rightarrow q)] \Rightarrow$
$[(p \Rightarrow r) \wedge (r \Rightarrow p)]$ By 31.21 and 31.24

(5) $\vdash$ Th By df 30.35

§ 43 - S'a-THEOREMS

43.1 -	$\vdash$	$\Box q \Rightarrow (p \Rightarrow q)$	(=**S′a**511)
(1)	$\vdash$	$\Box q \Rightarrow \Box(\sim p \vee q)$	From 41.11 Rp by 31.41
(2)	$\vdash$	Th	By 31.41 df 30.32 and 32.0
43.11 -	$\vdash$	$(\Box p \wedge \Box q) \Rightarrow (p \Leftrightarrow q)$	
(1)	$\vdash$	$\Box p \Rightarrow (q \Leftrightarrow p)$	43.1 subst
(2)	$\vdash$	$\Box q \Rightarrow (p \Rightarrow q)$	43.1
(3)	$\vdash$	$(\Box p \wedge \Box q) \Rightarrow [(q \rightarrow p) \wedge (p \Rightarrow q)]$	From (1) and (2) by 42.31
(4)	$\vdash$	Th	By 31.41 df, 30.32 and 32.02
43.2 -	$\vdash$	$\Box \sim p \Rightarrow (p \Rightarrow q)$	(=**S′a**512)
(1)	$\vdash$	$\Box \sim p \Rightarrow \Box(\sim p \vee q)$	41.11 subst
(2)	$\vdash$	Th	By 31.41 df, 30.32 and 32.02
43.21 -	$\vdash$	$(\Box \sim p \wedge \Box \sim q) \Rightarrow (p \Leftrightarrow q)$	

§ 44 - DISTRIBUTION OF MODALITIES (SECOND SET: EQUIVALENCES)

44.1 -	$\vdash$	$(\Box p \wedge \Box q) \Rightarrow \Box(p \wedge q)$	(=**Sm**21′)
(1)	$\vdash$	$(\Box p \wedge \Box q) \Rightarrow \Box \sim \sim p$	From 30.11 by 31.32
(2)	$\vdash$	$\Box \sim \sim p \Rightarrow (\sim p \Rightarrow p \wedge q)$	43.2 subst
(3)	$\vdash$	$(\Box p \wedge \Box q) \Rightarrow (\sim p \Rightarrow p \wedge q)$	From (1) and (2) by 30.15
(4)	$\vdash$	$(\Box p \wedge \Box q) \Rightarrow (\sim q \Rightarrow p \wedge q)$	Proofs as for (3)
(5)	$\vdash$	$(\Box p \wedge \Box q) \Rightarrow [(\sim p \Rightarrow p \wedge q) \wedge (\sim q \Rightarrow p \wedge q)]$	From (3) and (4) by 42.21
(6)	$\vdash$	$\{[\sim p \Rightarrow (p \wedge q)] \wedge [\sim q \Rightarrow (p \wedge q)]\} \Rightarrow [(\sim p \vee \sim q) \Rightarrow (p \wedge q)]$	42.22 subst
(7)	$\vdash$	$(\Box p \wedge \Box q) \Rightarrow [(\sim p \vee \sim q) \Rightarrow (p \wedge q)]$	Rp by 31.361
(8)	$\vdash$	$(\Box p \wedge \Box q) \Rightarrow [\sim (p \wedge q) \Rightarrow (p \wedge q)]$	Rp by 33.11
(9)	$\vdash$	Th	From (5) and (6) by 30.15
44.2 -	$\vdash$	$\Diamond(p \vee q) \Rightarrow (\Diamond p \vee \Diamond q)$	(=**Sm**23′) From 44.1 by duality
44.3 -	$\vdash$	$\Box(p \wedge q) \Leftrightarrow (\Box p \wedge \Box q)$	(=**Sm**21) From 41.4 and 44.1 by df 30.35
44.4 -	$\vdash$	$\Diamond(p \vee q) \Leftrightarrow (\Diamond p \vee \Diamond q)$	(=**Sm**23) From 44.3 by duality

§ 45 - STRICT EQUIVALENCE

45.1 - *Strict equivalence as necessary equivalence.*

$\vdash \Box(p\leftrightarrow q) \Leftrightarrow (p\Leftrightarrow q)$

(1) $\vdash \Box[(p\rightarrow q)\wedge(q\rightarrow p)] \Leftrightarrow [\Box(p\rightarrow q)\wedge\Box(q\rightarrow p)]$ 44.3

(2) $\vdash \Box(p\leftrightarrow q) \Leftrightarrow [\Box(p\rightarrow q)\wedge\Box(q\rightarrow p)]$ By 32.02 by df 30.33

(3) $\vdash$ Th By df 30.35

45.2 - *Strict implications transformed into strict equivalences.*

45.21 - $\vdash (p\Rightarrow q) \Leftrightarrow [p\Leftrightarrow(p\wedge q)]$ (= **Sa**44)

(1) $\vdash (p\rightarrow q) \Leftrightarrow [p\leftrightarrow(p\wedge q)]$ From APC by 34.42

(2) $\vdash \Box(p\rightarrow q) \Leftrightarrow [p\Leftrightarrow(p\wedge q)]$ By 31.19

(3) $\vdash$ Th Rp by 32.02 and 45.1

45.22 - $\vdash (p\Rightarrow q) \Leftrightarrow [q\Leftrightarrow(p\vee q)]$ (= **Sa**45)

(1) $\vdash (p\rightarrow q) \Leftrightarrow [q\leftrightarrow(p\vee q)$ From APC by 34.42

(2) $\vdash \Box(p\rightarrow q) \Leftrightarrow [q\Leftrightarrow(p\vee q)]$ By 31.19

(3) $\vdash$ Th By 32.02 and 45.1

45.23 - $\vdash \Box\sim p \Leftrightarrow [p\Leftrightarrow(p\wedge\sim p)]$

(1) $\vdash \Box\sim p \Leftrightarrow (p\Rightarrow\sim p)$ 33.12

(2) $\vdash$ Th Rp by 45.21

45.24 - $\vdash \Box p \Leftrightarrow [p\Leftrightarrow(p\vee\sim p)]$

(1) $\vdash \Box p \Leftrightarrow (\sim p\Rightarrow p)$ 33.11

(2) $\vdash$ Th Rp by 45.22

45.3 - *Lemmas.*

45.30 - If $\vdash Q\Rightarrow R$, then $\vdash (P\Rightarrow Q)\Rightarrow(P\Rightarrow R)$

(1) $\vdash Q\Rightarrow R$ By hp

(2) $\vdash Q\Leftrightarrow(Q\wedge R)$ By 45.21

(3) $\vdash [P\Rightarrow(Q\wedge R)] \Rightarrow [(P\Rightarrow Q)\wedge(P\Rightarrow R)]$ 42.23 subst

(4) $\vdash [(P\Rightarrow Q)\wedge(P\Rightarrow R)] \Rightarrow (P\Rightarrow R)$ 31.23 subst

(5) $\vdash [(P\Rightarrow(Q\wedge R)] \Rightarrow (P\Rightarrow R)$ From (3) and (4) by 30.15

(6) $\vdash (P\Rightarrow Q) \Rightarrow (P\Rightarrow R)$ Rp by (2)

45.31 - If $\vdash R\Rightarrow Q$, then $\vdash (Q\Rightarrow P)\Rightarrow(R\Rightarrow P)$

(1) If $\vdash \sim Q\Rightarrow\sim R$, then $\vdash (\sim P\Rightarrow\sim Q)\Rightarrow(\sim P\Rightarrow\sim R)$ 45.30 subst

(2) Th Rp by .34

45.32 - If $\vdash R\Rightarrow Q$, then $\vdash [S\Rightarrow(Q\Rightarrow P)] \Rightarrow [S\Rightarrow(R\Rightarrow P)]$

45.33 - If $\vdash R\Rightarrow Q$, then, if $\vdash S\Rightarrow(Q\Rightarrow P)$, then $\vdash S\Rightarrow(R\Rightarrow P)$

§ 46 - BECKER'S RULES

We extend the name of «*Becker's rules*» to all rules concluding from $\vdash P \Rightarrow Q$ to a strict implication having as antecedent P affected by a given modality and as consequent Q affected by the same modality. Such rules are valid in S2°.

46.1 - If $\vdash P \Rightarrow Q$, then $\vdash \Box P \Rightarrow \Box Q$.

(1)	$\vdash$	$P \Rightarrow Q$	By hp
(2)	$\vdash$	$P \Leftrightarrow (P \wedge Q)$	By 45.21
(3)	$\vdash$	$\Box P \Leftrightarrow \Box (P \wedge Q)$	By 31.19
(4)	$\vdash$	$\Box (P \wedge Q) \Rightarrow \Box Q$	From 41.21 by 31.21
(5)	$\vdash$	$\Box P \Rightarrow \Box Q$	Rp by (3)

46.2 - If $\vdash P \Rightarrow Q$, then $\vdash \Diamond P \Rightarrow \Diamond Q$.

Similarly, using 45.21, rule 31.191 and 40.1 instead of 41.21.

46.21 - If $\vdash P \Rightarrow Q$, then $\vdash \sim \Diamond Q \Rightarrow \sim \Diamond P$.

From 46.2 subst by 31.34

(This is the original form of Becker's rule.)

46.22 - If $\vdash P \Leftrightarrow Q$, then $\vdash \Box P \Leftrightarrow \Box Q$.

(1)	$\vdash$	$P \Leftrightarrow Q$	By hyp
(2)	$\vdash$	$(P \Rightarrow Q) \wedge (Q \Rightarrow P)$	By definition 30.15
(3)	$\vdash$	$[(P \Rightarrow Q) \wedge (Q \Rightarrow P)] \Rightarrow (P \Rightarrow Q)$	30.11 subst
(4)	$\vdash$	$(P \Rightarrow Q)$	By (3), (2) and 30.23
(5)	$\vdash$	$(\Box P \Rightarrow \Box Q)$	By 46.1
(6)	$\vdash$	$[(P \Rightarrow Q) \wedge (Q \Rightarrow P)] \Rightarrow (Q \Rightarrow P)$	31.23 subst
(7)	$\vdash$	$(Q \Rightarrow P)$	By (6), (2) and 30.23
(8)	$\vdash$	$\Box Q \Rightarrow \Box P$	By 46.1
(9)	$\vdash$	$(\Box P \Rightarrow \Box Q) \wedge (\Box Q \Rightarrow \Box P)$	By 30.22
(10)	$\vdash$	$(\Box P \Leftrightarrow \Box Q)$	By def 30.15

46.23 - *If* $\vdash P \Leftrightarrow Q$, then $\vdash \Diamond P \Leftrightarrow \Diamond Q$

(similarly, using 46.2 instead of 46.1)

46.3 - From rule 46.2 we can derive 40.1.

(1)	$\vdash$	$p \wedge q \Rightarrow p$	30.11
(2)	$\vdash$	$\Diamond (p \wedge q) \Rightarrow \Diamond p$	By 46.2

Since 46.2 has been derived from 40.1, rule 46.2 is shown de-

ductively equivalent to 40.1 and may be taken as postulate for S2° and S2 instead of 40.1.

Besides, the derivation of 40.1 from 46.2 proves that Becker's rules are independent of the axioms of S1° and of S1. For, if the rules in question were derivable from these axioms, then 40.1 would also be derivable, which is shown as impossible by 40.3.

46.4 - As consequences of Beckers's rules, we have rules leading to the same conclusions as the general method of 26.2 and 26.3.

46.41 - If $\vdash (P \rightarrow Q) \Rightarrow (R \rightarrow S)$,
then $\vdash (P \Rightarrow Q) \Rightarrow (R \Rightarrow S)$
By rule 46.1, then Rp by 32.02

46.42 - If $\vdash [(P \rightarrow P') \wedge (Q \rightarrow Q')] \Rightarrow (R \rightarrow S)$,
then $\vdash [(P \Rightarrow P') \wedge (Q \Rightarrow Q')] \Rightarrow (R \Rightarrow S)$
By rule 46.1, then Rp by 44.3 and 32.02

46.43 - The rules 46.41 and 46.42 remain valid if we replace some '$\rightarrow$' in the hypothesis by '$\leftrightarrow$' and if we replace the corresponding '$\Rightarrow$' by '$\Leftrightarrow$' in the conclusion.
Replace in the demonstrations 46.1 and 32.02 respectively by 31.19 and 45.1.

***46.5** - For another system deductively equivalent with S2°, see §80.23.

§ 47 - THEOREMS PROVABLE IN SYSTEM 2 ONLY

47.1 -	$\vdash$	$\Box p \Leftrightarrow (p \wedge \Box p)$	From 37.12 Rp by 45.21
47.11 -	$\vdash$	$p \Leftrightarrow (p \vee \Box p)$	From 37.12 Rp by 45.22

47.2 -	$\vdash$	$[p \Rightarrow (q \Rightarrow r)] \Rightarrow [(p \wedge q) \Rightarrow r]$	(compare with **Sa** 70″)
(1)	$\vdash$	$(q \Rightarrow r) \Rightarrow (q \rightarrow r)$	37.2 subst
(2)	$\vdash$	$[p \Rightarrow (q \Rightarrow r)] \Rightarrow [p \Rightarrow (q \rightarrow r)]$	By rule 45.30
(3)	$\vdash$	Th	Rp by 32.12

47.3	$\vdash$	$\Diamond(p \vee \sim p) \Leftrightarrow (p \vee \sim p)$	
(1)	$\vdash$	$\Box(p \vee \sim p)$	From APC by 34.1

(2)	$\vdash$	$\Box(p \vee \sim p) \Rightarrow [\Diamond(p \vee \sim p) \Rightarrow (p \vee \sim p)]$	By 43.1
(3)	$\vdash$	$\Diamond(p \vee \sim p) \Rightarrow (p \vee p)$	By (1) and (2)
(4)	$\vdash$	$(p \vee \sim p) \Rightarrow \Diamond(p \vee \sim p)$	36.0 subst
(5)	$\vdash$	Th	From (5) and (4) by df 30.35

47.31 - $\vdash$ $\Diamond \sim (\Diamond p \wedge \sim p)$

(1)	$\vdash$	$\Box \Diamond p \Rightarrow \Diamond p$	35.12 subst
(2)	$\vdash$	$\Box \Diamond p \rightarrow \Diamond p$	By 35.2
(3)	$\vdash$	$\sim \Diamond \sim \Diamond p \rightarrow \Diamond p$	Rp by 32.61
(4)	$\vdash$	$\Diamond \sim \Diamond p \vee \Diamond p$	Rp by 31.52 and 31.32
(5)	$\vdash$	$\Diamond(\sim \Diamond p \vee p)$	Rp 41.44
(6)	$\vdash$	Th	Rp 31.35 and 31.32

47.32 - We consider following matrix:
Values: 1, 2, 3, 4 Designated values: 1, 2

$\wedge$	1	2	3	4
1	1	2	3	4
2	2	2	4	4
3	3	4	3	4
4	4	4	4	4

p	$\sim p$	$\Diamond p$
1	4	2
2	4	1
3	2	1
4	2	4

47.33 - It is easy to verify that the matrix satisfies all axioms 30.1.

Moreover we verify that, whenever P and Q are designated, then $P \wedge Q$ is designated and that, whenever P and $P \Rightarrow Q$ are designated, then Q is designated. Hence every formula which is derivable from the axioms 30.1 by means of adjunction and inference is satisfied by the matrix.

47.34 - But the formula 47.31 is not derivable from the axioms 30.1 by means of adjunction and inference. For this formula gives the value 4 if $p=3$.

Thus formula 47.31 is an example of a formula which is provable in S2, but cannot be proved without using the rule of replacement for strict equivalents.

47.4 - $\vdash$ $\Diamond p \vee \Diamond \sim p$

(1)	$\vdash$	$\Box(p \vee \sim p)$	By 33.1
(2)	$\vdash$	$\Diamond(p \vee \sim p)$	By 35.41
(3)	$\vdash$	Th	By 44.4

§ 48 - UNDERIVABILITY OF FORMULAS

48.1 - There is only one set of **Sa**-formulas valid in M'PC which are not provable in system 2, namely:
Sa71 to **Sa**795 (**S**-transformations of «exported» theorems).
The **m**-formulas **m**5, **m**6, **m**7 with proper modalities, and the corresponding **sm**- and **Sm**-formulas are not valid in system 2. And the same for the rules **m**8 and **Sm**8.

48.2 - We shall consider the *underivability of theorems stating reductions*, i.e. of theorems stating that $Mp \Leftrightarrow M'p$, where 'M' and 'M'' are different proper modalities or, which amounts to the same thing, where 'M' and 'M'' are different sequences of symbols '$\diamond$' and '$\sim$', one symbol at least in the sequence being a diamond (a symbol '$\diamond$').
48.21 - Important results may be obtained by using the following infinite matrix M.

The elements of M consist of all sets of signed integers. The designated element is the universal set V. If A and B are elements of M, then $A \wedge B$ is the intersection AB of A and B. If A is any element of M, then $\sim A$ is the complement $\bar{A}$ of A and $\diamond A$ is $A + \vartheta A$, where '+' denotes union of sets and 'ϑA' denotes the set of all signed integers whose immediate predecessors are in A.

All axioms and primitive rules of System 2 satisfy the matrix.
48.22 - Let us now indicate by '$\diamond^n$' a sequence of n diamonds. It is first shown that $\diamond^n p \Leftrightarrow \diamond^m p$ only if $n = m$.
It is clear that the formula must be verifiable for every set A. Let us take $A = \{0\}$, then $\diamond A = \{0, 1\}$, $\diamond\diamond A = \{0, 1, 2\}$ and so on. It is clear that if we have $\diamond^n p \Leftrightarrow \diamond^m p$, we must have
$\{0, 1, 2, \ldots, n\} = \{0, 1, 2, \ldots, m\}$ and hence $n = m$.
It follows thus that we have an infinity of irreducible affirmative proper modalities, and in general an infinite number of irreducible proper modalities in S2.
48.23 - Using the same matrix, one can also show that, if α and β are infinite sequences of diamonds and negation signs, then, if $\alpha p \Leftrightarrow \beta p$ is provable, α and β have the same degree.

48.24 - The question is left open whether there can be two modalities α' and β' consisting of a finite sequence of '◇' and '∼' (where no two successive negation-signs occur in α' and β') and such that $\alpha' p \Leftrightarrow \beta' p$, α' and β' being different, but of the same degree.

§ 49 - S2-MATRICES AND DECISION-METHOD FOR S2

49.1 - Mc Kinsey arrives at the following results for S2-matrices (matrices satisfying S2):
49.11 - Let a *normal matrix* be defined as one satisfying conditions corresponding to the rules of procedure 30.22-23-24.
49.12 - A normal matrix is a Boolean algebra (Theorem I) for which necessary and sufficient conditions are stated (Theorem 3). As a consequence we have a «recipe» for the construction of all possible finite normal S2-matrices.
49.13 - If we have a finite S2 characteristic matrix, we should be provided with a decision method. But Dugundji has shown that there is no finite S2 characteristic matrix.

It is proved however (Theorem 4) that there is a normal S2 infinite characteristic matrix.
49.14 - Let now $a_1 \ldots a_r$ be a finite sequence of elements of a normal S2 matrix. Then there exists a finite normal S2 matrix with at most $2^{2^{r+1}}$ elements, which has (roughly said) the same rules of operation and in which a sequence $b_1 \ldots b_r$ corresponds to the sequence $a_1 \ldots a_r$.

49.2 - The decision procedure is then as follows: A sentence of S2 which contains just r sub-sentences is provable if and only if it is satisfied by every normal S2-matrix with no more than $2^{2^{r+1}}$ elements.
It must be conceded that, at the moment, this decision procedure is impractical, since it supposes that a given sentence must be tested by an enormous number of matrices.

***49.3** - For another decision method for S2, see § ***141.1**.

§ *49′ - AN ALTERNATIVE SET OF POSTULATES FOR S2

Lemmon (1957) has formulated a modal system, which he calls 'P2' and which he has shown to be equivalent to S2.

The postulates for P2 are the following:

I. The theorems of the APC.

II. The following three *rules*:

a) Rule of substitution for propositional variables;

b) If $\vdash P$ is a theorem of the APC or an axiom of P2, then $\vdash \Box P$;

c) If $\vdash \Box(P \rightarrow Q)$, then $\vdash \Box(\Box P \rightarrow \Box Q)$ (Becker's rule 46.1).

III. The following two *axioms*:

$\vdash \quad \Box p \rightarrow p$ (weaker than 37.12);

$\vdash \quad \Box(p \rightarrow q) \rightarrow (\Box p \rightarrow \Box q)$ (weaker than 33.311).

§ *49″ - AN ALTERNATIVE SET OF POSTULATES FOR S2°

Sobocinski (1962) has shown that one obtains a system deductively equivalent to S2° by adding to the system S1° the axiom:

$$40.1 \quad \vdash \quad \Diamond(p \wedge q) \Rightarrow \Diamond p.$$

SECTION 5 - SYSTEM 3

System 3 holds an intermediate position between System 2, with an infinity of irreducible modalities, and S4, just as System 3 is a system with a finite number of modalities.

§ 50 - POSTULATES FOR SYSTEM 3

50.0 - We call 'System 3' (or 'S3') the system derived from the postulates of System 1 (thus the postulates of 30, plus 36.0) with the following added:

50.01 - $\vdash (p \Rightarrow q) \Rightarrow (\Diamond p \Rightarrow \Diamond q)$.

It may be stressed that 50.01 is of degree 3, whereas the axioms previously stated were of degree 1 or 2.

50.1 - Postulate 50.01 can be shown independent of the ones of System 2 by the following matrix of Parry (Huntington's Example 0.4).

Values: 12345678; designated values: 1, 2

p	$\sim p$	$\Diamond p$
1	8	1
2	7	1
3	6	1
4	5	1
5	4	1
6	3	1
7	2	3
8	1	7

$p \wedge q$	q 12345678
p 1	12345678
2	22446688
3	34347878
4	44448888
5	56785678
6	66886688
7	78787878
8	88888888

And by virtue of the definitions:

p	$\sim\Diamond p$	$\Box p$
1	8	2
2	8	6
3	8	8
4	8	8
5	8	8
6	8	8
7	6	8
8	2	8

$p\Rightarrow q$	q 12345678
p 1	26888888
2	22888888
3	26268888
4	22228888
5	26882688
6	22882288
7	26262626
8	22222222

$p\Leftrightarrow q$	q 12345678
p 1	26888888
2	62888888
3	88268888
4	88628888
5	88882688
6	88886288
7	88888826
8	88888862

With this matrix, fulfilling the conditions for a demonstration of independence, 50.01 (and 51.12 below) has values 8 for values $p=7$ and $q=8$.

On the other hand, the matrix satisfies S2° and 36.0 (of S1). It shows thus that 50.01 is not provable even in S2.

50.2 - System 3 may be shown consistent, by the fact that it satisfies matrices 56.1-2-3 stated below.

50.3 - We may here state consequences concerning the «deduction-theorem» for the system 2.

Since we had Becker's rules 46.1-2 above in system 2, and since, according to the matrix, we have not there 50.01 or 51.12, so the deduction-theorem (concluding to $\vdash P\Rightarrow Q$ wherever $\vdash Q$ is derived from $\vdash P$) is not valid in system 2.

And since we have value 3 for $p=7$ and $q=8$ for the formula

$$(p\Rightarrow q)\rightarrow(\Diamond p\Rightarrow\Diamond q) \quad (\text{or } \sim[(p\Rightarrow q)\wedge\sim(\Diamond p\Rightarrow\Diamond q)]),$$

so, for system 2, we do not even have the deduction-theorem in the weaker form according to which if $\vdash Q$ derives from $\vdash P$, then $\vdash P\rightarrow Q$.

§ 51 - IMMEDIATE CONSEQUENCES

51.1 - *Implications of implications.*

51.11 - $\vdash$ $(p \Rightarrow q) \Rightarrow (\Box p \Rightarrow \Box q)$ (= **Sm** 31)
(1) $\vdash$ $(\sim q \Rightarrow \sim p) \Rightarrow (\Diamond \sim q \Rightarrow \Diamond \sim p)$ 50.01 subst
(2) $\vdash$ $(p \Rightarrow q) \Rightarrow (\sim \Diamond \sim p \Rightarrow \sim \Diamond \sim q)$ By 31.34
(3) $\vdash$ Th By df 30.36
51.12 - $\vdash$ $(p \Rightarrow q) \Rightarrow (\sim \Diamond q \Rightarrow \sim \Diamond p)$ From 50.01 by 31.34
In general
51.15 - M being an affirmative modality: $\vdash (p \Rightarrow q) \Rightarrow (Mp \Rightarrow Mq)$.
51.151 - M being an affirmative modality:
$\vdash [r \Rightarrow (p \Rightarrow q)] \Rightarrow [r \Rightarrow (Mp \Rightarrow Mq)]$.
51.16 - M' being a negative modality: $\vdash (p \Rightarrow q) \Rightarrow (M'q \Rightarrow M'p)$.
51.161 - M' being a negative modality:
$\vdash$ $[r \Rightarrow (p \Rightarrow q)] \Rightarrow [r \Rightarrow (M'q \Rightarrow M'p)]$.

51.2 - From 50.01 we can derive 40.1.
(1) $\vdash$ $(p \wedge q) \Rightarrow p$ 30.11
(2) $\vdash$ $[(p \wedge q) \Rightarrow p] \Rightarrow [\Diamond(p \wedge q) \Rightarrow \Diamond p]$ 50.01 subst
(3) $\vdash$ $\Diamond(p \wedge q) \Rightarrow \Diamond p$ From (1) and (2) by rule 30.23
Hence system 3 includes system 2.

51.3 - *Implications of equivalences.*
51.30 - $\vdash$ $(p \Leftrightarrow q) \Rightarrow (\Diamond p \Leftrightarrow \Diamond q)$ (= **Sm**34)
(1) $\vdash$ $(p \Rightarrow q) \Rightarrow (\Diamond p \Rightarrow \Diamond q)$ 50.01
(2) $\vdash$ $(q \Rightarrow p) \Rightarrow (\Diamond q \Rightarrow \Diamond p)$ 50.01 subst
(3) $\vdash$ $[(p \Rightarrow q) \wedge (q \Rightarrow p)] \Rightarrow [(\Diamond p \Rightarrow \Diamond q) \wedge (\Diamond q \Rightarrow \Diamond p)]$
By 42.31
(4) $\vdash$ Th Subst by df 30.35
51.31 - $\vdash$ $(p \Leftrightarrow q) \Rightarrow (\Box p \Leftrightarrow \Box q)$ (= **Sm**33)
From 51.11 similarly
51.32 - $\vdash$ $(p \Leftrightarrow q) \Rightarrow (\sim \Diamond p \Leftrightarrow \sim \Diamond q)$ From 51.12 similarly
51.35 - M being a modality: $\vdash$ $(p \Leftrightarrow q) \Rightarrow (Mp \Leftrightarrow Mq)$

51.4 - We can derive 50.01 from 51.30 added to the postulates of *system 2*.
(1) $\vdash$ $[p \Leftrightarrow (p \vee q)] \Rightarrow [\Diamond p \Leftrightarrow \Diamond(p \vee q)]$ 51.30 subst
(2) $\vdash$ $[p \Leftrightarrow (p \vee q)] \Rightarrow [\Diamond p \Leftrightarrow (\Diamond p \vee \Diamond q)]$ By 44.2
(3) $\vdash$ Th By 45.22
Hence 51.30 added to the postulates of system 2 gives a set of postulates for system 3, equivalent to the set 50.0.

§ 52 - EXPORTED THEOREMS AND OTHER CONSEQUENCES

52.1 - $\vdash$ $[(p\wedge q)\Rightarrow r] \Rightarrow [\Box p\Rightarrow(\Box q\Rightarrow\Box r)]$

(1)	$\vdash$	$[p\wedge(q\Rightarrow r)] \Rightarrow [p\Rightarrow(q\rightarrow r)]$	From 32.12 by rule 31.1
(2)	$\vdash$	$[p\Rightarrow(q\rightarrow r)] \Rightarrow [\Box p\Rightarrow(q\Rightarrow r)]$	From 51.11 subst by 32.
(3)	$\vdash$	$(q\Rightarrow r) \Rightarrow (\Box q\Rightarrow\Box r)$	51.11 subst
(4)	$\vdash$	$[\Box p\Rightarrow(q\Rightarrow r)] \Rightarrow [\Box p\Rightarrow(\Box q\Rightarrow\Box r)]$	By rule 45.30
(5)	$\vdash$	Th	From (1), (2), (4) by 32.

This is a kind of strict analogue of **a**70′.

We already had a kind of strict analogue of **a**70″ in 47.2.

52.11 - If $\vdash$ $[(P\rightarrow Q)\wedge(R\rightarrow S)] \rightarrow (P'\rightarrow Q')$,
then $\vdash$ $(P\Rightarrow Q) \Rightarrow [(R\Rightarrow S)\Rightarrow(P'\Rightarrow Q')]$ By 52.1 and 32.02

52.12 - If, in the premise of 52.11, one or more of the '$\rightarrow$' is replaced by '$\leftrightarrow$', the corresponding '$\Rightarrow$' in the conclusion must be replaced by '$\Leftrightarrow$'.

Use 45.1 instead of or together with 32.02.

52.2 - So the «exported analogues» **a**7 of theorems **a**6 may be **S**-transformed in System 3, e.g.:

52.21 - $\vdash$ $(p\Rightarrow q) \Rightarrow [(q\Rightarrow r)\Rightarrow(p\Rightarrow r)]$ (=**Sa72**)

52.22 - $\vdash$ $(q\Rightarrow r) \Rightarrow [(p\Rightarrow q)\Rightarrow(p\Rightarrow r)]$ (=**Sa721**)

52.3 - $\vdash$ $[p\Rightarrow(q\Rightarrow r)] \Rightarrow [\Box q\Rightarrow(p\Rightarrow r)]$

(1)	$\vdash$	$(q\Rightarrow r) \Rightarrow (q\rightarrow r)$	37.2 subst
(2)	$\vdash$	$[p\Rightarrow(q\Rightarrow r)] \Rightarrow [p\Rightarrow(q\rightarrow r)]$	From 32.12 by rule 31.16
(3)	$\vdash$	$[p\Rightarrow(q\rightarrow r)] \Rightarrow [q\Rightarrow(p\rightarrow r)]$	From 32.13 by rule 31.16
(4)	$\vdash$	$[q\Rightarrow(p\rightarrow r)] \Rightarrow [\Box q\Rightarrow(p\Rightarrow r)]$	From 42.31 subst by 32
(5)	$\vdash$	Th	From (2), (3), (4) by 32

This is a kind of a strict analogue of **a**705′.

52.4 - We have the following transformations of **S′a**-theorems.

52.41 - $\vdash$ $\Box q \Rightarrow (\Box p\Rightarrow\Box q)$ (see **S′a** 512)

(1)	$\vdash$	$\Box q \Rightarrow (p\Rightarrow q)$	41.31
(2)	$\vdash$	$(p\Rightarrow q) \Rightarrow (\Box p\Rightarrow\Box q)$	51.11
(3)	$\vdash$	Th	From (1) and (2) by 30

52.42 - $\vdash$ $\sim\Diamond q \Rightarrow (\sim\Diamond p\Rightarrow\sim\Diamond q)$ From 52.41 subst by 33

§ 53 - REDUCTION-THEOREMS

A striking peculiarity of system 3 (first mentioned by Parry, although system 3 had been formulated the first of all the Lewis's systems, in the *Survey* of 1918) is that one can prove reduction theorems which enable us to show that there are but a finite number of modalities, namely 42. The reductions depend on three key-theorems 53.2-3-4 which state a subordination of modalities.

53.1 - $\vdash \Box^2 p \Rightarrow \Box^3 p$

(1) $\vdash \Box\, q \Rightarrow (p \Rightarrow q)$ — 43.1

(2) $\vdash \Box^2 p \Rightarrow (p \Rightarrow \Box p)$ — By subst

(3) $\vdash \Box^2 p \Rightarrow (\Box^2 p \Rightarrow \Box^2 \Box p)$ — By rule 51.151

(4) $\vdash (\Box^2 p \Rightarrow \Box^2 \Box p) \Rightarrow (\Box^2 p \rightarrow \Box^3 p)$ — 37.2 subst

(5) $\vdash \Box^2 p \Rightarrow (\Box^2 p \rightarrow \Box^3 p)$ — From (3) and (4) by rule 30.25

(6) $\vdash (\Box^2 p \wedge \Box^2 p) \Rightarrow \Box^3 p$ — By 32.12

(7) $\vdash$ Th — Subst by 31.22

53.11 - $\vdash \Box^2 p \Leftrightarrow \Box^3 p$

(1) $\vdash \Box^2 p \Rightarrow \Box^3 p$ — 53.1

(2) $\vdash \Box^3 p \Rightarrow \Box^2 p$ — 37.12 subst

(3) $\vdash$ Th — From (1) and (2) by df 30.35

53.12 - $\vdash \Diamond^2 p \Leftrightarrow \Diamond^3 p$ — From 53.11 by duality

53.2 - $\vdash \Box p \Rightarrow \Box \Diamond \Box p$

(1) $\vdash \Box p \Rightarrow (\Box p \Rightarrow \Diamond \Box p)$ — 36.0 and 52.41, by 30.23

(2) $\vdash \Box p \Rightarrow (\Box \Diamond \sim p \Rightarrow \Box p)$ — 52.41 subst

(3) $\vdash \Box p \Rightarrow [(\Box \Diamond \sim p \Rightarrow \Box p) \wedge (\Box p \Rightarrow \Diamond \Box p)]$ — (2), (1) by 42.21

(4) $\vdash [(\Box \Diamond \sim p \Rightarrow \Box p) \wedge (\Box p \Rightarrow \Diamond \Box p)] \Rightarrow (\Box \Diamond \sim p \Rightarrow \Diamond \Box p)$ — 30.15 subst

(5) $\vdash \Box p \Rightarrow (\Box \Diamond \sim p \Rightarrow \Diamond \Box p)$ — (3), (4) by 30.15

(6) $\vdash \Box p \Rightarrow (\sim \Diamond \Box p \Rightarrow \Diamond \Box p)$ — (5) Rp by 33.23

(7) $\vdash$ Th — (6) Rp by 33.11

53.21 - $\vdash \Diamond \Box \Diamond p \Rightarrow \Diamond p$ — From 53.2 by duality

53.25 - $\vdash (\Box \Diamond)^2 p \Leftrightarrow \Box \Diamond p$

(1) $\vdash \Box \Diamond p \Rightarrow (\Box \Diamond)^2 p$ — 53.2 subst

(2) $\vdash (\Box \Diamond)^2 p \Rightarrow \Box \Diamond p$ — From 53.21 by 51.151

(3) $\vdash$ Th — By df 30.35

53.26 - $\vdash (\Diamond \Box)^2 p \Leftrightarrow \Diamond \Box p$ — From 53.25 by duality

53.3 -	$\vdash$	$\Box p \Rightarrow \Box\Diamond^2\Box^2 p$	
(1)	$\vdash$	$\Box\sim(\sim p) \Rightarrow (\sim p \Rightarrow \Box^2 p)$	43.2 subst
(2)	$\vdash$	$\Box p \Rightarrow (\sim p \Rightarrow \Box^2 p)$	Rp by 31.32
(3)	$\vdash$	$\Box p \Rightarrow (\Diamond^2\sim p \Rightarrow \Diamond^2\Box^2 p)$	By rule 51.151
(4)	$\vdash$	$\Box\Diamond^2\sim p \Rightarrow \Diamond^2\sim p$	37.12 subst
(5)	$\vdash$	$\Box^2\Diamond^2\sim p \Rightarrow \Box\Diamond^2\sim p$	37.12 subst
(6)	$\vdash$	$\Box^2\Diamond^2\sim p \Rightarrow \Diamond^2\sim p$	(4), (5), by 30.15
(7)	$\vdash$	$\Box p \Rightarrow (\Box^2\Diamond^2\sim p \Rightarrow \Diamond^2\Box^2 p)$	From (7) and (6), by rule 45.32
(8)	$\vdash$	$\Box p \Rightarrow (\sim\Diamond^2\Box^2 p \Rightarrow \Diamond^2\Box^2 p)$	Rp by 33.211 and 33.23
(9)	$\vdash$	Th	From (8) by 33.11
53.31 -	$\vdash$	$\Diamond\Box^2\Diamond^2 p \Rightarrow \Diamond p$	From 53.3 by duality
53.35 -	$\vdash$	$\Box^2\Diamond^2 p \Leftrightarrow \Box^2\Diamond p$	
(1)	$\vdash$	$\Box^2\Diamond^2 p \Rightarrow \Box\Diamond\Box^2\Diamond^2 p$	53.2 subst
(2)	$\vdash$	$\Box\Box^2\Diamond^2 p \Rightarrow \Box^2\Diamond\Box^2\Diamond^2 p$	By 31.15
(3)	$\vdash$	$\Box^2\Diamond^2 p \Rightarrow \Box^2\Diamond\Box^2\Diamond^2 p$	By 53.11
(4)	$\vdash$	$\Box^2\Diamond^2 p \Rightarrow \Box^2\Diamond p$	From (3) and 53.31 by 30.15
(5)	$\vdash$	$\Box^2\Diamond p \Rightarrow \Box^2\Diamond^2 p$	From 30.16 by 15.151
(6)	$\vdash$	Th	
53.36 -	$\vdash$	$\Diamond^2\Box^2 p \Leftrightarrow \Diamond^2\Box p$	From 53.35 by duality

53.4 - *Derived reduction-theorems.*

53.41 -	$\vdash$	$\Box^2\Diamond\Box^2 p \Leftrightarrow \Box^2\Diamond\Box p$	
(1)	$\vdash$	$\Box^2\Diamond\Box^2 p \Leftrightarrow \Box^2\Diamond^2\Box^2 p$	53.35 subst
(2)	$\vdash$	$\Box^2\Diamond\Box^2 p \Leftrightarrow \Box^2\Diamond^2\Box p$	By 53.36
(3)	$\vdash$	Th	By 53.35
53.42 -	$\vdash$	$\Diamond^2\Box\Diamond^2 p \Leftrightarrow \Diamond^2\Box\Diamond p$	From 53.41 by duality
53.43 -	$\vdash$	$\Box\Diamond^2\Box\Diamond p \Leftrightarrow \Box\Diamond^2 p$	
(1)	$\vdash$	$\Diamond\Box\Diamond p \Rightarrow \Diamond p$	53.21
(2)	$\vdash$	$(\Box\Diamond)\Diamond\Box\Diamond p \Rightarrow (\Box\Diamond)\Diamond p$	By 51.15
(3)	$\vdash$	$\Box\Diamond^2 p \Rightarrow \Box\Diamond^2\Box^2\Diamond^2 p$	53.3 subst
(4)	$\vdash$	$\Box\Diamond^2 p \Rightarrow \Box\Diamond^2\Box^2\Diamond p$	By 53.35
(5)	$\vdash$	$\Box\Diamond^2 p \Rightarrow \Box\Diamond^2\Box\Diamond p$	By 53.36
(6)	$\vdash$	Th	From (2) and (5) by df 30.35
53.44 -	$\vdash$	$\Diamond\Box^2\Diamond\Box p \Leftrightarrow \Diamond\Box^2 p$	From 53.42 by duality

§ 54 - REDUCTION OF ALL MODALITIES TO 42

54.1 - *Types of simplified proper modalities.*

We call «*simplified (proper) modalities*», proper modalities Mp or $M\sim p$ in which 'M' does not contain any negation-sign.

According to 33.21-23 all proper modalities reduce to (are strictly equivalent to) simplified modalities.

Simplified modalities are of 4 types.

Type A - Affirmative modalities Mp, 'M' beginning with '$\Box$';
Type B - Affirmative modalities Mp, 'M' beginning with '$\Diamond$';
Type C - Negative modalities $M\sim p$, 'M' beginning with '$\Box$';
Type D - Negative modalities $M\sim p$, 'M' beginning with '$\Diamond$'.

54.2 - *Reduction of type A-modalities to ten.*

54.21 - With one modality-sign, we have modality: $\Box p$.

54.22 - With two modality-signs, we have two distinct modalities:

$\Box^2 p$ and $\Box\Diamond p$.

54.23 - With three modality-signs, we have four modalities:

$\Box^3 p$, $\Box^2\Diamond p$, $\Box\Diamond\Box p$, $\Box\Diamond^2 p$.

But $\vdash \Box^3 p \Leftrightarrow \Box^2 p$ 53.11

Hence three modalities are left: $\Box^2\Diamond p$, $\Box\Diamond\Box p$, $\Box\Diamond^2 p$.

54.24 - With four modality-signs, we have six modalities:

$\Box^2\Diamond\Box p$, $\Box^2\Diamond^2 p$, $\Box\Diamond\Box^2 p$, $(\Box\Diamond)^2 p$, $\Box\Diamond^2\Box p$, $\Box\Diamond^3 p$.

But $\vdash \Box^2\Diamond^2 p \Leftrightarrow \Box^2\Diamond p$ 53.35

$\vdash (\Box\Diamond)^2 p \Leftrightarrow \Box\Diamond p$ 53.25

$\vdash \Box\Diamond^3 p \Leftrightarrow \Box\Diamond^2 p$ By 53.12

Hence three distinct modalities are left: $\Box^2\Diamond\Box p$, $\Box\Diamond\Box^2 p$, $\Box\Diamond^2\Box p$.

54.25 - With five modality-signs, we have six modalities:

$\Box^2\Diamond\Box^2 p$, $\Box(\Box\Diamond)^2 p$, $\Box\Diamond\Box^3 p$, $\Box\Diamond\Box^2\Diamond p$, $\Box\Diamond^2\Box^2 p$, $\Box\Diamond^2\Box\Diamond p$.

But $\vdash \Box^2\Diamond\Box^2 p \Leftrightarrow \Box^2\Diamond\Box p$ 53.41

$\vdash \Box(\Box\Diamond)^2 p \Leftrightarrow \Box(\Box\Diamond) p$ By 53.25

$\vdash \Box\Diamond\Box^3 p \Leftrightarrow \Box\Diamond\Box^2 p$ By 53.11

$\vdash \Box\Diamond^2\Box^2 p \Leftrightarrow \Box\Diamond^2\Box p$ By 53.36

$\vdash \Box\Diamond^2\Box\Diamond p \Leftrightarrow \Box\Diamond^2 p$ 53.43

Hence one modality is left: $\Box\Diamond\Box^2\Diamond p$.

54.26 - With six modality-signs, we have two modalities:
$\Box\Diamond\Box^2\Diamond\Box p$ and $\Box\Diamond\Box^2\Diamond^2 p$.
But $\vdash \Box\Diamond\Box^2\Diamond\Box p \Leftrightarrow \Box\Diamond\Box^2 p$ By 53.44
$\vdash \Box\Diamond\Box^2\Diamond^2 p \Leftrightarrow \Box\Diamond\Box^2\Diamond p$ By 53.35

54.37 - Hence there are at most ten distinct type A-modalities in System 3, viz.:
$\Box p$, $\Box^2 p$, $\Box\Diamond p$, $\Box^2\Diamond p$, $\Box\Diamond\Box p$, $\Box\Diamond^2 p$,
$\Box^2\Diamond\Box p$, $\Box\Diamond\Box^2 p$, $\Box\Diamond^2\Box p$, $\Box\Diamond\Box^2\Diamond p$.

54.3 - *Reduction of type B-, C-, D-modalities.*

54.31 - A *type B-modality,* say $M'p$, is the dual $(Mp)^*$ of a type A-modality Mp. But, according to 33.64:
If $\vdash Mp \Leftrightarrow M''p$, then $\vdash (Mp)^* \Leftrightarrow (M''p)^*$, i.e. if the type A-modality Mp reduces to $M''p$, the type B-modality $(Mp)^*$ reduces to $(M''p)^*$. Hence there are at most ten irreducible type B-modalities, which are the duals of the type A-modalities, viz.:
$\Diamond p$, $\Diamond^2 p$, $\Diamond\Box p$, $\Diamond^2\Box p$, $\Diamond\Box\Diamond p$, $\Diamond\Box^2 p$,
$\Diamond^2\Box\Diamond p$, $\Diamond\Box\Diamond^2 p$, $\Diamond\Box^2\Diamond p$, $\Diamond\Box\Diamond^2\Box p$.

54.32 - A *type C-modality,* say $M'p$, is a modality $M\sim p$, Mp being a type A-modality. But if $\vdash Mp \Leftrightarrow M''p$, then $\vdash M\sim p \Leftrightarrow M''\sim p$.
Hence there are at most ten irreducible type C-modalities, which are: $\Box\sim p$, $\Box^2\sim p$, $\Box\Diamond\sim p$, $\Box^2\Diamond\sim p$, $\Box\Diamond\Box\sim p$, $\Box\Diamond^2\sim p$,
$\Box^2\Diamond\Box\sim p$, $\Box\Diamond\Box^2\sim p$, $\Box\Diamond^2\Box\sim p$, $\Box\Diamond\Box^2\Diamond p$.

54.33 - Similarly there are at most ten irreducible *type D-modalities* corresponding to the type C-modalities, viz:
$\Diamond\sim p$, $\Diamond^2\sim p$, $\Diamond\Box\sim p$, $\Diamond^2\Box\sim p$, $\Diamond\Box\Diamond\sim p$, $\Diamond\Box^2\sim p$,
$\Diamond^2\Box\Diamond\sim p$, $\Diamond\Box\Diamond^2\sim p$, $\Diamond\Box^2\Diamond\sim p$, $\Diamond\Box\Diamond^2\Box\sim p$.

54.4 - Hence we have at most 40 *irreducible proper* modalities; if we add to them the 2 improper modalities, p and $\sim p$, we have *at most* 42 irreducible modalities: 21 affirmative and 21 negative ones.

§ 55 - IMPLICATIONS BETWEEN MODALITIES

55.1 - The strict implications (other than strict equivalences) between type A-modalities can be summed up in four series (we prove each implication separately).

55.11 -	$\vdash$	$\Box^2\Diamond p \Rightarrow \Box\Diamond\Box^2\Diamond p \Rightarrow \Box\Diamond p \Rightarrow \Box\Diamond^2 p$	
55.111 -	$\vdash$	$\Box^2\Diamond p \Rightarrow \Box\Diamond\Box^2\Diamond p$	53.2 subst
55.112 -	$\vdash$	$\Box^2\Diamond\Box^2\Diamond p \Rightarrow \Box\Diamond p$	
(1)	$\vdash$	$\Box^2\Diamond p \Rightarrow \Box\Diamond p$	35.12 subst
(2)	$\vdash$	$\Box\Diamond\Box^2\Diamond p \Rightarrow \Box\Diamond\Box\Diamond p$	By 50.01 and 51.11
(3)	$\vdash$	Th	Rp by 53.25
55.113 -	$\vdash$	$\Box\Diamond p \Rightarrow \Box\Diamond^2 p$	30.16 subst by 51.15
55.12 -	$\vdash$	$\Box^2 p \Rightarrow \Box^2\Diamond\Box p \Rightarrow \Box\Diamond\Box^2 p \Rightarrow \Box\Diamond\Box p \Rightarrow \Box\Diamond^2\Box p$	
55.121 -	$\vdash$	$\Box^2 p \Rightarrow \Box^2\Diamond\Box p$	53.2 subst
55.122 -	$\vdash$	$\Box^2\Diamond\Box p \Rightarrow \Box\Diamond\Box^2 p$	
(1)	$\vdash$	$\Box^2\Diamond\Box^2 p \Rightarrow \Box\Diamond\Box^2 p$	37.12 subst by 51.15
(2)	$\vdash$	Th	By 53.41
55.123 -	$\vdash$	$\Box\Diamond\Box^2 p \Rightarrow \Box\Diamond\Box p$	37.12 subst
55.124 -	$\vdash$	$\Box\Diamond\Box p \Rightarrow \Box\Diamond^2\Box p$	
(1)	$\vdash$	$\Diamond\Box p \Rightarrow \Diamond^2\Box p$	30.16 subst
(2)	$\vdash$	$\Box\Diamond\Box p \Rightarrow \Box\Diamond^2\Box p$	By 46.1
55.13 -	$\vdash$	$\Box^2 p \Rightarrow \Box p \Rightarrow \Box\Diamond\Box p$	
55.131 -	$\vdash$	$\Box^2 p \Rightarrow \Box p$	37.12 subst
55.132 -	$\vdash$	$\Box p \Rightarrow \Box\Diamond\Box p$	53.2
55.14 -	We have also		
55.141 -	$\vdash$	$\Box^2\Diamond\Box p \Rightarrow \Box^2\Diamond p$	35.12 by 51.15
55.142 -	$\vdash$	$\Box\Diamond\Box p \Rightarrow \Box\Diamond p$	35.12 by 51.15
55.143 -	$\vdash$	$\Box\Diamond^2\Box p \Rightarrow \Box\Diamond^2 p$	35.12 by 51.15

55.2 - We obtain the implications between type B-modalities by duality.
E.g. we have from 55.13 by duality:

$$\vdash \quad \Diamond\Box\Diamond p \Rightarrow \Diamond p \Rightarrow \Diamond^2 p$$

55.3 - Some type A-modalities imply some type B-modalities by virtue of 36.01 or 35.12.
E.g.

$$\vdash \quad \Box^2 p \Rightarrow \Diamond\Box^2 p,$$
$$\vdash \quad \Box^2\Diamond\Box p \Rightarrow \Diamond\Box\Diamond^2 p.$$

55.4 - The implications among type C- and D- (negative) modalities are those between type A- and B-modalities respectively, substituting '$\sim p$' for 'p'.

55.5 - With the improper modalities p and $\sim p$, we have by 37.12 and 30.16

$$\vdash \quad \Box p \Rightarrow p \Rightarrow \Diamond p,$$
$$\vdash \quad \Box \sim p \Rightarrow \sim p \Rightarrow \Diamond \sim p.$$

§ 56 - UNDERIVABILITY OF OTHER IMPLICATIONS BETWEEN MODALITIES

To prove in detail, using matrices, that no other strict implications exist between modalities, see Parry.

The matrices used, may be mentioned here for purpose of reference.

56.1 (Group I of Lewis-Langford)

As 30.5, but:

p	$\Diamond p$
1	1
2	1
3	1
4	3

56.2 Group II of Lewis-Langford)

As 30.5, but:

p	$\Diamond p$
1	1
2	2
3	1
4	4

56.3 Group III of Lewis-Langford)

As 30.5, but:

p	$\Diamond p$
1	1
2	1
3	1
4	4

56.4

As 30.5, but:

p	$\Diamond p$
1	1
2	1
3	3
4	3

It follows that no strict equivalence between modalities can be proved except those listed above, hence that system 3 has just 42 irreducible modalities.

§ 57 - ALTERNATIVE SET OF POSTULATES FOR SYSTEM 3

57.1 - Simons (1953, JSL XVIII, 4) gives for S3 a set of postulates, to be compared with 63.11 below, in which there is no other rule of inference than the rule of detachment for material implication.

Simons states this axioms as axiom-schemes; we state them with a rule of substitution. It is shown loc.cit. that the postulates are independent.

57.11 - *Axioms*:

57.111 - $\vdash$ $p \Rightarrow (p \vee p)$

57.112 - $\vdash$ $(p \wedge q) \Rightarrow q$

57.113 - $\vdash$ $[(r \wedge p) \wedge \sim (q \wedge r)] \Rightarrow (p \wedge \sim q)$

57.114 - $\vdash$ $\sim \Diamond p \Rightarrow \sim p$

57.115 - $\vdash$ $p \Rightarrow \Diamond p$

57.116 - $\vdash$ $(p \Rightarrow q) \Rightarrow (\sim \Diamond q \Rightarrow \sim \Diamond p)$

(These axioms are mutually independent.)

57.12 - *Rules*:

57.121 - The rule of substitution 30.21 (Axiom-schemes dispense from it).

57.122 - The rule of detachment for material implication: If $\vdash P$ and if $\vdash P \rightarrow Q$, then $\vdash Q$.

57.13 - *The definitions* of 30.3.

57.2 - *The postulate sets 57.1 and 50 are equivalent.*

57.21 - The postulates 57.1 are those of 50 or follow from them. The only problem arises with 57.113. If we replace by '$\rightarrow$' the '$\Rightarrow$' in it, we have a tautology (provable in APC), hence 57.113 is valid by 34.15.

57.22 - For the derivation of the postulates of 50 from the postulate set 57.1, see Simons (1957).

***57.3** - Lemmon (1957) has formulated a modal system, called 'P3' which he has shown to be deductively equivalent to S3.

The postulates of P3 are the following:

I. The theorems of the APC.

II. The following two *rules*:

a) Rule of substitution for propositional variables;

b) If $\vdash P$ is a tautology of the APC or an axiom of P3, then $\vdash \Box P$.

III. The following two *axioms*:

$\vdash$ $\Box p \rightarrow p$; (weaker than 37.12)

$\vdash$ $\Box (p \rightarrow q) \rightarrow \Box (\Box p \rightarrow \Box q)$ (weaker than 51.11).

***57.4** - A formulation by Ishimoto.

***57**.40 - Ishimoto (1954) has formulated a modal system equivalent to S3, taking as primitive operators the signs '|' (the Sheffer-Nicod stroke) and '||' (such that '$P \| Q$' is interpretable as, being '$\sim\Diamond(P\wedge Q)$').

For the assertion of the system we shall use the symbol '$\vdash$'. The symbols '$\sim$', '$\wedge$', '$\vee$', '$\Diamond$', '$\rightarrow$' and '$\Rightarrow$' will be introduced by definitions.

When the symbols '|' or '||' are put obliquely and appear as '/' or '//', their binding force shall then be stronger (i.e. their separating force weaker) than otherwise. Thus '$p\|q/r$' shall mean '$p\|(q|r)$', and '$p/q|r/s$' shall stand for '$(p|q)|(r|s)$'.
The operators '||', '|', '$\sim$', '$\vee$', '$\wedge$' and '$\Diamond$' have all equal binding force.
The operators '$\rightarrow$' and '$\Rightarrow$' have both weaker binding force than the other ones. Thus '$p \| q/r \Rightarrow (s \| q \Rightarrow p \| s)$' shall stand for '$(p \| (q \mid r)) \Rightarrow ((s \| q) \Rightarrow (p \| s))$'.

The system has the following *definitions*:

***57**.411 - '$P\Rightarrow Q$' for '$P \| Q/Q$',
***57**.412 - '$P\rightarrow Q$' for '$P \mid Q/Q$',
***57**.413 - '$\sim P$' for '$P \mid P$',
***57**.414 - '$P\vee Q$' for '$P/P \mid Q/Q$',
***57**.415 - '$P\wedge Q$' for '$P/Q \mid P/Q$',
***57**.416 - '$\Diamond P$' for '$P/\!/P \mid P/\!/P$'.

Axiom-schemata:

***57**.421 - $\vdash\ p \| q/r \Rightarrow (s \mid q \Rightarrow p \mid s)$
***57**.422 - $\vdash\ p \Rightarrow p$
***57**.423 - $\vdash\ p \| q/r \Rightarrow (s \| q \Rightarrow p \| s)$
***57**.424 - $\vdash\ p \| q \Rightarrow p \mid q$
***57**.425 - $\vdash\ p \| p \Rightarrow p \| q$
***57**.426 - $\vdash\ (p/q \mid p/q) \| (p/q \mid p/q) \Rightarrow p \| q$.

The system has the two following *rules*:

a) *Modus ponens* for '$\Rightarrow$':
If $\vdash P\Rightarrow Q$ and if $\vdash P$, then $\vdash Q$.
(This rule is restricted to propositional formulas 'P' and 'Q' containing no defined operators.)

b) *Rule of adjunction*:
If $\vdash P$ and if $\vdash Q$, then $\vdash P \wedge Q$.
(The substitutability of strict equivalent propositions, containing no defined operators, is a meta-theorem provable for the system).
Ishimoto has shown that this system is deductively equivalent to S3.

§ *58 - PROPER SUBSYSTEMS OF S3 (SYSTEMS 3° AND 3*)

***58.1** - Sobocinski (1962) has considered a proper subsystem of S3, constructed by adding to S1° the axiom:
***58.10** - $\vdash \sim\Diamond[\sim\Diamond(p\wedge\sim q) \wedge \sim\sim(\Diamond p\wedge\Diamond q)]$, or the axiom
50.01 - $\vdash (p\Rightarrow q) \Rightarrow (\Diamond p\Rightarrow\Diamond q)$.
He has called this system 'S3°'.
***58.11** - Thomas (1962) has shown that the formula 57.114 $\vdash \sim\Diamond p\rightarrow\sim p$ is not provable in S3°.
***58.12** - By adding to the system S3° the axiom:
36.0 $\vdash p \Rightarrow \Diamond p$,
one obtains a system deductively equivalent to S3.

***58.2** - Sobocinski has called 'S3*' the system formed by the following axioms:

$\vdash p \Rightarrow (p\wedge p)$

$\vdash (p\wedge p) \Rightarrow p$

$\vdash [(r\wedge p)\wedge\sim(q\wedge r)] \Rightarrow (p\wedge\sim p)$

$\vdash (p\Rightarrow q) \Rightarrow (\sim\Diamond q\Rightarrow\sim\Diamond p)$

$\vdash \sim\Diamond p \rightarrow \sim p$ (57.114)

He has shown that S3* plus 36.0 $\vdash p\Rightarrow\Diamond p$ added gives S3.
***58.21** - Ivo Thomas has shown that S3* does not contain the theorem
30.15 $\vdash [(p\Rightarrow q)\wedge(q\Rightarrow r)] \Rightarrow (p\Rightarrow r)$,
nor the theorem
44.1 $\vdash (\Box p\wedge\Box q) \Rightarrow \Box(p\wedge q)$.

SECTION 6 - SYSTEM 4

System 4 is very important; nearly all theorems provable in S5 are provable in S4; nevertheless S4 has not the trivial simplicity of S5, as it keeps 12 distinct proper modalities. Moreover, quite interesting interpretations have been found for S4.

§ 60 - POSTULATES FOR SYSTEM 4

60.0 - System 4 (or S4) will be defined as the system resulting from the postulates of system 1, plus the following one:

60.01 - $\vdash \quad \Diamond\Diamond p \Rightarrow \Diamond p.$

It is clear that instead of 60.01 one could take as axiom the dual of it:

60.02 - $\vdash \quad \Box p \Rightarrow \Box\Box p.$

60.1 - Axiom 60.01 leads to strict equivalences:

60.11 -	$\vdash$	$\Diamond\Diamond p \Leftrightarrow \Diamond p$	
(1)	$\vdash$	$\Diamond p \Rightarrow \Diamond\Diamond p$	36.0 subst
(2)	$\vdash$	$\Diamond\Diamond p \Rightarrow \Diamond p$	60.01
(3)	$\vdash$	Th	From (1) and (2) by df 30.35
60.12 -	$\vdash$	$\Box\Box p \Leftrightarrow \Box p$	From 60.11 by duality

So «possibility» is here the same as «possible possibility» or as «possibility affected an undeterminate number of times by possibility». And «necessity» is there the same as «necessary necessity» or as «necessity affected an undeterminate number of times by necessity».

60.2 - Axiom 60.01 is *independent* of the postulates of system 1, since, with matrix 30.5, satisfying system 1, it has value 3 for $p=4$.

60.3 - The postulates of system 4 are *consistent* with each other since matrix 56.3 satisfies them all.

60.4 - System 4 includes system 2 and system 3.
This is shown by the following theorems:

60.41 - $\vdash$ $\Box(p\Rightarrow q) \Leftrightarrow (p\Rightarrow q)$
(1) $\vdash$ $\Box\Box(p\rightarrow q) \Leftrightarrow \Box(p\rightarrow q)$ 60.12 subst
(2) $\vdash$ Th Subst by 32.02

60.42 - $\vdash$ $\Diamond(p\wedge q) \Rightarrow \Diamond p$ (=40.1)
(1) $\vdash$ $[(p\wedge q)\Rightarrow p] \Leftrightarrow \Box[(p\wedge q)\Rightarrow p]$ 60.41 subst
(2) $\vdash$ $\{[(p\wedge q)\Rightarrow p]\wedge\Diamond(p\wedge q)\} \Rightarrow \Diamond p$ 33.32 subst
(3) $\vdash$ $\Box[(p\wedge q)\Rightarrow p]$ From 31.10 by (1)
(4) $\vdash$ Th From (3) and (2) by 33.4

60.43 - $\vdash$ $(p\Rightarrow q) \Rightarrow (\Diamond p\Rightarrow\Diamond q)$ (=50.01)
(1) $\vdash$ $\Box(p\Rightarrow q) \Rightarrow \Box(\Diamond p\rightarrow\Diamond q)$
From 33.321 subst by rule 33.311
(2) $\vdash$ Th Subst by 60.41 and 32.02

60.44 - Systems 2 and 3 being derived from the postulates of system 1 with 40.1 (= 60.42) and 50.01 (=60.43) respectively added, these systems are included in system 4.

§ 61 - REDUCTION OF MODALITIES IN SYSTEM 4

There are in System 4 exactly 14 irreducible modalities, 12 proper modalities and 2 improper ones.

We might prove this along the same lines as in Parry, as follows. Since System 3 is contained is System 4 (60.44), the reductions of System 3 are valid in System 4. If now, by 60.11, we reduce $\Diamond\Diamond p$ to $\Diamond p$, and if, by 60.12, we reduce $\Box\Box p$ to $\Box p$, the 40 proper modalities reduce to 12.

But as some reductions of System 3 may seem artificial, it is worth to show that the S4 reductions may be proved simply and naturally.

61.1 - *Reduction theorems in S4.*

61.11 - $\vdash$ $\Box p \Rightarrow \Box\Diamond\Box p$

This is 53.2, but it may be proved more simply in S4 than in S3.

(1) $\vdash$ $\Box^2 p \Rightarrow \Diamond\Box p$ 37.13 subst
(2) $\vdash$ $\Box^3 p \Rightarrow \Box\Diamond\Box p$ By 46.1

(3)	$\vdash$	$\Box p \Rightarrow \Box^3 p$	By 60.12(bis)
(4)	$\vdash$	$\Box p \Rightarrow \Box\Diamond\Box p$	By (3) and (2), 31.21.
61.12 -	$\vdash$	$\Diamond\Box\Diamond p \Rightarrow \Diamond p$	From 61.11 by duality
61.13 -	$\vdash$	$(\Box\Diamond)^2 p \Rightarrow \Box\Diamond p$	Proof as in 53.25
61.14 -	$\vdash$	$(\Diamond\Box)^2 p \Leftrightarrow \Diamond\Box p$	From 61.13 by duality

61.2 - *Types of simplified modalities in S4.*

We call «*simplified* modalities» in System 4, modalities of the form Mp or $M{\sim}p$ in which 'M' 1° neither contains any negation-sign, 2° nor contains two '$\Diamond$' or two '$\Box$' in immediate succession.

According to 33.21-23 all affirmative modalities reduce to modalities M without negation-sign, and all negative modalities reduce to modalities $M{\sim}$, where 'M' does not contain any negation-sign.

According to 60.11 and 60.12, in System 4 two '$\Diamond$' in immediate succession may be replaced by one, and two '$\Box$' in immediate succession may be replaced by one.

Simplified modalities are of 4 types:

Type A: affirmative modalities Mp, 'M' beginning with '$\Box$',
Type B: affirmative modalities Mp, 'M' beginning with '$\Diamond$',
Type C: negative modalities $M{\sim}p$, 'M' beginning with '$\Box$',
Type D: negative modalities $M{\sim}p$, 'M' beginning with '$\Diamond$'.

61.3 - *Reduction of simplified modalities of type A to three.*

With one modality-sign, we have one modality: $\Box p$,
With two modality-signs, we have one modality: $\Box\Diamond p$,
With three modality-signs, we have one modality: $\Box\Diamond\Box p$,
With four modality-signs, we might have $(\Box\Diamond)^2 p$, but, according to 61.13, this reduces to $\Box\Diamond p$. Hence we have at most 3 type A-modalities: $\Box p$, $\Box\Diamond p$, $\Box\Diamond\Box p$.

61.4 - *Reduction of type B-, C-, D-modalities.*

Type B-modalities are the duals of type A-modalities. We have at most three irreducible type B-modalities: $\Diamond p$, $\Diamond\Box p$, $\Diamond\Box\Diamond p$.

Similarly there will be at most 3 type C-modalities: $\Box{\sim}p$, $\Box\Diamond{\sim}p$, $\Box\Diamond\Box{\sim}p$.

And there will be at most 3 type D-modalities: $\Diamond\sim p$, $\Diamond\Box\sim p$, $\Box\Diamond\Box\sim p$.

61.5 - Hence we have at most 12 irreducible proper modalities; if we add to them the 2 improper modalities p and $\sim p$, we have at most 14 irreducible modalities.

61.6 - *Implications between modalities.*

61.61 - $\vdash\ \Box p \Rightarrow \Box\Diamond\Box p \Rightarrow \left\{\begin{matrix}\Diamond\Box p\\ \Box\Diamond p\end{matrix}\right\} \Rightarrow \Diamond\Box\Diamond p \Rightarrow \Diamond p$

(1)	$\vdash$	$\Box p \Rightarrow \Box\Diamond\Box p$	61.11
(2)	$\vdash$	$\Box\Diamond\Box p \Rightarrow \Diamond\Box p$	37.12 subst
(3)	$\vdash$	$\Box\Diamond\Box p \Rightarrow \Diamond\Diamond p$	From 37.12 by 46.2 and 46.1
(4)	$\vdash$	$\Diamond\Box p \Rightarrow \Diamond\Box\Diamond p$	From 30.16 by 46.16 and 46.2
(5)	$\vdash$	$\Box\Diamond p \Rightarrow \Diamond\Box\Diamond p$	36.0 subst
(6)	$\vdash$	$\Diamond\Box\Diamond p \Rightarrow \Diamond p$	61.12
61.62 -	$\vdash$	$\Box p \Rightarrow p \Rightarrow \Diamond p$	37.12 and 36.0

61.7 - It may be shown by means of matrices that no other strict implications between modalities are valid in System 4 (for the detailed proof, see Parry).

§ 62 - THEOREMS AND RULES VALID IN SYSTEM 4

62.1 - $\vdash\ \Box q \Rightarrow (p \Rightarrow \Box q)$

(1)	$\vdash$	$\Box\Box q \Rightarrow (p \Rightarrow \Box q)$	43.10 subst
(2)	$\vdash$	Th	Rp by 60.12

62.2 - Theorems about importation and exportation become strict equivalences.

62.21 - $\vdash\ [(\Box p \wedge \Box q) \Rightarrow \Box r] \Leftrightarrow [\Box p \Rightarrow (\Box q \Rightarrow \Box r)]$ (= **S'a**70)

(1) $\vdash\ [(\Box p \wedge \Box q) \Rightarrow \Box r] \Rightarrow [\Box\Box p \Rightarrow (\Box\Box q \Rightarrow \Box\Box r)]$ 52.1 subst

(2) $\vdash\ [(\Box p \wedge \Box q) \Rightarrow \Box r] \Rightarrow [\Box p \Rightarrow (\Box q \Rightarrow \Box r)]$ Subst by 60.12

(3) $\vdash\ [\Box p \Rightarrow (\Box q \Rightarrow \Box r)] \Rightarrow [(\Box p \wedge \Box q) \Rightarrow \Box r]$ 47.2 subst

(4) $\vdash$ Th From (2) and (3) by df 30.35

62.22 - $\vdash$ $[\Box p \Rightarrow (\Box q \Rightarrow \Box r)] \Leftrightarrow [\Box q \Rightarrow (\Box p \Rightarrow \Box r)]$ (= **S'a**705)
(1) $\vdash$ $[\Box p \Rightarrow (\Box q \Rightarrow \Box r)] \Rightarrow [\Box \Box q \Rightarrow (\Box p \Rightarrow \Box r)]$ 52.3 subst
(2) $\vdash$ $[\Box p \Rightarrow (\Box q \Rightarrow \Box r)] \Rightarrow [\Box q \Rightarrow (\Box p \Rightarrow \Box r)]$ Subst by 60.12
(3) $\vdash$ $[\Box q \Rightarrow (\Box p \Rightarrow \Box r)] \Rightarrow [\Box p \Rightarrow (\Box q \Rightarrow \Box r)]$ Similarly
(4) $\vdash$ Th From (2) and (3) by df 30.35

62.3 - If $\vdash P$, then $\vdash \Box p$ (This is rule 22.2 of M″PC).
To prove this rule it suffices to show that if P is an axiom of system 4 or a formula derived in it, then $\vdash \Box P$.
(1) All axioms of system 4 (i.e. 30.11 to 30.15, 36.0 and 60.01) are of the form $P \Rightarrow Q$; by 60.41, if $\vdash P \Rightarrow Q$, then $\vdash \Box (P \Rightarrow Q)$. Thus if R is an axiom of system 4, then $\vdash \Box R$.
(2) If Q is derived from P by the substitution rule 30.21, then obviously $\vdash \Box Q$ can be derived from $\vdash \Box P$.
(3) If $P \wedge Q$ is derived from P and Q by the rule of adjunction 30.22, then, by 44.1, $\vdash \Box (P \wedge Q)$ from $\vdash \Box P$ and $\vdash \Box Q$.
(4) If Q is derived from P and $P \Rightarrow Q$ by the rule of detachment 30.23, then, by 33.31, $\vdash \Box Q$ from $\vdash \Box P$ and $\vdash P \Rightarrow Q$ (which is strictly equivalent to $\vdash \Box (P \Rightarrow Q)$ by 60.41).
(5) If Q is derived from P by the rule of replacement of strict equivalents 30.24 or by definitions, then, obviously, $\vdash \Box Q$ from $\vdash \Box P$.

62.4 - We have, in consequence of 62.3, rules of inferences such as:
62.41 - If $\vdash P \rightarrow Q$, then $\vdash \Box P \rightarrow \Box Q$.
(1) $\vdash$ $P \rightarrow Q$ By hyp
(2) $\vdash$ $P \Rightarrow Q$ By 62.3 and 32.02
(3) $\vdash$ $\Box P \rightarrow \Box Q$ By 32.311
62.42 - *If* $\vdash P \leftrightarrow Q$, then $\vdash P \Leftrightarrow Q$ By 62.3 and 45.1
62.43 - *Rule of replacement of material equivalents.*
If $\vdash P \leftrightarrow Q$, then a valid formula remains valid if 'P' is replaced by 'Q' somewhere in it. From 30.24 by 62.42.

62.5 - *Some other theorems.*
62.51 - $\vdash$ $\Box (p \vee \sim p) \Leftrightarrow (p \vee \sim p)$

(1) $\vdash$ $\Box(p \vee \sim p)$ From APC by 34.1
(2) $\vdash$ $\Box\Box(p \vee \sim p)$ Subst by 60.12
(3) $\vdash$ $\Box(p \vee \sim p) \Leftrightarrow \sim(p \wedge \sim p)$ From (2) and (1) by 43.2

62.52 - $\vdash$ $\Diamond(p \wedge \sim p) \Leftrightarrow (p \wedge \sim p)$ (By duality)

62.53 - Let us define:
'Fp' for '$p \wedge \sim p$',
'Vp' for '$p \vee \sim p$'.
As a consequence:
$\vdash$ $\sim \mathrm{F}p \Leftrightarrow \mathrm{V}p$,
$\vdash$ $\sim \mathrm{V}p \Leftrightarrow \mathrm{F}p$.

62.54 - We have:
$\vdash$ $\Diamond \mathrm{F}p \Leftrightarrow \mathrm{F}p$ 62.52
$\vdash$ $\Box \mathrm{V}p \Leftrightarrow \mathrm{V}p$ 62.51

62.55 - We had already in System 2:
$\vdash$ $\Diamond \mathrm{V}p \Leftrightarrow \mathrm{V}p$ 47.03
$\vdash$ $\Box \mathrm{F}p \Leftrightarrow \mathrm{F}p$ by duality

62.56 - We had also in System 2:
$\vdash$ $\Box \sim p \Leftrightarrow (p \Leftrightarrow \mathrm{F}p)$ 45.23
$\vdash$ $\Box p \Leftrightarrow (p \Leftrightarrow \mathrm{V}p)$ 45.24

§ 63 - ALTERNATIVE SETS OF POSTULATES FOR SYSTEM 4

63.1 - The following is a set of postulates with the same primitive rules as for APC (§13).

63.11 - *Axioms*:

63.110 - The axioms of §60 (i.e. 30.11 to 30.15, 36.0 and 60.01).

63.111 - $\vdash$ $(p \Rightarrow q) \rightarrow (p \rightarrow q)$

63.112 - $\vdash$ $p \rightarrow [q \rightarrow (p \wedge q)]$

63.113 - $\vdash$ $(p \Rightarrow q) \Rightarrow (\sim q \Rightarrow \sim p)$ (= **Sa31'**)

63.114 - $\vdash$ $[(p \Rightarrow q) \wedge (r \Rightarrow s)] \Rightarrow [(p \wedge r) \Rightarrow (q \wedge s)]$

63.115 - $\vdash$ $(p \Rightarrow q) \Rightarrow (\Diamond p \Rightarrow \Diamond q)$ (= **Sm32**)

63.12 - As *rules*:

63.120 - The rule of substitution 30.21 (which might be dispensed with using axiom-schemata).

63.121 - The rule of detachment for material implication:
If $\vdash P$ and if $\vdash P \rightarrow Q$, then $\vdash Q$.

63.13 - The definitions of §60, i.e. the definitions 30.3.

63.2 - The postulate sets 63.1 and 60 are equivalent.

63.21 - The postulates of 63.1 are those of 60 or follow from these. We have to prove this last for the axioms 63.111 to 63.115 and for the rule 63.121.

(63.111)	$\vdash$	$(p \Rightarrow q) \rightarrow (p \rightarrow q)$	
(1)	$\vdash$	$(p \Rightarrow q) \Rightarrow (p \rightarrow q)$	37.2
(2)	$\vdash$	Th	By 32.42 and 37.12
(63.112)	$\vdash$	$p \rightarrow [q \rightarrow (p \wedge q)]$	From APC by 34.3

(63.113) From 31.34 by rule .16.
(63.114) Proved like 42.31.
(63.115) Proved like 60.43.
(63.121) Proved like 32.211.

63.22 - The postulates of 60 are these of 63.1 or follow from them. The only postulates proper to 60 are now rules 30.22-23-24. These are derived by means of the additional axioms.

(30.22) If $\vdash P$ and if $\vdash Q$, then $\vdash P \wedge Q$.

(1)	$\vdash$	P	By hp
(2)	$\vdash$	$P \rightarrow [Q \rightarrow (P \wedge Q)]$	63.112
(3)	$\vdash$	$Q \rightarrow (P \wedge Q)$	By rule 63.121
(4)	$\vdash$	Q	By hp
(5)	$\vdash$	$P \wedge Q$	By rule 63.121

(30.23) If $\vdash P$ and if $\vdash P \Rightarrow Q$, then $\vdash Q$.

(1)	$\vdash$	$P \Rightarrow Q$	By hp
(2)	$\vdash$	$(P \Rightarrow Q) \rightarrow (P \rightarrow Q)$	63.111
(3)	$\vdash$	$P \rightarrow Q$	By rule 63.121
(4)	$\vdash$	P	By hp
(5)	$\vdash$	Q	By rule 63.121

(30.24) Rule of replacement of strict equivalents. This follows from 63.113-114-115.

63.3 - Another set of postulates differs from that in § 23 (for M″PC) only by the fact that 23.32 is replaced by 63.313 (stated below).

63.31 - *Axioms*:

63.310 - The axioms of APC (13.11-12-13-14),

63.311 - $\vdash$ $\Box p \rightarrow p$,

63.312 - $\vdash$ $\Box(p \rightarrow q) \rightarrow (\Box p \rightarrow \Box q)$,

63.313 - $\vdash$ $\Box p \rightarrow \Box\Box p$.

63.32 - *Rules*:
63.320 - the rule of substitution (30.21 or 13.2);
63.321 - the rule of detachment for material implication (13.3);
(13.3);
63.322 - If $\vdash P$, then $\vdash \Box P$.
63.33 - *Definitions*:
63.330 - The definitions of 13 (13.41-42-43),
63.331 - '$\Diamond P$' for '$\sim\Box\sim P$', (23.51),
63.332 - '$P \Rightarrow Q$' for '$\Box(P \rightarrow Q)$', (23.52),
63.333 - '$P \Leftrightarrow Q$' for '$\Box(P \leftrightarrow Q)$'. (23.53).

63.4 - The postulate sets 63.3 and 63.1 are equivalent.
63.41 - The postulates of 63.3 are these of 63.1 or follow from them. The postulates proper to 63.3 are the axioms 63.31, the rule 63.32, the definitions 63.331-332-333. We may derive these (or corresponding theorems) from the postulate set 60 (proved equivalent with the postulate set 63.1).
(63.310) Follows from 34.3.
(63.311) From 37.12 by 37.2.
(63.312) From 32.311 by 32.02 and 37.2.
(63.313) From 60.02 by 37.2.
(63.323) Proved as 62.3.
The three definitions are proved as strict equivalences (allowing replacement by virtue of the rule 30.24).
(63.331) Proved as strict equivalence in 32.22.
(63.332) Proved as strict equivalence in 32.02.
(63.333) Proved as strict equivalence in 45.1.
63.42 - The postulates of 63.1 are these of 63.3 or follow from them. The postulates proper to 63.1 are the axioms 63.11 and the definitions 30.34-35-36.

A. All the **a**-formulas are valid, all postulates of APC being provable by 63.3.

B. In particular $\vdash p \rightarrow [q \rightarrow (p \wedge q)]$ (= 63.112)
From which follows the rule of adjunction, as in 63.22.

C. $\vdash (p \Rightarrow q) \rightarrow (p \rightarrow q)$ (= 63.111)
By 63.311 and df 63.332

And, as a consequence, the rule 30.23 (detachment for strict implication) is valid.

D. The axioms 63.113-114-114 are provable as follows:

Da (60.113) (1) $\vdash$ $(p \rightarrow q) \rightarrow (\sim q \rightarrow \sim p)$ APC
(2) $\vdash$ $\Box[(p \rightarrow q) \rightarrow (\sim q \rightarrow \sim p)]$ By 63.322
(3) $\vdash$ $\Box(p \rightarrow q) \rightarrow \Box(\sim q \rightarrow \sim p)$ By 63.312
(4) $\vdash$ $\Box[\Box(p \rightarrow q) \rightarrow \Box(\sim q \rightarrow \sim p)]$ By 63.322
(5) $\vdash$ Th By df 63.332

Db Lemma $\vdash (\Box p \wedge \Box q) \rightarrow \Box(p \wedge q)$
(1) $\vdash$ $p \rightarrow [q \rightarrow (p \wedge q)]$ APC
(2) $\vdash$ $\Box\{p \rightarrow [q \rightarrow (p \wedge q)]\}$ By 63.322
(3) $\vdash$ $\Box p \rightarrow \Box[q \rightarrow (p \wedge q)]$ By 63.312
(4) $\vdash$ $\Box p \rightarrow [\Box q \rightarrow \Box(p \wedge q)]$ By (3) and 63.312
(5) $\vdash$ Th By APC

Dc (63.114) (1) $\vdash$ $[(p \rightarrow q) \wedge (r \rightarrow s)] \rightarrow [(p \wedge r) \rightarrow (q \wedge s)]$ APC
(2) $\vdash$ $\Box\{[(p \rightarrow q) \wedge (r \rightarrow s)] \rightarrow [(p \wedge r) \rightarrow (q \wedge s)]\}$ By 63.312
(3) $\vdash$ $\Box[(p \rightarrow q) \wedge (r \rightarrow s)] \rightarrow \Box[(p \wedge r) \rightarrow (q \wedge s)]$ By 63.312
(4) $\vdash$ Th By (3) and Lemma Db

Dd (61.115) (1) $\vdash$ $\Box(\sim q \rightarrow \sim p) \rightarrow (\Box \sim q \rightarrow \Box \sim p)$ 63.312
(2) $\vdash$ $\Box(\sim q \rightarrow \sim p) \rightarrow (\sim \Box \sim p \rightarrow \sim \Box \sim q)$ By 63.312
(3) $\vdash$ $\Box(p \rightarrow q) \rightarrow (\Diamond p \rightarrow \Diamond q)$ By 63.312
(4) $\vdash$ $\Box[\Box(p \rightarrow q) \rightarrow (\Diamond p \rightarrow \Diamond q)]$ By APC
(5) $\vdash$ $\Box\Box(p \rightarrow q) \rightarrow \Box(\Diamond p \rightarrow \Diamond q)$ By df 63.331
(6) $\vdash$ $\Box(p \rightarrow q) \rightarrow \Box(\Diamond p \rightarrow \Diamond q)$ By 63.313
(7) $\vdash$ Th By df 63.332

From these axioms follows a rule of a strict equivalence replacement under the form: If $\vdash P \Rightarrow Q$ and $\vdash Q \Rightarrow P$, then a valid formula remains valid if 'P' is replaced by 'Q' somewhere in it.

E. By the methods of M″PC the following couples of strict implications, corresponding to the definitions 30.34-35-36, may be derived from the postulates 63.3:

(30.34) $\vdash$ $(p \Rightarrow q) \Rightarrow \sim \Diamond(p \wedge \sim q)$
$\vdash$ $\sim \Diamond(p \wedge \sim q) \Rightarrow (p \Rightarrow q)$

(30.35) $\vdash$ $(p \Leftrightarrow q) \Rightarrow [(p \Rightarrow q) \wedge (q \Rightarrow p)]$
$\vdash$ $[(p \Rightarrow q) \wedge (q \Rightarrow p)] \Rightarrow (p \Leftrightarrow q)$
(30.36) $\vdash$ $\Box p \Rightarrow \sim\Diamond\sim p$
$\vdash$ $\sim\Diamond\sim p \Rightarrow \Box p$

63.5 - The postulates for system 3, with the rule 62.3 added, form a postulate set for system 4.

63.51 - $\vdash$ $\Box\Box q \Rightarrow (\Box p \Rightarrow \Box\Box p)$

(1)	$\vdash$	$\Box p \Rightarrow (q \Rightarrow p)$	43.1 subst
(2)	$\vdash$	$\Box p \Rightarrow (\Box\Box q \Rightarrow \Box\Box p)$	By 51.151
(3)	$\vdash$	$\Box\Box\Box q \Rightarrow (\Box p \Rightarrow \Box\Box p)$	By 52.3
(4)	$\vdash$	Th	Subst by 53.11

63.52 - Since 63.51 is valid in system 3, it suffices that a certain formula $\vdash \Box\Box Q$ be proved, in order to have $\vdash \Box p \Rightarrow \Box\Box p$, which is 60.02, and that may be taken as a postulate for system 4 (if added to the postulates of some system containing system 1).

63.53 - This condition is fulfilled if we have the rule 62.3. Then we have, e.g.

(1)	$\vdash$	$p \Rightarrow p$	.11
(2)	$\vdash$	$\Box(p \rightarrow p)$	Rp by 32.02
(3)	$\vdash$	$\Box\Box(p \rightarrow p)$	By rule 62.3
(4)	$\vdash$	$\Box\Box(p \rightarrow p) \Rightarrow (\Box p \Rightarrow \Box\Box p)$	63.51 subst
(5)	$\vdash$	$\Box p \Rightarrow \Box\Box p$	(60.02) From (3) and (4) by 30.12

63.54 - The condition is fulfilled also if we add to System 3 the postulate:

$$(p \vee \sim p) \Rightarrow \Box(p \vee \sim p), \quad \text{or} \quad Vp \Rightarrow \Box Vp.$$

(1)	$\vdash$	$(p \vee \sim p) \Rightarrow \Box(p \vee \sim p)$	By hp
(2)	$\vdash$	$(\Box p \vee \sim p) \Rightarrow \Box\Box(p \vee \sim p)$	By 46.1
(3)	$\vdash$	$\Box\Box(p \vee \sim p)$	From (1) and (2), a06, 31.021, and 63.42

63.6 - The postulates 57.1 for System 3, with 60.01 added, form a postulate set equivalent to the postulate set 60.0.

The postulate set 63.5 shares with 63.1 the peculiarity of using no other inference rules than the rule of detachment for material implication. But they are more simple than those of 60.0 and they are shown as independent by Simons (1957).

As the postulates 57.1 are postulates for System 3, it is clear that System 4 follows from these postulates with 60.01 added.

On the other hand, the postulates 57.1 follow from the postulates 60.0 and 60.01 is a part of the postulate set 60.0.

§ 64 - VARIOUS FORMS OF THE DEDUCTION THEOREM IN SYSTEM 4

To prove the various forms of the deduction theorem we start from the postulates 63.1.

64.0 - We say that $P_1, P_2, \ldots, P_n \vdash Q$ if there is a finite sequence $Q_1, Q_2, \ldots, Q_r$ of formulas, where $Q_r = Q$, and such that, for $i = 1, \ldots, r$, either:

(1) Q_i is an axiom, or results from an axiom by substitution; or

(2) Q_i is one of the formulas P_j (for $i \leqslant j \leqslant n$); or

(3) there exist integers j and k, less than i, such that $Q_j = (Q_k \rightarrow Q_i)$.

64.1 - A necessary and sufficient condition that $P_1, P_2, \ldots, P_n \vdash Q$ is that there exists a finite sequence $Q_1, Q_2, \ldots, Q_r$ of formulas, where $Q_r = Q$, and such that, for each $i = 1, \ldots, r$, either:

(1a) Q_i is a provable formula; or

(1b) there is a j, less than i, such that Q_i results from Q_j by substituting some formula for a variable which occurs in Q_j, but which does not occur in any one of the formulas $P_1, P_2, \ldots, P_n$; or

(2) Q_i is one of the formulas P_j (for $i \leqslant j \leqslant n$); or

(3) there exist integers j and k, less than i, such that $Q_j = (Q_k \rightarrow Q_i)$.

(Conditions 2 and 3 are thus the same in 64.0 and in 64.1.)

64.11 - The condition is necessary, since every Q_i which satisfies one of the three conditions of 64.0 will clearly satisfy one of the four conditions of 64.1.

64.12 - To see that the condition is sufficient (that if 1a, 1b, 2, or 3 is satisfied, then $P_1, P_2, \ldots, P_n \vdash Q$), we make an induction on r.

64.13 - If $r = 1$, the sequence consists simply of Q: thus the hypotheses of conditions 1b and 3 cannot be satisfied, so we need to consider only conditions 1a and 2.

If Q satisfies condition 1a, then Q is provable, and hence there exists a sequence $R_1, R_2, \ldots, R_s$ of formulas, such that $R_s = Q$ and such that, for $i = 1, \ldots, s$, R_i either results from a substitution in an axiom, or is obtained by modus ponens for material implication (63.121) from preceding members of the sequence; this sequence $R_1, R_2, \ldots, R_s$ satisfies a condition of 64.0, and hence $P_1, P_2, \ldots, P_n \vdash Q$, as was to be shown.

If Q satisfies condition 2, which is a condition of 64.0, we have again $P_1, P_2, \ldots, P_n \vdash Q$, and this completes this part of the proof.

64.14 - Now suppose the condition is sufficient for all $r < k$, and let $Q_1, \ldots, Q_{k-1}, Q_k$ be a sequence satisfying a condition of 64.1. Then, for each $i < k$, there is a sequence $Q_{i,1}, Q_{i,2}, \ldots, Q_{i,ri}$, which satisfies a condition of 64.0, and such that $Q_{i,r_i} = Q_i$. If we form the new sequence:

$$Q_{1,1},\ Q_{1,2}, \ldots, Q_{1,r1},\ Q_{2,r2}, \ldots,\ Q_{k-1,1}, \ldots,\ Q_{k-1,rk-1},\ Q_k,$$

then each member of this sequence except the last one will satisfy one of the three conditions of 64.0. To simplify the notation, let the elements of this sequence be denoted by 'R_1', 'R_2', ..., 'R_s'. Then the sequence $R_1, R_2, \ldots, R_s$ is such that $R_s = Q$; and moreover, for $i < s$, R_i satisfies one of the three conditions of 64.0, and R_s satisfies one of the four conditions of 64.1, i.e. 1a, 1b, 2 or 3.

If R_s satisfies either 2 or 3, which are conditions of 64,0, then the sequence $R_1, \ldots, R_s$ suffices to show that $P_1, \ldots, P_n \vdash Q$. Then we need to consider only the cases where R_s satisfies 1a or 1b.

If R_s satisfies 1a, the proof is as in 64.13.

Suppose, finally, that R_s satisfies 1b, i.e., suppose that R_s results from some R_j $(j<s)$ by substituting for a variable not occurring in any one of the formulas $P_1, \ldots, P_n$. Now let $R'_1, R'_2, \ldots, R'_j$ be the formulas into which $R_1, R_2, \ldots, R_j$ are carried by the substitution which carries R_j into R_s (thus we must have in particular, $R'_j = R_s = Q$). Then every element of the sequence of formulas $R'_1, R'_2, \ldots, R'_j$ satisfies one of the three conditions of 64.0; so that again $P_1, \ldots, P_n \vdash Q$, which completes the proof.

64.2 - $P \vdash Q$ is true if and only if $P \rightarrow Q$ is provable.
64.21 - If $P \rightarrow Q$ is provable, then the sequence P, $P \rightarrow Q$, Q satisfies a condition of 64.1, and hence $P \vdash Q$ is true.
64.22 - If $P \vdash Q$ is true, then there exists a sequence $Q_1, \ldots, Q_r$ which satisfies a condition of 64.0. In order to show that $P \rightarrow Q$ is provable, we make an induction on r.
64.23 - If $r = 1$, the sequence $Q_1, \ldots, Q_r$ reduces to Q_1 (and hence to Q. Hence, as in 64.12 it can only satisfy condition 1a (Q is provable) or condition 2 (and then $Q = P$).

If Q is provable, and since $Q \rightarrow (P \rightarrow Q)$ is provable, (being a formula of APC) we conclude that $P \rightarrow Q$ is provable by an application of modus ponens.

If $Q = P$, then $P \rightarrow Q$ is provable because it is the formula $P \rightarrow P$ of APC.
64.24 - Now suppose the theorem is true for $r < k$, and let $r = k$, so that the sequence $Q_1, Q_2, \ldots, Q_k$ satisfies a condition of 64.0.

If Q is an axiom (condition 1) or if $Q = P$ (condition 2), the proof is the same as in 64.23.

Hence we suppose (condition 3) that there are integers u and v, less than k, such that $Q_u = (Q_v \rightarrow Q_k)$. Since u and v are less than k, we see by the induction hypothesis that the formulas

$$P \rightarrow Q_v$$
$$P \rightarrow (Q_v \rightarrow Q_k)$$

are provable, and hence that $P \rightarrow Q_k$ is provable, as was to be shown.

64.3 - $P_1, P_2, \ldots, P_n \vdash Q$ if and only if $(P_1 \wedge P_2 \wedge \ldots \wedge P_n) \vdash Q$.
63.31 - Suppose first that $P_1, P_2, \ldots, P_n \vdash Q$, and let $Q_1, Q_2, \ldots, Q_r$ be formulas satisfying a condition of 64.1 with respect to $P_1, P_2, \ldots, P_n$ and Q. Let $R_1, \ldots, R_n$ be defined as follows:

$$R_1 = [(P_1 \wedge \ldots \wedge P_n) \rightarrow P_1],$$
$$R_2 = [(P_1 \wedge \ldots \wedge P_n) \rightarrow P_2],$$
$$\ldots\ldots$$
$$R_n = [(P_1 \wedge \ldots \wedge P_n) \rightarrow P_n].$$

Since the formulas $R_1, \ldots, R_n$ are formulas of APC, and hence provable, we see that the sequence of formulas:

$$(P_1 \wedge \ldots \wedge P_n), R_1, R_2, \ldots, R_n, P_1, P_2, P, \ldots, P_n, Q_1, \ldots, Q_r$$

suffices, by 64.1, to show that $(P_1 \wedge P_2 \wedge \ldots P_n) \vdash Q$, as was to be shown.

64.32 - Now suppose, on the other hand, that $(P_1 \wedge \ldots \wedge P_n) \vdash Q$, and let a sequence of formulas satisfy a condition of 64.0 with respect to $P_1, \ldots, P_n$ and Q. Let the sequence of formulas $R_1, R_2, \ldots, R_n$ be defined as follows:

$$R_n = [P_n \rightarrow (P_1 \wedge \ldots \wedge P_n)]$$
$$R_{n-1} = (P_{n-1} \rightarrow R_n)$$
$$R_2 = (P_2 \rightarrow R_3)$$
$$R_1 = (P_1 \rightarrow R_2)$$

Then the formula R_1 is a formula of APC, and we see that the sequence of formulas:

$$P_1, P_2, \ldots, P_n, R_1, R_2, \ldots, R_n, (P_1 \wedge \ldots \wedge P_n), Q_1, \ldots, Q_n$$

suffices, by 64.1, to show that $P_1, P_2, \ldots, P_n \vdash Q$, as was to be shown.

64.4 - $P_1, P_2, \ldots, P_n \vdash Q$ if and only if $(P_1 \wedge \ldots \wedge P_n) \rightarrow Q$ is provable. By 64.3 and 64.2.

64.5 - $P_1, \ldots, P_n \vdash Q$ if and only if $(P \wedge \ldots \wedge P_n) \Rightarrow Q$ is provable By 64.4 and 62.3.

64.6 - If $P_1, \ldots, P_n \vdash Q$, where $n > 1$, then $P_1, \ldots, P_{n-1} \vdash (P \rightarrow Q)$.

(1)	$P_1, \ldots, P_n \vdash Q$	By hp
(2)	$(P_1 \wedge \ldots \wedge P_n) \rightarrow Q$	By 64.4
(3)	$(P_1 \wedge \ldots \wedge P_{n-1}) \rightarrow (P_n \rightarrow Q)$	By **a**70 (provable by 33.3)
(4)	$P_1, \ldots, P_{n-1} \vdash (P_n \rightarrow Q)$	By 64.4

64.7 - Suppose that $P_1, P_2, \ldots, P_n \vdash Q$, where $n > 1$, and that for $1 \leqslant i \leqslant n-1$, there is a formula R_i such that $P_i \Leftrightarrow \Box R_i$ is provable. Then $P_1, P_2, \ldots, P_{n-1} \vdash (P_n \Rightarrow Q)$.

(1)	$\vdash \quad P_1, \ldots, P_{n-1}, P_n \vdash Q$	By hp
(2)	$\vdash \quad (P_1 \wedge \ldots \wedge P_{n-1} \wedge P_n) \rightarrow Q$	By 64.4
(3)	$\vdash \quad (P_1 \wedge \ldots \wedge P_{n-1}) \rightarrow (P_n \rightarrow Q)$	By **a**70
(4)	$\vdash \quad (P_1 \wedge \ldots \wedge P_{n-1}) \Rightarrow (P_n \rightarrow Q)$	By 62.3 and 32.02
(5)	$\vdash \quad \Box(P_1 \wedge \ldots \wedge P_{n-1}) \Rightarrow (P_n \Rightarrow Q)$	By 46.1 and 32.02
(6)	For $i \leqslant n-1 \quad \vdash \quad P_i \Leftrightarrow \Box R_i$	By hp
(7)	For $i \leqslant n-1 \quad \vdash \Box R_i \Leftrightarrow \Box\Box R_i$	60.02 subst

(8)	For $i \leqslant n-1$	$\vdash P_i \Leftrightarrow \Box P_i$	By (6) and (7)
(9)	$\vdash$	$\Box(P_1 \wedge \ldots \wedge P_{n-1}) \Leftrightarrow (\Box P_1 \wedge \ldots \wedge \Box P_{n-1})$	44.3 subst
(10)	$\vdash$	$\Box(P_1 \wedge \ldots \wedge P_{n-1}) \Leftrightarrow (P_1 \wedge \ldots \wedge P_{n-1})$	Subst by (8)
(11)	$\vdash$	$(P_1 \wedge \ldots \wedge P_{n-1}) \Rightarrow (P_n \Rightarrow Q)$	From (5) subst by (10)
(12)	$\vdash$	$P_1, \ldots, P_{n-1} \vdash (P_n \Rightarrow Q)$	By 64.5

§ 65 - L-SYSTEM EQUIVALENT TO SYSTEM 4

The principles of a L-system equivalent to System 4 have been laid down by Curry. The system he actually formulated is not equivalent to S4; hence we shall modify his rules so to make it (presumably) equivalent to S4. This section supposes the reader is acquainted with the L-systems in Curry's formulation. Besides pure notational particularities, our formulation will differ from that of Curry on the following points:

(a) we omit the rules Pr and Er; hence we have not to introduce into our schemata a distinct notation for assertions valid in the inner system;

(b) we confine ourselves to classical logic with negation; as what regards necessity, our rules are those of LKY;

(c) we admit definitions 63.331-332-333 respectively for '◇', for '⇒' and for '⇔'. Hence in the present system, '◇' is exactly dual to '□'.

65.0 - We write '$\Box\mathfrak{X}$' for the prosequence obtained by prefixing '□' to all sentences of $\mathfrak{X}$ not already of the form $\Box P$.

65.1 - We have, in addition to the schemata of LK, both schemata of Curry's system LKY:

$$\Box l \quad \frac{\mathfrak{X}, P \Vdash \mathfrak{Y}}{\mathfrak{X}, \Box P \Vdash \mathfrak{Y}} \qquad \text{and} \qquad \Box r \quad \frac{\Box\mathfrak{X} \Vdash P}{\Box\mathfrak{X} \Vdash \Box P}$$

The intuitive sense of both schemata will be explained in 65.5. As may be seen, □r admits but one consequent.

65.2 - The elimination theorem has been proved by Curry for LKY.

65.3 - We derive from our L-system the postulates of S4 under the form stated in 63.3.

Axioms.

To prove 63.311	(1)	$p \Vdash p$	
	(2)	$\Box p \Vdash p$	$\Box$l
	(3)	$\Vdash \Box p \rightarrow p$	Pr
To prove 63.312	(1)	$p \Vdash p \quad q \Vdash q$	
	(2)	$p, p \rightarrow q \Vdash q$	Pl
	(3)	$\Box p, \Box(p \rightarrow q) \Vdash q$	$\Box$l
	(4)	$\Box p, \Box(p \rightarrow q) \Vdash \Box q$	$\Box$r
	(5)	$\Box(p \rightarrow q) \Vdash \Box p \rightarrow \Box q$	Pr
	(6)	$\Vdash \Box(p \rightarrow q) \rightarrow (\Box p \rightarrow \Box q)$	Pr
To prove 63.313	(1)	$\Box p \Vdash \Box p$	
	(2)	$\Box p \Vdash \Box\Box p$	$\Box$r
	(3)	$\Vdash \Box p \rightarrow \Box\Box p$	Pr

Rules.

Rule 63.320 of substitutions may be dispensed with.
For rule 63.321 of detachment with material implication:

$$\dfrac{\dfrac{p \Vdash p \qquad q \Vdash q}{p, p \rightarrow q \Vdash q}\,\text{Pl} \qquad \Vdash p \qquad \Vdash p \rightarrow q}{\Vdash q}$$

by the elimination theorem (twice)

Definitions are the same in both systems.

65.4 - Inversely, the postulates of the L-system may be derived from those of S4, if we admit following translation:

65.40 - $P_1, P_2, \ldots, P_m \Vdash Q_1, Q_2, \ldots, Q_n$ is translated by:
$\vdash (P_1 \wedge P_2 \wedge \ldots \wedge P_m) \rightarrow (Q_1 \vee Q_2 \vee \ldots \vee Q_n)$.

65.41 - Under this translation, the schemata of LK are provable in APC.

65.42 - Let $\mathfrak{X}$ be $P_1, P_2, \ldots, P_m$ and $\mathfrak{Y}$ be $Q_1, Q_2, \ldots, Q_n$.
Then in $\Box$l $\mathfrak{X}, P \Vdash \mathfrak{Y}$ becomes
$\vdash \quad (P_1 \wedge P_2 \wedge \ldots \wedge P_m \wedge P) \rightarrow (Q_1 \vee Q_2 \vee \ldots \vee Q_n)$.
and $\mathfrak{X}, \Box P \Vdash \mathfrak{Y}$ becomes
$\vdash \quad (P_1 \wedge P_2 \wedge \ldots \wedge P_m \wedge \Box P) \rightarrow (Q_1 \vee Q_2 \vee \ldots \vee Q_n)$.
From 35.12 $\vdash \Box p \rightarrow p$ by APC.

65.43 - Let $\mathfrak{X}$ be $P_1, P_2, \ldots, P_m, \Box Q_1, \Box Q_2, \ldots, \Box Q_n$.
Then, according to definition 65.0, $\Box\mathfrak{X}$ is:
$\Box P_1, \Box P_2, \ldots, \Box P_m, \Box Q_1, \Box Q_2, \ldots, \Box Q_n$.
In schema $\Box$r, $\Box\mathfrak{X} \Vdash P$ becomes:

(1) $\vdash \quad (\Box P_1 \wedge \Box P_2 \wedge \ldots \wedge \Box P_m \wedge \Box Q_1 \wedge \Box Q_2 \wedge \ldots \wedge \Box Q_n) \rightarrow P$

(2) $\vdash \quad \Box(\Box P_1 \wedge \Box P_2 \wedge \ldots \wedge \Box P_m \wedge \Box Q_1 \wedge \Box Q_2 \wedge \ldots \wedge \Box Q_n) \rightarrow P$
By 62.41

(3) $\vdash \quad (\Box\Box P_1 \wedge \Box\Box P_2 \wedge \ldots \wedge \Box\Box P_m \wedge \Box\Box Q_1 \wedge \Box\Box Q_2 \wedge \ldots \wedge \Box\Box Q_n) \rightarrow \Box P$ By 44.31

(4) $\vdash \quad (\Box P_1 \wedge \Box P_2 \wedge \ldots \wedge \Box P_m \wedge \Box Q_1 \wedge Q_2 \wedge \ldots \wedge \Box Q_n) \rightarrow \Box P$,
which is the translation of $\Box\mathfrak{X} \Vdash \Box P$.

65.44 - Since the translations of the schemata of LK, and of the schemata $\Box$l and $\Box$r are provable in S4, and since the definitions are the same in both systems (S4 being derived from the postulates 6.3), the L-System may be derived from S4.

65.45 - By 65.3 and 65.4, both systems are deductively equivalent. We shall from now on call our system the «S4-L system».

65.5 - There is a method of decision for the S4-L system.

For the L-systems are constructive in this sense that they prove a theorem by introduction of the connectives without any elimination. A connective can only be introduced by one determinate schema, and each conclusion of a step in the reasoning can be the consequence of determinate premisses by a determinate schema. Hence if a proposition is provable, it must be possible to reach it in a finite series of determinate steps. (For the schemata of contraction, see Curry.) If this is not possible, the proposition is not provable.

65.6 - For the practice of the L-method, it may be useful to introduce, by virtue of the definition of '$\Diamond$', following schemata for $\Diamond$:

$$\Diamond l \ \frac{P \Vdash \Diamond \mathfrak{X}}{\Diamond P \Vdash \Diamond \mathfrak{X}} \quad \text{and} \quad \Diamond r \ \frac{\mathfrak{X} \Vdash P, \mathfrak{Y}}{\mathfrak{X} \Vdash \Diamond P, \mathfrak{Y}}$$

There may be only one antecedent in $\Diamond$l.
For instance, to derive 61.11 $\vdash \Box p \Rightarrow \Box\Diamond\Box p$.

(1)	$\Box p \Vdash \Box p$	
(2)	$\Box p \Vdash \Diamond\Box p$	$\Diamond$r
(3)	$\Box p \Vdash \Box\Diamond\Box p$	$\Box$r
(4)	$\Vdash \Box p \rightarrow \Box\Diamond\Box p$	Pr
(5)	$\Vdash \Box(\Box p \rightarrow \Box\Diamond\Box p)$	$\Box$r
(6)	$\Vdash \Box p \Rightarrow \Box\Diamond\Box p$	Rp by 32.02

65.7 - We shall only mention the schemata for necessity in a T-system (the equivalent of Gentzen N-systems).

These schemata have to be added to a classical T-system (e.g. to the schemata of TJ plus $\vdash p \vee \sim p$). They do not lead to a decision procedure.

§ 66 - DECISION PROCEDURES FOR SYSTEM 4

Several kinds of decision-procedures are known for S4.

66.0 - The first one, based upon the L-methods, has been mentioned in 65.5.

66.1 - McKinsey's decision procedure for S2 (49.2) can be adapted to S4.

66.2 - Decision-procedures using truth-tables have been stated by Leonard, von Wright, and Anderson.

Their principle is as follows. It is possible to reduce a modal proposition (on the same lines as this may be done for propositions with quantifiers) into a normal form, which is truth-function of degree 0, 1, 2, ... modalities. This truth-function may be tested by means of a truth-table assigning truth-values to all arguments of the truth-function.

But here we have one difficulty. The variables to which truth-values are assigned in APC are independent of each other. The constituents to which truth-values are assigned in the present methods are not independent. In other words some relations will in most cases exist between the components, by virtue of postulates proper to modal logic. So take a somewhat trivial example. It is absurd to assign value 1 to a component p and value 0 to a component $\Diamond p$, for, by postulate 36.0, p implies $\Diamond p$.

In consequence it will be necessary to «delete» rows of truth-values which correspond to cases excluded by postulates proper to modal logic. Let us suppose we have to test the proposition $\Diamond p \rightarrow (p \wedge \Diamond p)$. If we give to p and $\Diamond p$ independent values, the truth-table will be:

$\Diamond p$	$\rightarrow$	$(p$	$\wedge$	$\Diamond p)$
1	1	1	1	1
0	1	1	0	0
1	0	0	0	1
0	1	0	0	0

But the third row must be deleted, because, according to postulate 36.0, p implies $\Diamond p$; hence p may not have value 1 when $\Diamond p$ has value 0. The table with the third row deleted gives the designated value 1 for all rows.

We explain first the method of Anderson, and shall then give an idea of the methods of von Wright and Leonard.

66.3 - The proposition is first reduced to a normal form in which

(1) there are no other connectives than '$\sim$', '$\wedge$', '$\Diamond$',

(2) no part of the proposition is of the form '$\sim\sim\alpha$', or '$\Diamond\sim(\alpha\wedge\beta)$'.

66.4 - Constituents are (1) the variables, (2) parts of the form '$\Diamond\alpha$'. Truth-values are assigned to each constituent, and a truth-table constructed as usual. The proposition is valid if and only if each row has the designated value 1, with the exceptions now to be explained.

66.5 - The exceptions concern the rows excluded by the modal postulates, i.e. no account is taken of their having truth-value 0. Modal postulates in 63.3 are the three axioms 63.311-313 and the rule 63.323.

66.51 - Axiom 63.311 $\vdash \Box p \rightarrow p$, is equivalent to $\vdash p \rightarrow \Diamond p$. Hence a first exception: there may not be a row in which value 1 is attributed to P and value 0 to $\Diamond P$. In particular, if in some row P is a variable with value 1, $\Diamond P$ has value 1 also. (This is in accordance with 62.51.)

66.52 - A second exception takes care of axioms 63.312 and 63.313. To take care of axiom 63.312 we might formulate the exceptions as follows: If $\vdash P \rightarrow (Q_1 \vee \ldots \vee Q_m)$, then we have $\vdash \Diamond P \rightarrow (\Diamond Q_1 \vee \ldots \vee \Diamond Q_m)$. Hence there may not be a row in which value 1 is assigned to $\Diamond P$, and value 0 is assigned to all components $\Diamond Q_1, \ldots, \Diamond Q_m$. In particular, if Q_1 is a variable with truth-value, $\Diamond Q_1$ has truth-value 0 (this is in accordance with 62.5).

But by virtue of axiom 63.313 (or of 60.11): If $\vdash P \rightarrow \Diamond Q'$, then we have $\vdash \Diamond P \rightarrow \Diamond Q'$. To take care of both axioms the exception has to be formulated summarily as follows: If $\vdash P \rightarrow (Q_1 \vee \ldots \vee Q_m \vee \Diamond Q'_1 \vee \ldots \Diamond Q'_n)$, there may not be a row in which $\Diamond Q_1, \ldots, \Diamond Q_m, \Diamond Q'_1, \ldots, \Diamond Q'_n$ have all value 0, and in which $\Diamond P$ has value 1.

66.53 - A third exception takes care of rule 63.322, according to which: if $\vdash P$, then $\vdash \Box P$, and if $\vdash \sim P$, then $\vdash \sim \Diamond P$. We formulate it summarily as follows: There is no row in which $\sim P$ is a tautology and in which $\Diamond P$ has value 1.

66.6 - von Wright's rules are enunciated somewhat informally. The proposition has to be reduced to an «absolutely perfect disjunctive normal form». The constituents of a proposition P of degree 1 (with no $\Diamond$ «under» a $\Diamond$) are not any propositions $\Diamond Q$ occurring in P, but all propositions $\Diamond Q'$, Q' being any disjunction of the variables and their negations. In a proposition P in which two variables, p and q, are occurring, the degree 1-constituents will be $\Diamond(p \wedge q)$, $\Diamond(p \wedge \sim q)$, $\Diamond(\sim p \wedge q)$, $\Diamond(\sim p \wedge \sim q)$.

The proposition is expressed as a truth-function of the constituents and values are assigned to all constituents. But rows are to be omitted in which occur such truth-values as are impossible by virtue of the postulates mentioned in 63.323, and by virtue of 47.4.

*66.7 - For other decision procedures, see §§ *141.3 and *142.1.

§ *67 - SOME ALTERNATIVE SETS OF POSTULATES FOR SYSTEM 4

*67.1 - Lemmon (1957) has formulated a modal system, called 'P4', which he has shown to be deductively equivalent to S4.

The postulates of P4 are the following:

I. The theorems of the APC.

II. The two rules:

a) Substitution for propositional variables,

b) If $\vdash P$ (in P4), then $\vdash \Box P$.

III. The two axioms:

$\vdash \quad \Box p \rightarrow p,$

$\vdash \quad \Box(p \rightarrow q) \rightarrow \Box(\Box p \rightarrow \Box q).$

N.B. The system P4 differs from P3 only by the rule IIb. Here the premise $\vdash P$ must not be a tautology of APC or an axiom of the new system, but may be a theorem, already proved.

*67.2 - Yonemitsu (1957) has shown that one obtains a modal system deductively equivalent to S4 by adding to the system S3 the axiom:

$\vdash \quad \Box(p \Rightarrow p),$

or the axiom:

$\vdash \quad \Diamond(p \wedge \sim p) \Rightarrow (p \wedge \sim p).$

*67.3 - Prior (1963) has formulated a modal system deductively equivalent to S4, taking as sole operators the signs '→', '⇒' and '0' (the «false» proposition).

The postulates are the following:

I. *Definitions*:

'$\Box P$' for '$(P \Rightarrow P) \Rightarrow P$',

'$\sim P$' for '$P \rightarrow 0$',

'$\Diamond P$' for '$\sim \Box \sim P$'.

II. *Axioms*:

$\vdash \quad (p \Rightarrow q) \Rightarrow (s \Rightarrow ((q \Rightarrow r) \Rightarrow (p \Rightarrow r)))$

$\vdash \quad ((p \rightarrow q) \rightarrow p) \Rightarrow p$

$\vdash \quad (p \Rightarrow (p \Rightarrow q)) \Rightarrow (p \Rightarrow q)$

$\vdash \quad (p \Rightarrow q) \Rightarrow (p \rightarrow q)$

$\vdash \quad 0 \Rightarrow p.$

III. *Rules*:

a) Substitution for the propositional variables.
b) Substitution of '$\rightarrow$' for '$\Rightarrow$' in any thesis.
c) If $\vdash P$ and if $\vdash P \Rightarrow Q$, then $\vdash Q$.
d) If $\vdash P \rightarrow Q$, then $\vdash P \Rightarrow Q$.

***67.4** - Ishimoto (1956) has formulated two modal systems deductively equivalent to S4, taking the same primitive operators as in his system *57.4.

***67.41** - A first system takes as postulates:

I. The *definitions* *57.411-416.

II. The *axioms* *57.421 and *57.425-426, plus the following one:

***67.324** - $\vdash \quad p \,\|\, q \rightarrow p \mid q$ (instead of *57.424).

III. The following *rules*:

a) The substitution for propositional variables.
b) A detachment rule for material implication under the form:

If $\vdash P$ and if $\vdash P \mid Q / R$, then $\vdash R$.

***67.42** - A second system has the same definitions and the same rules, but the following axioms:

***67.431** - $\vdash \quad p \Rightarrow p;$

***67.432** - $\vdash \quad (p \,\|\, q/r) \,\|\, (s \mid q \Rightarrow p \mid s)/(t \,\|\, u \Rightarrow t \mid u);$

***67.433** - $\vdash \quad (p \,\|\, q/r) \,\|\, (s \,\|\, q \Rightarrow p \,\|\, s)/(t \wedge u \,\|\, t \wedge u \Rightarrow t \,\|\, u);$

***67.434** - $\vdash \quad p /\!/ q \mid (p/q \mid (r \,\|\, r \Rightarrow \Diamond r \,\|\, \Diamond r)).$

§ *68 - THE SYSTEM S4^0

Sobocinski (1962) has proposed a proper sub-system of S4, constructed by adding to the system S1^0 the axiom:

*68.01 - $\vdash$ $\sim\Diamond(\Diamond\Diamond p \wedge \sim p)$, or the axiom
60.01 - $\vdash$ $\Diamond\Diamond p \Rightarrow \Diamond p$.

He calls this system 'S4°'.

The addition to S4° of the axiom 36.0 $\vdash p \Rightarrow \Diamond p$ gives a system deductively equivalent to S4.

Sobocinski has shown that his system S4° is deductively equivalent with the system which Feys has called 'T' and which he calls here 'S2'' (see below the §81.1), and also to the system called 'M' by von Wright (see below §81.2).

(Sobocinski has shown that, in S4° one can replace the two axioms $\vdash \Box p \Rightarrow p$ and $\vdash p \Rightarrow \Diamond p$, by the following one: $\vdash \Box(p \Rightarrow \Diamond p)$.)

The system S4° plus the axiom $\vdash p \Rightarrow \Box\Diamond p$ gives S5.

SECTION 7 - SYSTEM 5

§ 70 - POSTULATES FOR SYSTEM 5

70.0 - System 5 (or S5) will be defined as the system resulting from the postulates of system 1, together with the additional axiom:

70.01 - $\vdash \quad \Diamond p \Rightarrow \Box\Diamond p$.

70.02 - Axiom 70.01 is *independent* of the postulates for system 1, as, with matrix 30.5, it has value 4 for $p=3$.

70.03 - Axiom 70.01 is *consistent* with the postulates of system 1, as matrix 56.3 satisfies these postulates and 70.01.

70.1 - We derive the strict equivalences:

70.11 -	$\vdash$	$\Box\Diamond p \Leftrightarrow \Diamond p$	
(1)	$\vdash$	$\Box\Diamond p \Rightarrow \Diamond p$	37.12 subst
(2)	$\vdash$	Th	From (1) and 70.01
70.12 -	$\vdash$	$\Diamond\Box p \Leftrightarrow \Box p$	From 70.11 by duality

70.2 - We can derive 60.01 $\vdash \Diamond\Diamond p \Rightarrow \Diamond p$ in system 5, and so system 5 contains system 4.

(1)	$\vdash$	$\Box\Diamond p \Rightarrow \Diamond p$	37.12 subst
(2)	$\vdash$	$\Diamond\Box\Diamond p \Rightarrow \Diamond p$	Rp by 70.12
(3)	$\vdash$	$\Diamond\Diamond p \Rightarrow \Diamond p$	Rp by 70.11

§ 71 - REDUCTION OF MODALITIES

71.1 - The reductions of system 4 being valid in system 5, we have, according to 61.5, but 7 distinct affirmative (and 7 distinct negative) modalities to consider.

Four affirmative modalities were of degree higher than 1; in system 5 they all reduce to modalities of degree 1:

$\vdash$	$\Diamond\Box p \Leftrightarrow \Box p$	70.12
$\vdash$	$\Box\Diamond p \Leftrightarrow \Diamond p$	70.11
$\vdash$	$\Box\Diamond\Box p \Leftrightarrow \Diamond\Box p \Leftrightarrow \Box p$	By 70.11-12
$\vdash$	$\Diamond\Box\Diamond p \Leftrightarrow \Box\Diamond p \Leftrightarrow \Diamond p$	By 70.12-11

Similarly the four negative modalities of degree higher than 1 reduce to modalities of degree 1.

So there remain in system 5 only *six* irreducible modalities. Four of them are proper modalities, and they are of degree one:

Possibility, $\Diamond p$, and impossibility, $\sim\Diamond p$ or $\Box\sim p$.

Necessity, $\Box p$, and non-necessity or contingency, $\sim\Box p$ or $\Diamond\sim p$.

In addition to there, there are the two zero-degree modalities: p and $\sim p$.

Three modalities are affirmative, with the implications:

$\Box p \Rightarrow p \Rightarrow \Diamond p$.

Three are negative, with the implications:

$\sim\Diamond p \Rightarrow p\sim \Rightarrow \sim\Box p$.

This is the «*traditional*» system of modalities since Theophrastus (02.1).

71.2 - The reductions of modalities in system 5 may be summed up as follows:

71.21 - If M is an affirmative modality: $\vdash M\Box P \Leftrightarrow \Box P$

71.211 - If M' is a negative modality: $\vdash M'\Box P \Leftrightarrow \sim\Box P$

71.22 - If M is an affirmative modality: $\vdash M\Diamond P \Leftrightarrow \Diamond P$

71.221 - If M' is a negative modality: $\vdash M'\Diamond P \Leftrightarrow \sim\Diamond P$

71.23 - If M is an affirmative modality and M'' a proper modality: $\vdash$ MM$''P \Leftrightarrow M''P$

71.5-8 - The following rules for proper modalities are valid in system 5:

If M is a proper modality:

71.51 - $\vdash \Box MP \Leftrightarrow MP$

71.52 - $\vdash \Diamond MP \Leftrightarrow MP$

71.53 - $\vdash \Box MP \Leftrightarrow \Diamond MP$

71.62 - $\vdash (MP \vee \Box Q) \Leftrightarrow \Box(MP \vee Q)$

71.64 - $\vdash (MP \wedge \Diamond Q) \Leftrightarrow (MP \wedge Q)$

71.71 - $\vdash (MP \Rightarrow Q) \Leftrightarrow (MP \Rightarrow \Box Q)$

71.72 - $\vdash (P \Rightarrow MQ) \Leftrightarrow (\Diamond P \Rightarrow MQ)$

71.81 - If $\vdash Mp \Rightarrow Q$, then $\vdash MP \Rightarrow \Box Q$

71.82 - If $\vdash P \Rightarrow MQ$, then $\vdash \Diamond P \Rightarrow MQ$

These were, among the rules valid in M'PC, the last to be proved.

§ 72 - REDUCTION OF MODAL FUNCTIONS IN SYSTEM 5

72.0 - *Modal functions* are formulas which are built up from propositional variables and the operations $\sim$, $\Diamond$ and $\wedge$, or formulas which are strictly equivalent to such ones.

72.1 - $\vdash$ $[\Diamond p \wedge (p \Rightarrow \sim \Diamond q)] \Rightarrow \sim \Diamond q$

(1)	$\vdash$	$(p \Rightarrow \sim \Diamond q) \Rightarrow (\Diamond p \Rightarrow \Diamond \sim \Diamond q)$	50.01 subst
(2)	$\vdash$	$(p \Rightarrow \sim \Diamond q) \Rightarrow (\Diamond p \Rightarrow \sim \Diamond q)$	By 71.23
(3)	$\vdash$	$[\Diamond p \wedge (p \Rightarrow \sim \Diamond q)] \Rightarrow [\Diamond p \wedge (\Diamond p \Rightarrow \sim \Diamond q)]$	By 42.11
(4)	$\vdash$	$[\Diamond p \wedge (\Diamond p \Rightarrow \sim \Diamond q)] \Rightarrow \sim \Diamond q$	37.3 subst.
(5)	$\vdash$	Th	From (3) and (4) by 30.15

72.2 - $\vdash$ $\Diamond(p \wedge \Diamond q) \Leftrightarrow (\Diamond p \wedge \Diamond q)$

(1)	$\vdash$	$[\Diamond p \wedge (p \Rightarrow \sim \Diamond q)] \Rightarrow \sim \Diamond q$	72.1
(2)	$\vdash$	$(\Diamond p \wedge \sim \sim \Diamond q) \Rightarrow \sim (p \Rightarrow \sim \Diamond q)$	By 32.11
(3)	$\vdash$	$(\Diamond p \wedge \Diamond q) \Rightarrow \sim \sim \Diamond (p \wedge \sim \sim \Diamond q)$	By 31.32 and by df 30.34
(4)	$\vdash$	$(\Diamond p \wedge \Diamond q) \Rightarrow \Diamond (p \wedge \Diamond q)$	By 31.32
(5)	$\vdash$	$\Diamond (p \wedge \Diamond q) \Rightarrow (\Diamond p \wedge \Diamond \Diamond q)$	41.3 subst
(6)	$\vdash$	$\Diamond (p \wedge \Diamond q) \Rightarrow (\Diamond p \wedge \Diamond q)$	By 60.11
(7)	$\vdash$	Th	From (4) and (6) by df 30.35

72.3 - $\vdash$ $\Diamond(p \wedge \sim q) \Leftrightarrow (\Diamond p \wedge \sim \Diamond q)$

(1)	$\vdash$	$\Diamond(p \wedge \Diamond \sim \Diamond q) \Leftrightarrow (\Diamond p \wedge \Diamond \sim \Diamond q)$	72.2 subst
(2)	$\vdash$	Th	By 71.23

74.4 -	$\vdash$	$[(p \wedge \sim p) \wedge r] \Leftrightarrow (p \wedge \sim p)$	From APC by 34.4
72.41 -	$\vdash$	$[(p \vee \sim p) \vee r] \Leftrightarrow (p \vee \sim p)$	From APC by 34.4

72.5 - Each formula built up from the single variable p by means of the operations $\sim$, $\wedge$ and $\Diamond$, is in system 5 equivalent to one of the following 16 formulas:

(1) p, (2) $\sim p$, (3) $p\Diamond$, (4) $\sim\Diamond p$, (5) $\Diamond\sim p$, (6) $\sim\Diamond\sim p$, (7) $p\wedge\sim p$, (8) $p\vee\sim p$, (9) $p\wedge\Diamond\sim p$, (10) $\sim p\vee\sim\Diamond\sim p$, (11) $\sim p\wedge\Diamond p$, (12) $p\vee\sim\Diamond p$, (13) $\Diamond p\wedge\Diamond\sim p$, (14) $\sim\Diamond p\vee\sim\Diamond\sim p$, (15) $\Diamond p\wedge(\sim p\vee\sim\Diamond\sim p)$, (16) $\Diamond\sim p\wedge(p\vee\sim p)$.

The theorem can be proved by an induction on the length of the formula built up from p. Since p is one of the 16 formulas, it clearly suffices to show that this class of 16 formulas has the following properties:

(1) if α is in the class, then there exists in the class a formula β such that $\sim\alpha\Leftrightarrow\beta$ is provable in system 5;

(2) If α is in the class, then there exists in the class a formula β such that $\Diamond\alpha\Leftrightarrow\beta$ is provable in system 5;

(3) if α and β are in the class, then there exist in the class a formula γ such that $(\alpha\wedge\beta)\Leftrightarrow\gamma$ is provable in system 5.

The proof offers no difficulty, using the theorems 70.1 to 71.23, together with the theorems 41.33 and 62.5.

72.6 - In particular, as the 16 formulas are at most of degree 1, this proves that in system 5 each formula involving only one variable reduces to a formula of degree 1 at most.

72.7 - And from the theorems already proved it follows that every formula in system 5 reduces to a formula of degree 1 at most.

§ 73 - ALTERNATIVE SETS OF POSTULATES FOR SYSTEM 5

73.1 - The set of postulates 23 for M″PQC is a set of postulates for system 5.

The set 23 differs from the set 63.3 only by the fact that 63.313, $\vdash(\Box p\rightarrow\Box\Box p)$, is replaced in it by 23.32: If P is a proper modality, then $\vdash P\rightarrow\Box P$.

73.11 - The set 23 can be derived from the postulates 70.0 of system 5.

(1) The set 63.3 is derivable from the postulates of system 5, as system 4 (by 55.2) is included in system 5.

(2) The additional postulate 23.32 is (by 31.16 and 35.2) a consequence of 71.23, which has been derived in system 5.

73.12 - The postulate set 70.0 (consisting of the postulates of system 1, with 70.01 $\vdash \Diamond p \Rightarrow \Box\Diamond p$ added) is derivable from the set 23.

(1) The set 63.3 is derivable from the set 23, as the only postulate proper to 63.3 is 63.313 ($\vdash \Box p \rightarrow \Box\Box p$), which is a special case of 23.32. The postulates of system 1 are derivable from the set 63.3, as set 63.3 is a set for system 4, which includes system 1.

(2) The axiom 70.01 is a consequence of 23.32 (by 23.2 and 23.52).

73.2 - If we add 73.20 (given below) to postulates of system 4, and even to postulates of system 3 (¹), we have a set of postulates for system 5.

73.20 - $\vdash p \Rightarrow \Box\Diamond p$.

73.21 - A set of postulates for system 4, with 73.20 added, is a set for system 5, for 70.01, the only axiom proper to system 5, can be derived from it.

(1) $\vdash$ $\Diamond p \Rightarrow \Box\Diamond\Diamond p$

(2) $\vdash$ $\Diamond p \Rightarrow \Box\Diamond p$

73.22 - A set of postulates for system 3, with 73.20 added, is a set for system 5.

(1)	$\vdash$	$\Box(p\rightarrow p) \Rightarrow \Box\Box\Diamond(p\rightarrow p)$	From 73.20 subst, by rule 46.1
(2)	$\vdash$	$\Box(p\rightarrow p)$	From 31.11 by 32.42
(3)	$\vdash$	$\Box\Box\Diamond(p\rightarrow p)$	From (1) and (2) by 30.23
(4)	$\vdash$	$\Box\Box\Diamond(p\rightarrow p) \Rightarrow (\Box p \Rightarrow \Box\Box p)$	63.51 subst
(5)	$\vdash$	$\Box p \Rightarrow \Box\Box p$	From (3) and (4) by 30.23

(6) By 60.02, the system includes the system 4.

(7) By 73.21, the system reduces to system 5 (¹).

73.3 - For another postulate reducing system 4 to system 5, see 87.3.

***73.4** - *Some other alternative sets of postulates for* S5.

***73**.41 - Anderson (1956) has obtained a system deductively equivalent to S5 by taking the Simons axiom-schemata 57.111-116 for S3 (with the sole rule of detachment for material im-

(¹) Sobocinski has shown that 57.115 is derivable from the axioms 57.111-114, 57.116 plus 70.01 (or 73.20). (*Notre Dame Journal of Symbolic Logic*, 1962, pp. 51-60.) (The editor)

plication) and adding the following axiom-schema:
$\vdash (\sim\Diamond\sim p \Rightarrow \Diamond p) \Rightarrow (p \Rightarrow \sim\Diamond\sim p)$ (or $\vdash (\Box p \Rightarrow \Diamond p) \Rightarrow (p \Rightarrow \Box p)$.
The axiom-schemata are shown to be independent.

***73.42** - Simons (1957) has shown that one obtains a system deductively equivalent with S5 by adding to the axiom-schemata 57.111-116 for S3 the axiom-schema:

$\vdash \Diamond p \Rightarrow \sim\Diamond\sim\Diamond p$ (or $\vdash \Diamond p \Rightarrow \Box\Diamond p$, i.e. 70.01).

Sobocinski has shown that the axiom-schema 57.115 is not independent of the others in this formulation for S5.

Thomas (1963) has shown that one obtains a system equivalent to S5 by adding to S1° one of the following so-called «generalized S5-axioms»:

$\vdash \Diamond^j p \Rightarrow \Box^j \Diamond p$ (with any natural number j), or
$\vdash \Diamond^k p \Rightarrow \Box^{k+2} \Diamond p$ (with any natural number k). (See also § *80.5.)

***73.43** - Sobocinski (1962) has shown that one obtains a system deductively equivalent to S5 by adding to the system S1° the axiom 70.01 (just cited in *73.42).

***73.44** - Sobocinski (1962) has shown that one obtains a system deductively equivalent to S5 by adding the axiom:

$\vdash p \Rightarrow \sim\Diamond\sim\Diamond p$ (or $\vdash p \Rightarrow \Box\Diamond p$, i.e. the C12 of Lewis-Langford)

either to his system S3°(see § 58), or to the system S2° (see § 40).

Thomas (1963) has shown that one obtains a system equivalent to S5 by adding to S1° one of the following pairs of so-called «Brouwerian axioms»:

a) $\vdash p \Rightarrow \Box\Diamond p$ and
$\vdash p \Rightarrow \Box^{2k}\Diamond p$ (with any natural number $k > 0$);
b) $\vdash p \Rightarrow \Box^{m-1}\Diamond p$ and
$\vdash p \Rightarrow \Box^{n-1}\Diamond p$ (with any pair of natural numbers m, n both greater than 2, and co-prime).
(See also § *80.4.)

***73.5** - Prior (1963) has formulated a modal system deductively equivalent to S5, taking as sole operators the symbols '→', '⇒' and '0' (as in 67.3).

The system has the same definitions and the same rules as in 67.3.

67.3. The axioms are here the following:

$\vdash \quad \{[(p \Rightarrow q) \Rightarrow r] \Rightarrow s\} \Rightarrow [(q \Rightarrow s) \Rightarrow (p \Rightarrow s)],$

$\vdash \quad p \Rightarrow (q \rightarrow p),$

$\vdash \quad [p \Rightarrow (p \rightarrow q)] \Rightarrow (p \Rightarrow q),$

$\vdash \quad (p \Rightarrow q) \Rightarrow (p \rightarrow q),$

$\vdash \quad 0 \Rightarrow p.$

***73.6** - Prior (1953, with corrections by Łukasiewicz and Bausch, 1955) has constructed a modal system deductively equivalent to S5 by adding a system of deduction rules to the APC.

The rules are the following:

L1: If $\vdash P \rightarrow Q$, then $\vdash \Box P \rightarrow Q$;

L2: If $\vdash P \rightarrow Q$, and if all the variables appearing in 'P' are in the scope of an operator '$\Box$' or '$\Diamond$', then $\vdash P \rightarrow \Box Q$;

M1: If $\vdash P \rightarrow Q$, and if all the variables appearing in 'Q' are in the scope of an operator '$\Box$' or '$\Diamond$', then $\vdash \Diamond P \rightarrow Q$;

M2: If $\vdash P \rightarrow Q$, then $\vdash P \rightarrow \Diamond Q$.

This procedure amounts to a kind of Gödel L-formulation for S5.

***73.7** - Lemmon and Gjertsen (1959) did propose a modal system deductively equivalent to S5, constructed by adding to the APC an undefined modality '**Q**' for «contingency» (i.e. «neither necessity nor impossibility»).

Definitions:

'$\Box P$' for '$P \wedge \sim \mathbf{Q} P$';

'$\Diamond P$' for '$\sim \Box \sim P$'.

Axiom-schemata:

$\vdash \quad \mathbf{Q}p \leftrightarrow \mathbf{Q} \sim p;$

$\vdash \quad \sim \mathbf{Q}(p \leftrightarrow q) \rightarrow (\mathbf{Q}p \rightarrow \mathbf{Q}q);$

$\vdash \quad \mathbf{Q}(p \rightarrow q) \rightarrow (\sim \mathbf{Q}p \rightarrow p);$

$\vdash \quad \sim \mathbf{Q}(p \rightarrow \mathbf{Q}p).$

Sole *rule*:

If $\vdash P$, then $\vdash \sim \mathbf{Q}P$.

***73.8** - Prior (1957) says that one obtains a system deductively equivalent to S5 by taking the system 67.42 of Ishimoto for S4 and replacing his axiom 67.434 by the following:

$\vdash \quad p /\!/ q \mid \{p / q \mid [\Diamond(r \parallel r) \Rightarrow r \parallel r]\}.$

SECTION 8 - EXTENSIONS

A system S′ is called a (proper) *extension* of system S if every provable formula of S is also provable in S′, but not inversely.

We do not state here general theorems about extensions of modal systems, but we comment only some particular extensions of the modal systems studied hitherto. In this §8 we confine ourselves to extensions which may be considered as intermediary between two of the systems S1 to S5, namely extensions of S2 (81-85), of S3 (86) and S4 (87), then extensions which reduce the system to non-modal logic (88). We leave for §9 extensions generated by axioms of «universal possibility» or by «existence-axioms».

§*80 - SOME EXTENSIONS OF SYSTEM 1°

***80.1** - Sobocinski (1962) has called 'T^0' a modal system constructed by adding to $S1^0$ an arbitrary formula $\vdash \Box\Box Q$ with a 'Q' such that one has $\vdash \Box Q$ in $S1^0$.

He has shown that his system T^0 is a proper extension of $S1^0$ and a proper subsystem of the system S2′ (also called 'T') of the §81 below.

In the system T^0 one cannot prove the formulas:

$p \Rightarrow \Diamond p$,

$\Diamond \sim (p \wedge \sim p) \Leftrightarrow \sim (p \wedge \sim p)$,

nor $\Box (p \wedge \sim p) \Leftrightarrow \sim (p \wedge \sim p)$,

as can be shown by the matrix 36.1 satisfying T^0.

***80.2** - Sobocinski has called 'System T^x' a modal system obtained by adding to his system T^0 the axiom:

***80**.20 - $\vdash \Diamond \Box p$.

***80**.21 - He has shown that the system T^x is a proper extension of T^0, and a quasi-normal extension of T^0 in the sense of Scroggs.

In T^x one does not have the theorem: $\vdash \Box \Diamond \Box p$.

***80**.22 - The same are true of systems obtained by adding the axiom *80.20 to any of Sobocinski's system $S2^0$, $S3^0$ or $S4^0$, which are defined as follows:

***80**.23 - Sobocinski's system $S2^0$ is obtained by adding to $S1^0$ the axiom:

$\vdash \quad \sim\Diamond[\Diamond(p\wedge q)\wedge\sim\Diamond p]$

or the axiom: $\vdash \quad \Diamond(p\wedge q)\Rightarrow\Diamond p$.

By adding to the system S2° the axiom: $\vdash p\Rightarrow\Diamond p$, one obtains a system deductively equivalent to S2.

***80**.24 - For the system S3°, see §*58.

***80**.25 - For the system S4°, see §*68.

***80.3** - Thomas (1962) has shown that the system called 'S1*', obtained by adding to S1° the axiom $\vdash p\Rightarrow\Box\Diamond p$, does not contain the theorem $\vdash \quad \sim\Diamond(p\wedge\sim\Diamond p)$,

nor $\vdash \quad \Box p\Rightarrow p$,

nor $\vdash \quad p\Rightarrow\Diamond p$.

***80.4** - Thomas (1963) has shown that the addition to S1° of one of the following so-called «Brouwerian» axioms:

$\vdash p\Rightarrow\Box\Diamond p$ or

$\vdash p\Rightarrow\Box^{2k+1}\Diamond p$ (with some natural number k)

gives a system weaker than S5. (See also § *73.44.)

***80**.5 - Thomas (1963) has shown that a system formed by adding to S1° a so-called «generalized S5-axiom» of the form:

$\vdash \Diamond^{j}p\Rightarrow\Box^{k}\Diamond p$ (with j and k at least equal to 1, but with $j+k$ = an odd number)

should be weaker than S5. (See also § *73.42.)

***80**.6 - Sobocinski (1963) has shown that the system formed by adding to S1° the axiom:

$\vdash p\rightarrow\Diamond p$ (instead of $\vdash p\Rightarrow\Diamond p$)

is stronger than S1°, but weaker than S1.

§ 81 - EXTENSION OF SYSTEM 2: SYSTEM 2′ (OR T)

81.1 - Feys states, for a system designated as 'system **t**' or 'T', but which shall be called here «system 2′» ,postulates which are those of 63.3, except 63.313.

81.11 - *Axioms*:

81.110 - The postulates of APC.

81.111 - $\vdash \quad \Box p\rightarrow p$ (=63.311 or 37.12)

81.112 - $\vdash \quad \Box(p\rightarrow q)\rightarrow(\Box p\rightarrow\Box q)$ (=63.312) (weaker than 33.311)

81.12 - *Rules*:
81.120 - The rule of substitution (=63.120)
81.121 - The rule of detachment for material implication (=63.121)
81.122 - If $\vdash P$, then $\vdash \Box P$ (=62.3) (stronger than 34.15)

81.13 - *Definitions*:
81.131 - '$\Diamond P$' for '$\sim\Box\sim P$',
81.132 - '$P \Rightarrow Q$' for '$\Box(P \rightarrow Q)$',
81.133 - '$P \Leftrightarrow Q$' for '$\Box(P \leftrightarrow Q)$'.

81.2 - von Wright takes as postulates for his system called «system M»:
81.21 - *Axioms*:
81.210 - The postulates of APC.
81.211 - $\vdash \quad p \rightarrow \Diamond p$
81.212 - $\vdash \quad [\Diamond(p \vee q)] \leftrightarrow (\Diamond p \vee \Diamond q)$
81.22 - *Rules*:
81.221 - The rule of detachment with material implication.
81.222 - If $\vdash P$, then $\vdash \Box P$.
81.223 - If $\vdash P \leftrightarrow Q$, then $\vdash \Diamond P \leftrightarrow \Diamond Q$.
81.23 - *Definition*:
81.231 - '$\Box P$' for '$\sim\Diamond\sim P$'.

81.3 - The deductive equivalence of the postulates 81.1 and 81.2 has been proved by Sobocinski.

***81.4** - We obtain also a system deductively equivalent to S2′ by adding to the postulates of S1 the rule:

If $\vdash P$, then $\vdash \Box P$.

§ 82 - RELATIONS BETWEEN SYSTEM 2′ AND OTHER SYSTEMS

82.1 - The postulates of S2 are provable by means of the postulates of S2′. Hence S2′ contains S2.

82.11 - *Axioms*.

Axioms 30.11-12-13-14 are provable from APC, by 81.122 and df 81.132 or 81.133.

Lemma 63.42 Da is provable without 63.313, hence by postulates 81.1.

To prove axiom 30.15 $\vdash [(p \Rightarrow q) \wedge (q \Rightarrow r)] \Rightarrow (p \Rightarrow r)$

(1)	$\vdash$	$[(p \rightarrow q) \wedge (q \rightarrow r)] \rightarrow (p \rightarrow r)$	APC
(2)	$\vdash$	$\Box\{[(p \rightarrow q) \wedge (q \rightarrow r)] \rightarrow (p \rightarrow r)\}$	By 81.122
(3)	$\vdash$	$\Box[(p \rightarrow q) \wedge (q \rightarrow r)] \rightarrow \Box(p \rightarrow r)$	By 81.112
(4)	$\vdash$	$[\Box(p \rightarrow q) \wedge \Box(q \rightarrow r)] \rightarrow \Box(p \rightarrow r)$	By lemma 63.42 Da
(5)	$\vdash$	$\Box\{[\Box(p \rightarrow q) \wedge \Box(q \rightarrow r)] \rightarrow \Box(p \rightarrow r)\}$	By 81.122
(6)	$\vdash$	Th	By df 81.132

Axiom 36.0 $\vdash p \Rightarrow \Diamond p$ is provable from 81.111, by 81.122 and 81.132.

Axiom 40.1 $\vdash \Diamond(p \wedge q) \Rightarrow \Diamond p$

(1)	$\vdash$	$\sim p \rightarrow \sim(p \wedge q)$	APC
(2)	$\vdash$	$\Box[\sim p \rightarrow \sim(p \wedge q)]$	By 81.122
(3)	$\vdash$	$\Box \sim p \rightarrow \Box \sim (p \wedge q)$	By 81.122
(4)	$\vdash$	$\sim \Box \sim (p \wedge q) \rightarrow \sim \Box \sim p$	By APC
(5)	$\vdash$	$\Diamond(p \wedge q) \rightarrow \Diamond p$	By df 81.131
(6)	$\vdash$	Th	By 81.122 and df 81.132

82.12 - *Rules.*

82.121 - Rule of substitution is not necessary.

82.122 - Rule of detachment with strict implication results from 81.121 by means of 81.111.

82.123 - Rule of replacement of strict equivalents.

A. $\vdash (p \Rightarrow q) \Rightarrow (\sim q \Rightarrow \sim p)$ — Proved as in 63.42 Da

B. $\vdash [(p \Rightarrow q) \wedge (r \Rightarrow s)] \Rightarrow [(p \wedge r) \Rightarrow (q \wedge s)]$ — Proved as in 63.42 Dc

C. If $\vdash P \Leftrightarrow Q$, then $\vdash \Diamond P \Leftrightarrow \Diamond Q$

(1) If $\vdash P \leftrightarrow Q$, then $\vdash \Diamond P \leftrightarrow \Diamond Q$ — Proved in Sobocinski 3.1 as rule R II

(2) If $\vdash P \Leftrightarrow Q$, then $\vdash \Diamond P \leftrightarrow \Diamond Q$ — By 81.111

(3) If $\vdash P \Leftrightarrow Q$, then $\vdash \Diamond P \Leftrightarrow \Diamond Q$

From A, B, C, the rule of replacement of strict equivalents may be proved.

82.13 - *Definitions.*

Definition 30.31 follows from 81.131.

Definitions 30.32-33 are common to both systems.

82.2 - System 2′ possesses an infinite number of modalities. It suffices to show that the matrix of McKinsey (§ 49) satisfies the system 2′. For the proof, see Sobocinski.

82.3 - System 2′ does not contain System 3; hence it does not contain System 4.

It can be shown that rule 81.122 is not provable in System 3; moreover there is but a finite number of irreducible modalities in system 3.

§ 83 - THEOREMS PROVABLE IN SYSTEM 2′

83.1 - $\vdash$ $\Box(p \Rightarrow p)$

(1) $\vdash$ $p \Rightarrow p$

(2) $\vdash$ Th By 81.122

83.11 - In general, if $\vdash P$ in S2, then P preceded by any number of '$\Box$' is valid in S2′.

83.2 - All rules 62.4 are valid in S2′.

The demonstration of these rules presupposes only the postulates of S2 with rule 81.122 added.

83.3 - All theorems 62.5 are valid in S2′. For the same reason.

§ *84 - OTHER SYSTEMS EQUIVALENT TO SYSTEM 2′

***84.1** - Anderson (1957) has shown that one obtains a modal system equivalent to S2′ by taking the axiom-schemata 57.111-116 of Simons for S3 with the definition:

'$P \Rightarrow Q$' for '$\sim\Diamond\sim(P \rightarrow Q)$',

and the sole rule of inference:

If $\vdash P$ and if $\vdash \sim\Diamond\sim P \rightarrow Q$, then $\vdash Q$.

He has called this system 'system M*'.

He has shown that the axiom-schemata of this system are mutually independent.

***84.2** - Yonemitsu (1955 and 1957) has shown that one obtains modal systems deductively equivalent to system S2′ in the four following manners:

1° By adding to the system S1 an arbitrary axiom of the form $\vdash \Box\Box Q$ having as 'Q' a proposition for which $\vdash \Box Q$ is provable in the system S1;

2° By adding to the system S1 an arbitrary axiom of the form $\vdash \Box\Box Q$ having as 'Q' a tautology of the APC. He has called this system the system 'S′';

3° By adding to the system S2 the axiom $\vdash \Box(p \Rightarrow p)$;

4° By adding to the system S2 the axiom $\vdash \Diamond(p \wedge \sim p) \Rightarrow (p \wedge \sim p)$.

***84.3** - Sobocinski has formulated a system, which he calls 'S2°′', by adding to the postulates of S1° the axiom:

81.41 $\vdash$ $\Box(p \Rightarrow p)$.

He has shown that all the theorems of S2° are provable in this S2°′.

By adding to the postulates of S2°′ the axiom:

36.0 $\vdash$ $p \Rightarrow \Diamond p$ (or the axiom $\vdash \Box p \Rightarrow p$), one obtains a system equivalent to S2′.

§ 85 - EXTENSIONS OF SYSTEM 2′

85.1 - Between system 2′ and system 4, there is an infinite number of systems, called here '$S4^1$' (=S4), '$S4^2$', $S4^3$', etc., which we can obtain by adding to the postulates of S1° axioms of the form:

$$\vdash \quad \Box^n p \Rightarrow \Box^{n+1} p,$$

where '$\Box^n$' stands for a sequence of n signs '$\Box$', n corresponding to the index figuring in the name of the system.

Evidently the same result holds if we add

$$\vdash \quad \Diamond^{n+1} p \Rightarrow \Diamond^n p,$$

where '$\Diamond^n$' stands for a sequence of n diamonds.

For any n, the system $S4^n$ contains $S4^{n+1}$, but does not contain $S4^{n-1}$. Thus $S4^2$ is weaker than $S4^1$ or S4.

For the proofs, see a forthcoming paper of Sobocinski.

***85.2** - Sugihara has proved that in $S4^2$ and in the weaker systems $S4^3$, ..., the number of irreducible modalities is infinite.

§ 86 - EXTENSIONS OF SYSTEM 3

We obtain extensions of system 3 by adding to the postulates of system 3 some implication between modalities which holds in system 4, but not in system 3. Here are a few examples, after Parry.

86.1 - Let us add to system 3 the postulate:

86.10 - $\vdash \quad \Box\Diamond^2 p \Rightarrow \Box\Diamond p.$

Then we have:

86.11 - $\vdash \quad \Box\Diamond^2 p \Leftrightarrow \Box\Diamond p$ from 86.10 and 55.113, by df 30.35

86.12 - $\vdash \quad \Diamond\Box^2 p \Leftrightarrow \Diamond\Box p$ from 86.11 by duality

86.13 - We have the following reductions of type A-modalities, irreducible in system 3:

$\vdash \quad \Box\Diamond^2 p \Leftrightarrow \Box\Diamond p$ 86.11

$\vdash \quad \Box^2\Diamond^2 p \Leftrightarrow \Box^2\Diamond p$ from 86.11 by 46.1

$\vdash \quad \Box\Diamond^2\Box p \Leftrightarrow \Box\Diamond\Box p$ from 86.11 subst

$\vdash \quad \Box^2\Diamond^2\Box p \Leftrightarrow \Box^2\Diamond\Box p$ from 86.11 subst and 46.1

86.14 - Hence there remain only 6 types A-irreducible modalities:

$\Box p,\ \Box^2 p,\ \Box\Diamond p,\ \Box^2\Diamond p,\ \Box\Diamond\Box p,\ \Box^2\Diamond\Box p.$

86.15 - Hence for the four types, 24 irreducible proper modalities; plus the 2 improper modalities, 26 in all.

For the implications between them, see Parry.

86.2 - Let us add to system 3 the postulate:

86.20 - $\vdash \quad \Box\Diamond\Box p \Rightarrow \Box p.$

Then we have:

86.21 - $\vdash \quad \Box\Diamond\Box p \Leftrightarrow \Box p$ from 86.20 and 53.2 by df 30.35

86.22 - $\vdash \quad \Diamond\Box\Diamond p \Leftrightarrow \Diamond p$ from 86.21 by duality

86.23 - We have the following reductions of type A-modalities, irreducible in system 3:

$\vdash \quad \Box\Diamond\Box p \Leftrightarrow \Box p$ 86.21

$\vdash \quad \Box\Diamond\Box^2 p \Leftrightarrow \Box^2 p$ from 86.22 subst

$\vdash \quad \Box^2\Diamond\Box p \Leftrightarrow \Box^3 p$ from 86.21 by 46.1

$\vdash \quad \Box\Diamond\Box^2\Diamond p \Leftrightarrow \Box^2\Diamond p$ from 86.21 subst

86.24 - Hence there remain only 6 type-A irreducible modalities:

$$\Box p,\ \Box^2 p,\ \Box\Diamond p,\ \Box^2\Diamond p,\ \Box\Diamond^2 p,\ \Box\Diamond^2\Box p.$$

86.25 - Hence, for the four types, 24 irreducible proper modalities; plus the two impropers; this gives 26 in all.

86.3 - The systems 86.1-2 suggest a few remarks.

(a) Both systems have the same number, i.e. 26, of irreducible modalities; nevertheless they are not equivalent, as the reductions are not the same in both. The difference between systems is not based only on the number of distinct modalities.

(b) Although system 4 has fewer modalities than 86.2, system 86.2 is not even included in system 4. For there is in 86.2 a reduction $\Box\Diamond\Box p \Leftrightarrow \Box p$ which is not valid in system 4.

86.4 - Halldén (JSL, XIV, p. 233) mentions a system that he calls 'K' obtained by adding to the postulates of system 3 the following axiom:

86.40 - $\vdash \Diamond(\Box p \Rightarrow \Box^2 p)$.

This system K is shown to be stronger than system 3, but weaker than system 4.

§ 87 - EXTENSIONS OF SYSTEM 4

87.1 - Let us add to system 4 the postulate:

87.10 - $\vdash \ \Diamond\Box p \Leftrightarrow \Box\Diamond p$. We have then:

87.11 - $\vdash \ \Box\Diamond\Box p \Leftrightarrow \Box\Box\Diamond p \Leftrightarrow \Box\Diamond p$

$\vdash \ \Diamond\Box\Diamond p \Leftrightarrow \Diamond\Diamond\Box p \Leftrightarrow \Diamond\Box p \Leftrightarrow \Box\Diamond p$.

87.12 - So, from the affirmative modalities of system 4, viz.
$p,\ \Box p,\ \Diamond p,\ \Box\Diamond p,\ \Diamond\Box p,\ \Box\Diamond\Box p,\ \Diamond\Box\Diamond p,$
only 4 remain distinct: $p,\ \Box p,\ \Diamond p,\ \Box\Diamond p,$
with the implications: $\Box p \Rightarrow \left\{\begin{matrix}\Box\Diamond p\\ p\end{matrix}\right\} \Rightarrow \Diamond p.$

87.13 - And there are 8 modalities in all (the 4 affirmative ones, and the 4 negative ones, being the negations of them).

87.14 - System 87.1 is an example of a system not included in system 5, although system 5 has fewer modalities. For $\Diamond\Box p \Leftrightarrow \Box\Diamond p$ is not valid in system 5, where it would make $\Diamond p \Leftrightarrow \Box p$.

87.2 - Of a more particular nature is the system called '4.1' in McKinsey, obtained by adding to S4 the axiom:

87.20 - $\vdash \quad (\Box\Diamond p \wedge \Box\Diamond q) \Rightarrow \Diamond(p \wedge q)$.

It can be proved that:

87.21 - $\vdash \quad (\Box\Diamond p \wedge \Box\Diamond q) \Leftrightarrow \Box\Diamond(p \wedge q)$

87.22 - $\vdash \quad \Box\Diamond p \Rightarrow \Diamond\Box p$

87.23 - $\vdash \quad \Box\Diamond\Box p \Leftrightarrow \Diamond\Box p$

87.24 - $\vdash \quad \Diamond\Box\Diamond p \Leftrightarrow \Box\Diamond p$

From 87.23 and 87.24 it results that, from the 6 irreducible affirmative proper modalities of S4, only 4 remain irreducible in System 4.1. As it can be shown that no other reduction is possible, the system has 10 modalities in all: 4 affirmative proper, 4 negative proper and the 2 improper.

Since the implication 87.22 is not valid in System 5, System 4.1 is not included in system 5.

87.3 - The system obtained by adding postulate 87.30 below to system 4 has been called by Parry 'System 4.5'. We prove by theorems 87.32 to 87.36 that this system reduces simply to system 5.

87.30 -	$\vdash$	$\Box\Diamond\Box p \Rightarrow \Box p$	
87.31 -	$\vdash$	$\Box\Diamond\Box p \Leftrightarrow \Box p$	By 53.2
87.32 -	$\vdash$	$\Diamond\Box\Diamond p \Leftrightarrow \Diamond p$	from 87.31 by duality
87.33 -	$\vdash$	$\Diamond(\Diamond p \wedge \Diamond q) \Leftrightarrow (\Diamond p \wedge \Diamond q)$	
(1)	$\vdash$	$(\Diamond p \wedge \Diamond q) \Rightarrow \Diamond p$	31.23 subst
(2)	$\vdash$	$\Diamond(\Diamond p \wedge \Diamond q) \Rightarrow \Diamond^2 p$	By 46.2
(3)	$\vdash$	$\Diamond(\Diamond p \wedge \Diamond q) \Rightarrow \Diamond p$	Rp by 70.01
(4)	$\vdash$	$\Diamond(\Diamond p \wedge \Diamond q) \Rightarrow \Diamond q$	similarly
(5)	$\vdash$	$\Diamond(\Diamond p \wedge \Diamond q) \Rightarrow (\Diamond p \wedge \Diamond q)$	From (3) and (4) by 42.2
(6)	$\vdash$	$(\Diamond p \wedge \Diamond q) \Rightarrow \Diamond(\Diamond p \wedge \Diamond q)$	36.0 subst
(7)	$\vdash$	Th	From (5) and (6) by df 30.3
87.34 -	$\vdash$	$(p \wedge \sim\Diamond p) \Leftrightarrow (q \wedge \sim q)$	
(1)	$\vdash$	$p \Rightarrow \Diamond p$	36.0
(2)	$\vdash$	$\Box\sim(p \wedge \sim\Diamond p)$	by 32.01
(3)	$\vdash$	$q \Rightarrow q$	31.11
(4)	$\vdash$	$\Box\sim(q \wedge \sim q)$	By 32.01
(5)	$\vdash$	Th	From (2) and (4) by 43.2

87.35 - $\vdash$ $(\Diamond p \wedge \Diamond \sim \Diamond p) \Leftrightarrow \Diamond (q \wedge \sim q)$
(1) $\vdash$ $(\Box \Diamond p \wedge \sim \Diamond \Box \Diamond p) \Leftrightarrow (q \wedge \sim q)$ 87.34 subst
(2) $\vdash$ $(\Diamond p \wedge \Diamond \sim \Diamond p) \Leftrightarrow \Diamond (\Diamond p \wedge \Diamond \sim \Diamond p)$ 87.33 subst
(3) $\vdash$ $(\Diamond p \wedge \Diamond \sim \Diamond p) \Leftrightarrow \Diamond \Box \Diamond (\Diamond p \wedge \Diamond \sim \Diamond p)$ Rp by 87.32
(4) $\vdash$ $(\Diamond p \wedge \Diamond \sim \Diamond p) \Leftrightarrow \Diamond \Box (\Diamond p \wedge \Diamond \sim \Diamond p)$ Rp by 87.33
(5) $\vdash$ $(\Diamond p \wedge \Diamond \sim \Diamond p) \Leftrightarrow \Diamond (\Box \Diamond p \wedge \Box \Diamond \sim \Diamond p)$ By 44.2
(6) $\vdash$ $(\Diamond p \wedge \Diamond \sim \Diamond p) \Leftrightarrow \Diamond (\Box \Diamond p \wedge \sim \Diamond \Box \Diamond p)$ By 33.21
(7) $\vdash$ Th Rp by (1)

87.36 - $\vdash$ $\Diamond p \Rightarrow \Box \Diamond p$
(1) $\vdash$ $\sim \Diamond (q \wedge \sim q)$ From 32.11 by 30.34
(2) $\vdash$ $\sim \Diamond^2 (q \wedge \sim q)$ Rp by 60.11
(3) $\vdash$ $\sim \Diamond (\Diamond p \wedge \Diamond \sim \Diamond p)$ Rp by 87.35
(4) $\vdash$ $\sim \Diamond (\Diamond p \wedge \sim \sim \Diamond \sim \Diamond p)$ Rp by 31.32
(5) $\vdash$ Th Rp by 30.36 and 30.34.

***87.4** - Lemmon and Dawson have called «System 4.2» a system obtained by adding to system 4 the axiom:
***87**.41 - $\vdash \Diamond \Box p \rightarrow \Box \Diamond p$.
The system 4.2 is not contained in system 5.

§ 88 - EXTENSIONS REDUCING MODAL SYSTEMS TO APC

88.1 - System 1 can obviously be reduced to APC by the addition of a postulate reducing proper to improper modalities:
88.10 - $\vdash$ $p \Rightarrow \Box p$.
88.11 - $\vdash$ $\Diamond p \Rightarrow p$ might as well be used as postulate.
We have then:
88.12 - $\vdash$ $p \Leftrightarrow \Box p$ 88.10 and 37.12
88.13 - $\vdash$ $p \Leftrightarrow \Diamond p$ 88.11 and 37.0

88.2 - In order to fill up the gaps in the tables of strict implications between modalities, so as to have a «linear» series of modalities, some logicians have proposed the following postulates; but these have been shown to reduce various systems to APC. These are:
88.20 - $\vdash \Box \Diamond p \Rightarrow p$ (Churchman)
88.201 - $\vdash$ $\Box \Diamond p \Rightarrow \Box p$ (Becker)
88.202 - $\vdash$ $\Box \Diamond p \Leftrightarrow \Box p$ (Churchman. C14)

It is clear that if we have 88.202, we have 88.201, and if we have 88.201, we have 88.20, by 37.12.

88.21 - To prove that the postulate 88.20 (hence also 88.201 and 88.202) reduces system 2 to APC, we prove first a lemma (demonstrable in system 2):

88.211 - $\vdash$ $\Box\Diamond(p\rightarrow\Box p)$

(1)	$\vdash$	$\Box p \Rightarrow \Diamond\Box p$	36.0 subst
(2)	$\vdash$	$\Box(\Box p\rightarrow\Diamond\Box p)$	Rp by 32.02
(3)	$\vdash$	$\Box(\Diamond\sim p\vee\Diamond\Box p)$	By APC and 33.21
(4)	$\vdash$	$\Box\Diamond(\sim p\vee\Box p)$	Rp by 44.4
(5)	$\vdash$	Th	Rp by 32.02

88.212 - $\vdash$ $p \Rightarrow \Box p$

(1)	$\vdash$	$p \rightarrow \Box p$	From 88.211 by 88.20
(2)	$\vdash$	$(p\rightarrow\Box p) \rightarrow \Box(p\rightarrow\Box p)$	(1) subst
(3)	$\vdash$	Th	From (1) and (2) by rule 32.211 and 32.02
(4)	$\vdash$	$\sim\Diamond(\Diamond p\wedge\sim\sim\Diamond\sim\Diamond p)$	Rp by 31.32
(5)	$\vdash$	Th	Rp by 30.36 and 30.34

Hence, by the lemma 88.211 (valid in System 2), and 30.02 System 2 reduces to APC.

88.3 - Postulate 88.202 $\vdash\Box\Diamond p\Leftrightarrow\Box p$ would even reduce System 1 to APC, as can be proved by the following lemma:

88.31 - $\vdash$ $\Box p \Leftrightarrow \Box^2 p$

(1)	$\vdash$	$\Box p \Leftrightarrow \Box\Diamond p$	From 88.202 by 31.17
(2)	$\vdash$	$\Box p \Leftrightarrow \Box\sim\Box\sim p$	By 33.22
(3)	$\vdash$	$\Box p \Leftrightarrow \Box\sim\Box\Diamond\sim p$	Rp by 88.202
(4)	$\vdash$	$\Box p \Leftrightarrow \Box\Diamond\sim\Diamond\sim p$	Rp by 33.23
(5)	$\vdash$	$\Box p \Leftrightarrow \Box\Diamond\Box p$	By df 30.36
(6)	$\vdash$	Th	Rp by 88.202

88.32 - By virtue of 88.31 the system then reduces to System 4, containing system 2. Hence, by 88.21, the system reduces to APC.

SECTION 9 - EXTENSIONS (CONTINUED)

§ 91 - EXTENSIONS GENERATED BY POSTULATES OF UNIVERSAL POSSIBILITY

91.0 - The simplest postulate of universal possibility, which may be informaly discussed here, would be a postulate:

$\vdash \quad \Diamond p,$

i.e .«Everything is possible».

Such a postulate would be equivalent to $\vdash \sim\Box\sim p$; whence, if we substitute $\sim p$ for p, we would have $\vdash \sim\Box p$, «Every necessary proposition is false».

Such an axiom would be inconsistent with all systems studied up to this point, because all their axioms are of the form $\vdash \Box P$.

91.1 - There is however a real interest in the systems obtained by the addition to one of our preceding systems of the axiom:

91.10 - $\vdash \quad \Diamond^2 p.$

This is equivalent to $\vdash \sim\Box^2\sim p$, from which, by substitution of $\sim p$ for p, $\vdash \sim\Box^2 p$ may be derived, viz. «Every necessarily necessary proposition is false».

91.11 - Axiom 91.10 is independent from the postulate sets for S3 (and also for S1°, S1 and S2), for it is not satisfied by matrix 56.3 for $p = 4$.

Axiom 91.10 is consistent with the postulates for system 3 (and with those for S1°, S1 and S2), for it is satisfied by matrix 56.1.

Halldén (1949) calls (after Alban) 'system 6' the system generated by the addition of 91.10 to system 2, and 'system 7' the one generated by the addition of 91.10 to system 3.

91.12 - Axiom 91.10 is inconsistent with the postulates of system 4 (and with those of system 5).

We have e.g. 30.11 $\vdash \; (p\wedge q) \Rightarrow p$ or $\vdash \Box[(p\wedge q)\rightarrow p]$.

By 60.02 $\vdash \; \Box^2[(p\wedge q)\Rightarrow p]$.

But by 91.10 $\vdash \; \sim\Box^2[(p\wedge q)\rightarrow p]$, and so we have a contradiction.

91.2 - We may, also with Halldén (1949), consider the systems generated by the addition of the axiom:

91.20 - $\vdash \quad \Box\Diamond^2 p$.

91.21 - This postulate is also independent from and consistent with the postulates of system 3 (and of systems 1°, 1, 2), which may be proved as in 91.11 and 91.12.

Halldén has called 'system 8' the system generated by system 3 plus 91.20.

91.22 - Axiom 91.20 is inconsistent with the postulates of system 4 (and with these for system 5).

For 91.10 is an immediate consequence of 91.20.

§ 94 - POSTULATES OF IRREDUCIBILITY

We may combine reduction-postulates and postulates of irreducibility, as is done in the various systems called '$S2_n$' by McKinsey (JSL, IX, p. 42).

Let us put:

'Fp' for '$p \wedge \sim p$'.

Then $S\,2_1$ is derived from the postulates of system 2, plus:

$\vdash \quad \sim(\mathrm{F}p \Leftrightarrow \Diamond\mathrm{F}p)$,

$\vdash \quad \Diamond\mathrm{F}p \Leftrightarrow \Diamond^2\mathrm{F}p$.

And $S\,2_n$ is derived from the postulates of system 2, plus:

$\vdash \quad \sim(\mathrm{F}p \Leftrightarrow \Diamond\mathrm{F}p)$,

$\vdash \quad \sim(\Diamond\mathrm{F}p \Leftrightarrow \Diamond^2\mathrm{F}p)$,

. . . .

$\vdash \quad \sim(\Diamond^{n-1}\,\mathrm{F}p \Leftrightarrow \Diamond^n\,\mathrm{F}p)$,

$\vdash \quad \Diamond^n\,\mathrm{F}p \Leftrightarrow \Diamond^{n+1}\,\mathrm{F}p)$.

$\vdash \quad \Diamond^2\mathrm{F}p \Leftrightarrow \Diamond^3\mathrm{F}p$.

§ 95 - PROPOSITIONAL VARIABLES

95.0 - Some systems make use — as does the Polish school — of propositions or formulas about all or some propositions, mentioning propositional variables as bound variables. We have e.g. formulas such as **A***P R*, **E***P R*, '*P*' being the designation of a propositional variable and '*R*' the designation of a formula. There may also be formulas such as **A***p***A***q R*, **E***p***E***q R*, **A***p***E***q R*, and so on.

95.01 - These formulas may be interpreted as follows. An object-variable may have as values all different individuals supposed as existing in the logical universe; '**A**x R' says that R is valid for all values of x, thus whatever individuals may be designated by 'x'; and '**E**x R' says that R is valid for some individual taken as the value of x. Similarly 'p', 'q', 'r' may represent all different propositions; that does not mean the designata of all sentences worded differently, but all propositions, which may be taken as different. In APC, equivalent propositions may be considered as identical; as all true propositions are equivalent and all false propositions are equivalent, we may assume that there are two different propositions in APC and only two. In modal calculus strictly equivalent propositions may be taken as identical; it may be assumed that there are as many different propositions in a given system as there are non-strictly-equivalent modal functions in it.

95.02 - Propositional bound variables might be used simply as part of a metalanguage, in order to formulate some statements, e.g. some supplementary axioms such as 96.10 below.

But if theorems and rules are stated for the manipulation of formulas involving bound propositional variables, we have to do with special forms of logical calculi. Such calculi have in fact been developed at some extent in Lewis-Langford, but somewhat informally, in the context of a discussion based upon intuitive considerations. It would, of course, be easy to develop such systems axiomatically.

95.1 - Let us here consider what may be called an *assertoric functional calculus* (of first order) *with bound propositional variables* (AF^1PC). This calculus is an extension of APC, but, of course, not a modal one; it may be set forth as follows:

95.10 - A formula or rule of AF^1C will be said to undergo a **fp**-transformation (functional-propositional transformation) if 'x', 'y', 'X', 'Y' are replaced everywhere in it by 'p', 'q', 'R', 'S' (we shall not need here transformations for which this rule would create an ambiguity).

If n is the number of a formula or rule, **fp** n will be the number of the **fp**-transformed formula or rule. And so, e.g.:

Rule 16.2 is: If $\vdash P$, then $\vdash \mathbf{AX}\, P$,
Rule **fp** 16.2 is: If $\vdash P$, then $\vdash \mathbf{A}P\, R$,
Theorem 17.23 is: $\vdash \mathbf{EX}(P \vee Q) \leftrightarrow (\mathbf{EX}\, P \vee \mathbf{EX}\, Q)$,
Theorem **fp** 17.23 is: $\vdash \mathbf{E}P(R \vee S) \leftrightarrow (\mathbf{E}P\, R \vee \mathbf{E}P\, S)$.

95.11 - We take the theorems and rules **fp** 16 as postulates for AF'PC. Then if a theorem or rule is valid in AF'C, the corresponding **fp**-theorem or rule is valid in AF'PC.

In particular all theorems and rules **fp** 17 are valid.

By virtue of **fp** 16.1 all theorems and rules of APC are valid in AF^1PC; such are in particular the derived rules 14.3. The terminology based on them may be used in AF^1PC.

95.2 - We shall need here only some rules derivable in AF^1PC.

95.20 - If 'R' is a formula, then '$\mathbf{A}P\, R$' and '$\mathbf{E}P\, R$' are formulas.

95.21 - If $\vdash R$, then $\vdash \mathbf{A}P\, R$. By **fp** 16.2

95.22 - If $\vdash \mathbf{A}P\, R$, then $\vdash \mathbf{E}P\, R$. By **fp** 17.13

95.23 - If $\vdash (P/Q)R$, then $\vdash \mathbf{E}P\, R$. By **fp** 17.12

This covers the «principle of converse substitution» of Lewis-Langford.

95.24 - If $\vdash R$ and if $\vdash \mathbf{E}P\, S$, then $\vdash \mathbf{E}P(R \wedge S)$.

This follows from $\vdash \mathbf{A}P\, R \rightarrow [\mathbf{E}P\, R \rightarrow \mathbf{E}P(R \wedge S)]$ provable in AF^1PC.

95.3 - Statements involving bound propositional variables and symbols of modal propositional calculi can only be derived in some *modal* calculus with bound propositional variables, MF^1PC, and not in AF^1PC. There will be as many such different calculi as there are different systems of MPC.

95.31 - We might take as postulates for such calculi the postulates for MF^1C which have been stated by Barcan. So we would have:

(1) The postulates of a system of MPC;
(2) The postulates proper to AF^1PC (i.e. the postulates **fp** 16, except 16.1);
(3) Axioms such as $\vdash \Box \mathbf{A}P\, R \Rightarrow \mathbf{A}P \Box R$.

95.32 - If the theorems or rules derivable from these postulates 95.31 are **s**- or **S**-transformations of **fp**-theorems or rules, we number them as in section 24.

95.4 - We shall use the following theorems or rules, derivable in some MF¹PC:

95.41 - ⊢ □**A***P R* ⇒ **E***P R*. (**sfp** 17.13)

95.42 - If ⊢ **A***P*(*R*⇒*S*) and if ⊢**E***P R*, then ⊢**E***P S*. By **sfp** 17.325

95.43 - If '*P*' is not free in '*R*', then ⊢**A***P*(*R*⇒*S*) ⇔ (*R*⇒**A***P S*).

95.44 - If '*P*' is not free in '*S*', then ⊢**A***P*(*R*⇒*S*) ⇔ (**E***P R*⇒*S*) (¹).

§ 96 - EXTENSIONS WITH BOUND PROPOSITIONAL VARIABLES

96.0 - Let us consider the additional axiom:

96.01 - ⊢ **E***p***E***q*[~(*p*⇒*q*) ∧ ~(*p*⇒~*q*)].

96.02 - The significance of this axiom may best be grasped if we contrast it with a theorem derivable in AF¹PC:

⊢ **A***p***A***q*[(*p*→*q*) ∨ (*p*→~*q*)] From **a**542 by rule 65.21

i.e. «For two formulas *p* and *q* whatever, *p* implies materially *q* or ~*q*»).

The axiom ⊢**E***p***E***q*[~(*p*⇒*q*) ∧ ~(*p*⇒~*q*)]
is equivalent, by APC, with
⊢**E***p***E***q* ~[(*p*⇒*q*) ∨ (*p*⇒~*q*)], and by AF¹C with
⊢ ~**U***p***U***q*[(*p*⇒*q*) ∨ (*p*⇒~*q*)], the formal negation of the analogue of 96.02.

The two operators having incompatible theorems, it is proved that they are not the same. (In the systems S1° to S5 is was not possible to prove that they are the same.)

96.03 - Matrix 56.1 shows that 96.01 is consistent with the postulates of systems 1°, 1, 2, 3, 4, 5 (and also of their extensions). These postulates are satisfied by matrix 56.1, which also gives a designated value for ~(*p*⇒*q*) ∧ ~(*p*⇒~*q*) with *p* = 1 and *q* = 2 or *q* = 3 (²).

(¹) Lewis-Langford add as metatheorem 21.03:
If '*P*' is not free in '*R*', then ⊢**E***P*(*R*⇒*S*)⇔(*R*⇒**E***P S*).
The analogy of MF¹C (Barcan, metatheorem 48) suggests that only the strict *implication* is provable (that the '⇔' has to be replaced by '⇒'). In fact Lewis-Langford use theorem 21.03 only to prove their 21.11, and they add that this 21.11 is «unimportant».

(²) It is not possible to prove this way that 96.01 is consistent with 91.10 and 91.20.

96.04 - Axiom 96.01 is independent of the other postulates of the systems just enumerated.

This can be proved by means of a matrix which is the usual matrix 15.1 for APC, but to which we add:

p	$\Diamond p$
1	1
0	0

This matrix (identifying $\Diamond p$ with p, and $\Box p$ with p, and so $p \Rightarrow q$ with $p \rightarrow q$) satisfies every postulate of the systems in question, but not 96.01.

96.1 - From the axiom 96.01 it may be concluded (by means of the rules 95.2 of AF¹PC):

96.11 - $\vdash$ **E**p**E**q**E**$r[\Diamond p \wedge \Diamond q \wedge \Diamond r \wedge \sim (p \Leftrightarrow q) \wedge \sim (p \Leftrightarrow r) \wedge \sim (q \Leftrightarrow r)]$

(«There are at least three distinct propositions which are possible».)

96.12 - $\vdash$ **E**p**E**q**E**r**E**s $[\sim (p \Leftrightarrow q) \wedge \sim (p \Leftrightarrow r) \wedge \sim (p \Leftrightarrow s)$
$\wedge \sim (q \Leftrightarrow r) \wedge \sim (q \Leftrightarrow s) \wedge \sim (r \Leftrightarrow s)]$.

(«There are at least four distinct propositions».)

96.2 - Axiom 96.01 may be contrasted with theorems derivable from modal propositional logic (by means of MF¹PC):

We have in system 2:

96.20 - $\vdash$ $[(p \Rightarrow q) \wedge (p \Rightarrow \sim q)] \Leftrightarrow \Box \sim p$. (**S'a** 69)

We derive in MF¹PC:

96.21 - $\vdash$ **A**$q \Box \sim p \Leftrightarrow \Box \sim p$, Subst in **sfp** 17.51

96.22 - $\vdash$ **E**$q \Box \sim p \Leftrightarrow \Box \sim p$. Subst in **sfp** 17.52

Hence:

96.23 - $\vdash$ **A**$q[(p \Rightarrow q) \wedge (p \Rightarrow \sim q)] \Leftrightarrow \Box \sim p$.

(1) $\vdash$ **A**$q[p \Rightarrow q \wedge (p \Rightarrow \sim q)] \Leftrightarrow$ **A**$q \Box \sim p$ from 96.20 by rule 30.2

(2) $\vdash$ Th Subst by 96.21

96.24 - $\vdash$ **E**$q[(p \Rightarrow q) \wedge (p \Rightarrow \sim q)] \Leftrightarrow \Box \sim p$. Similarly by 96.22

96.25 - $\vdash$ **A**$q[(p \Rightarrow q) \wedge (p \Rightarrow \sim q)] \Leftrightarrow$ **E**$q[(p \Rightarrow q) \wedge (p \Rightarrow \sim q)]$.
By 96.23-24 ([1])

([1]) In systems 1° and 1 it is only possible to prove (Lewis-Langford 21.3 and 21.31):

$\vdash$ **E**$q[(p \Rightarrow q) \wedge (p \Rightarrow \sim q)] \Rightarrow \Box \sim p$,

$\vdash$ $\{\Box \sim p \wedge [p \Rightarrow (p \vee \sim p)]\} \Rightarrow$ **E**$q[(p \Rightarrow q) \wedge (p \Rightarrow \sim q)]$.

SECTION *9′ - SOME OTHER MODAL SYSTEMS

§*9′1 - Halldén (1948) formulated a modal system which he called 'S0' and which is weaker than S1°.

The system is formed by taking the same postulates as system 1 (§37), but without the definition 30.34. The operator '$\Rightarrow$' is taken as primitive.

Halldén has shown that in S0 one cannot prove the formulas:

$$\vdash \quad p \Rightarrow (p \vee q),$$
$$\vdash \quad (p \wedge \sim p) \Rightarrow q,$$

nor $\vdash \quad \{[(p \wedge q) \Rightarrow r] \wedge [(p \wedge \sim q) \Rightarrow r]\} \Rightarrow (p \Rightarrow r).$

§*9′2 - Lemmon (1957) has called 'S0.5' a modal system defined by the following postulates:

I. The theorems of the APC.

II. The sole *rule*:

If $\vdash P$ is a tautology of the APC, then $\vdash \Box P$.

III. The two *axiom-schemata*:

$$\vdash \quad \Box p \rightarrow p,$$
$$\vdash \quad \Box(p \rightarrow q) \rightarrow (\Box p \rightarrow \Box q).$$

§*9′3 - Moh Shaw-Kwei (1958) proposed a modal system, which he calls «system B» (basic system) and which is notably weaker than any of the Lewis's systems. The system uses but three symbols, namely: '$\sim$', '$\Rightarrow$' and '$\Box$'.

***9′3.1** - System B has the following postulates:

I. Three *axioms*:

$$\vdash \quad p \Rightarrow \sim\sim p,$$
$$\vdash \quad \sim\sim p \Rightarrow p,$$
$$\vdash \quad \Box p \Rightarrow p.$$

II. Five fundamental *rules*:

a) The rule of substitution for propositional variables;

b) The rule of substitutivity for strictly equivalent propositions (two propositions P and Q being considered as strictly equivalent if one has the theorems: $\vdash P \Rightarrow Q$ and $\vdash Q \Rightarrow P$.);

c) If $\vdash P \Rightarrow Q$, then $\vdash \sim Q \Rightarrow \sim P$;
d) If $\vdash P \Rightarrow Q$ and if $\vdash Q \Rightarrow R$, then $\vdash P \Rightarrow R$;
e) If $\vdash P \Rightarrow Q$, then $\vdash \Box P \Rightarrow \Box Q$.
In this system SB, one has infinitely many irreducible modalities.

***9′3.2** - One can form several extensions of the system B, which will be designated as 'B_n' (for $n = 1, 2, 3, \ldots$).

A system B_n is formed by adding to the basic system B, the two following axioms:

$$\vdash \quad \sim \Box^{n+1} p \Rightarrow \sim \Box^n p,$$
$$\vdash \quad \sim \Box^{n-1} \sim \Box \sim \Box p \Rightarrow \sim \Box p.$$

Thus, the system B_1 has the axioms:

$$\vdash \quad \sim \Box \Box p \Rightarrow \sim \Box p,$$
$$\vdash \quad \sim \sim \Box \sim \Box p \Rightarrow \sim \Box p.$$

The system B_1 admits precisely the 14 irreducible modalities of S4.

The system B_2 has the following axioms:

$$\vdash \quad \sim \Box^3 p \Rightarrow \sim \Box^2 p,$$
$$\vdash \quad \sim \Box \sim \Box \sim \Box p \Rightarrow \sim \Box p.$$

In B_2 there are no more than 126 irreducible modalities.

Generally, for a given n, a system B_n has no more than $(4m+2)$ irreducible modalities, where

$$m = (3n^2 - n + 1) \sum_{k=0}^{n-1} \binom{n}{k} \binom{n-1}{k} - \sum_{k=1}^{n-1} \sum_{h=k}^{n-1} h \binom{n}{k} \binom{h-1}{k-1}$$

***9′3.3** - By adding to the system B_2 the axiom:

$$\vdash \quad \sim \Box^2 \sim \Box p \Rightarrow \sim \Box^2 \sim \Box^2 p,$$

one obtains a system, called 'S′3', which has precisely the 42 irreducible modalities of S3.

§*9′4 - Porte (1955) has proposed a set of modal systems based upon the APC and starting with a very weak modal system called 'Sa'.

*9′4.1 - The system Sa consists of the following postulates:

I. The *definitions*:

'$P \rightarrow Q$' for '$\sim (P \wedge \sim Q)$';
'$P \Rightarrow Q$' for '$\Box (P \rightarrow Q)$';
'$P \leftrightarrow Q$' for '$(P \rightarrow Q) \wedge (Q \rightarrow P)$';
'$P \Leftrightarrow Q$' for '$(P \Rightarrow Q) \wedge (Q \Rightarrow P)$'.

II. The *axiom-schemata*:

$\vdash [p \rightarrow (q \rightarrow r)] \Rightarrow [(p \rightarrow q) \rightarrow (p \rightarrow r)]$;
$\vdash p \Rightarrow (q \rightarrow p)$;
$\vdash (\sim p \rightarrow \sim q) \Rightarrow (q \rightarrow p)$;
$\vdash (p \rightarrow q) \Rightarrow [r \wedge p) \rightarrow (r \wedge q)]$.

III. The following *rules*:

Rule D: If $\vdash P$ and $\vdash P \rightarrow Q$, then $\vdash Q$ (Detachment for '$\rightarrow$');

Rule A: If $\vdash \Box P$, then $\vdash P$ (Weakening, «affaiblissement»);

Rule Ra: If $\vdash P \Leftrightarrow Q$, then $P \mathbf{E} Q$;

Rule Rb: If $P \mathbf{E} Q$, then $\vdash P \Leftrightarrow Q$
('**E**' is here a dyadic predicate holding between strictly equivalent expressions; **E** forms assertions of the system, without the need of the assertion-sign '$\vdash$');

Rule νD: If $\vdash \Box P$ and if $\vdash P \Rightarrow Q$, then $\vdash \Box Q$ («Normalization» of the rule D, see below).

The rules Ra and Rb, taken together with the other postulates, have the effect that the relation **E** is reflexive, symmetric, transitive and monotone with respect to the operations of negation and of conjonction. It is not postulated, in Sa, that the relation **E** where also monotone with respect to the operation of necessity, '$\Box$')

*9′4.2 - One forms a new system, called 'Sb' by adding to the postulates of Sa the rule:

Cf: If $\vdash P \Leftrightarrow Q$, then $\vdash \Box P \leftrightarrow \Box Q$. (Weak comptability of **E** or '$\Leftrightarrow$' for '$\Box$').

*9′4.3 - One forms another system, called 'Sc', by adding to the postulates of Sa the rule:

CF: If ⊢P⇔Q, then ⊢□P⇔□Q (Bekker's rules, strong compatibility, or monotony of '**E**' or '⇔' with respect to '□').

***9′4**.4 - Starting with one of the systems Sa, Sb or Sc, one can form several new systems by modifying some postulates in one of the two following manners: 1°. by «strengthening» («renforcement») and 2°. by «normalization».

These modifications are defined for systems which are called «semi-canonical», a «*semi-canonical*» system being defined as a system which contains the rules D, Ra and Rb, but no other rule mentioning the relation '**E**'.

A «*canonical*» system is defined as a semi-canonical system having no other rules than the rules A, Ra and Rb.

***9′4**.41 - Let us first define the strengthening («renforcement») of a rule.

The strengthening of a rule R, is the axiom-schema 'ϱR' obtained by replacing by the material implication '→' the inferential relation authorised by the rule R.

Thus, the strengthening of a rule R of the form: If ⊢P, then ⊢Q, is the axiom-schema ϱR: ⊢P→Q.

For a rule R (having two premisses), of the form: If ⊢P and if ⊢Q, then ⊢S, the axiom-schema ϱR will be: ⊢P→(Q→S).

The «*strengthening*» of a semi-canonical-system Sx is the system called 'ϱSx', which one obtains by strengthening all the rules of Sx, with the sole exception of the rules D, Ra and Rb. (The axiom-schemata of Sx remain unchanged in the system ϱSx, even as the rules D, Ra and Rb.)

***9′4**.42 - The modification called «*normalization*» concerns the axiom-schemata as well as the rules.

The normalization of an axiom-schema X of the form: ⊢P is the corresponding axiom-schema, called 'νX', of the form: ⊢□P (obtained by prefixing a '□').

The normalization of a rule R is the corresponding rule, called 'νR', obtained by prefixing a '□' to the several premisses and to the conclusion of the rule R.

Nevertheless, the normalization of the rule Ra will be the rule:

νRa: If $\vdash \Box(P \Leftrightarrow Q)$, then $P \mathbf{E} Q$,
and the normalization of the rule Rb will be the rule:
νRb: If $P \mathbf{E} Q$, then $\vdash \Box(P \Leftrightarrow Q)$.
(No '$\Box$' are to be prefixed to assertions of the form '$P \mathbf{E} Q$'.)

The normalization of a semi-canonical system Sx will be denoted by 'νSx' and consists of:

a) all the postulates of the system Sx;
b) the normalizations of all the axiom-schemata of Sx;
c) the normalization of all the rules of Sx, with the sole exception of the rule νD (which is already the normalization of the rule D).

Generally speaking, the normalization of a semi-canonical system is not necessarily a semi-canonical system.

But one can always make it semi-canonical by adding to it the supplementary rule, called «Normalization-rule»:

Rν: If $\vdash \Box p$, then $\vdash \Box\Box P$.

When one has a normalized system, one can always obtain another system deductively equivalent to this normalization by deleting all the non-normalized axiom-schemata, and adding to the postulates the rule A (weakening) and the normalization-rule Rν.

A «normal» system is defined here as a system which is equivalent to its own normalization. All normalized systems are also normal, being equivalent to their own normalization.

***9'4**.43 - Porte has shown that, by starting with some given system S, and applying to S successive strengthening and normalization, we cannot get more than *six* non-equivalent proper extensions of this system S, namely the systems ϱS, νS, $\nu\varrho$S, $\varrho\nu$S, $\varrho\nu\varrho$S and $\nu\varrho\nu$S (this last being equivalent with $\nu\varrho\nu\varrho$S).

Between these 7 systems one finds the relations, which are represented by the arrows in the figure (an arrow going from one system to another which is included in the first one):

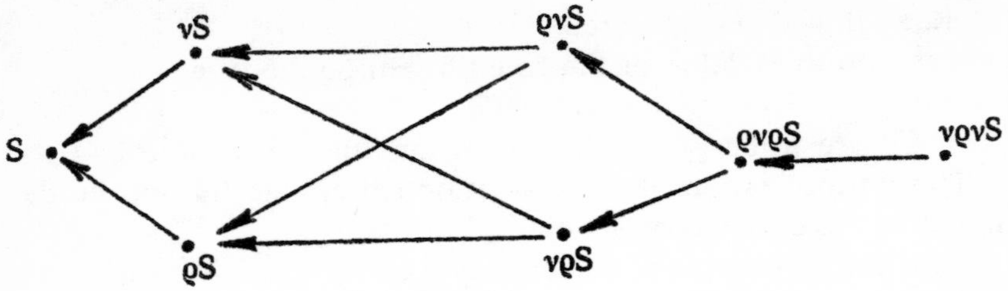

*9′4.43 - Starting from the system Sa, and adding the rules Rf, RF and using the strengthening and the normalization, one cannot obtain more than the *twelve* non-equivalent systems, which are listed is the following figure, where the arrows state the explained relation between them.

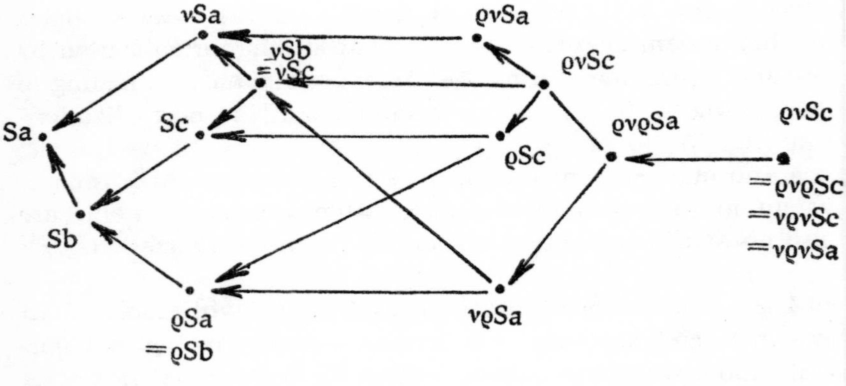

The system νϱSc is the weakest modal system being both normal and canonical.

The system ϱSa is the weakest canonical system.

The system νSa is the weakest normal system.

The system νϱSc is deductively equivalent to Lewis's system S4.

Other relations existing between these Porte systems and the Lewis's systems are not yet much known.

CHAPTER III

MODAL FUNCTIONAL LOGIC

Functional logic (even with identity included) will hold much less place in our outline than propositional logic did. Little has been written upon the subject and it seems that modal first-order functional logic (MF^1C) is closely parallel to assertoric first-order functional logic (AF^1C). On the other hand the theory of identity and descriptions founded upon a second order function logic (MF^2C), has led to paradoxical results and to deep-rooted difficulties.

To gain a first conspectus of MFC ,and to have at some extent a key to the relative triviality of MF^1C and to the difficulties of MF^2C, we shall resort to the same kind of «heuristical introduction» as in Chapter I. We shall start from a calculus with variables for cases, which will be called 'MFQ' instead of 'MFC', as modal propositions in this calculus reduce to propositions quantified «for all cases» and «for some cases». We shall, as in Chapter I, state a precise correspondence between MFC and MFQ, and between the axioms of MFC and a plausible system of axioms for MFQ.

SECTION 10 - OUTLINE OF MFQ, WITHOUT ABSTRACTION

We now have to deduce from axioms an associated modal functional calculus (MFQ), namely a modal functional calculus of first order MF^1Q and such parts of a calculus MF^2Q of second order as are required for a theory of identity and descriptions. Abstraction will be reserved for section 11.

§ 101 - ATOMIC PROPOSITIONS IN MFQ

We have to consider atomic propositions which are not just true or false, but true or false in some case *t*, propositions which are, so to speak, not absolute propositions but propositions relative to the case *t*.

Atomic propositions of APC were *p*, *q*, ... Atomic propositions of MFQ were p*t*, q*t*, .

Atomic propositions in AFC are of the form *AX*, *RXY*, ..., i.e such as *ax*, *bx*, *rxy*, i*xy* ('i' being the relation of identity). The corresponding modal atomic propositions will be (ax)*t*, (bx)*t*, (rxy)*t*, (ixy)*t* (with roman variables «a», «b», «r», «x», «y», ..., and one italic variable «*t*»). Using association to the left, as in combinatory logic, we shall write in the future simply 'ax*t*', 'bx*t*', 'rxy*t*', 'ixy*t*'.

More precisely an atomic proposition of MF^1Q may be either:

1° a proposition of the form P*T*, with a (roman) p-variable and a *t*-variable;

2° a proposition containing three kinds of elements:

a) one n^{ary} predicate ($n \geqslant 1$),

b) *n* (roman) variables for individuals,

c) one case-variable '*t*', ranging over all possible cases; and it must be recalled here that there is no notation for a privileged «real» case; what is characteristic of a modal atomic proposition is the fact that it is relative to some variable case.

Expressions such as 'p', 'ax', 'rxy', if taken as expressions in MFQ, are incomplete expressions, not well-formed expressions. Of course such expressions may be introduced, and will be introduced by way of abbreviation (after italization), and then they will be expressions of an extension of MFQ.

MFQ is not properly an extension of AFC, as it does not include among its well-formed expressions the well-formed expressions of AFC. But there is a correspondence between the calculi MFQ and AFC: a modal proposition attributing a predicate to n individuals behaves like that attributing a $(n+1)^{th}$ relation in AFC. This is also true of MFQ. If a proposition in MFC is considered as the attribution of a predicate to zero individual, it corresponds to (i.e. it has the same logical laws as) the attribution of a predicate to one individual in AFC.

§ 102 - PURELY QUANTIFIED AND MOLECULAR PROPOSITIONS IN MFQ

102.1 - *A purely quantified proposition of MFQ is formed from* an atomic proposition of MFQ by quantification alone.

102.2 - As there are three kinds of variables in atomic propositions of MFQ, we may use three kinds of quantifiers to form purely quantified propositions of MFQ. These quantifiers are:

a) quantifiers '**A***t*' and '**E***t*' (upon *t*-variables); these occurred already in MFQ;

b) quantifiers such as '**A**x, '**E**x' (or '**A**y', '**E**y', ...) which may occur at least in the first-order calculus MF^1Q;

c) quantifiers such as '**A**a', '**E**a' (or '**A**b', '**E**b', ...) which are peculiar to second-order modal logic MF^2Q, and which are left for later (§105).

102.3 - There may be zero, one or more quantifiers of the kind a) or b) in a purely quantified proposition of MF^1Q.

Let '*M*' be any atomic or purely quantified proposition of MF^1Q, then the following are purely quantified propositions of MF^1Q:

'**A***t***A**x *M*', '**A***t***E**x *M*', '**E***t***A**x *M*', '**E***t***E**x *M*', '**A**x**A***t M*', '**E**x**A***t M*', '**A**x**E***t M*', '**E**x**E***t M*'.

102.4 - A purely quantified proposition of MF^1Q may be interpreted as:

a) an enunciation involving *n* individuals or general considerations of individuals (we speak of a «general consideration of an individual» if the corresponding variable is quantified upon),
b) one *n*-ary predicate upon these individuals,
c) one or more specifications of a singular case or of cases in general (when '*t*' is quantified upon).

102.5 - A *proposition* of MF^1Q may be defined recursively as follows:
102.51 - An atomic proposition of MF^1Q is a proposition of MF^1Q.
102.52 - A proposition formed from a proposition of MF^1Q by quantification of a *t*-variable is a proposition of MF^1Q.
102.53 - A proposition formed from a proposition of MF^1Q by quantification of a variable for individuals is a proposition of MF^1Q.
102.54 - A truth-function of propositions of MF^1Q is a proposition of MF^1Q.

102.6 - Propositions of MF^1Q which are neither atomic nor purely quantified may be called *molecular propositions* of MF^1Q.

§ 103 - DERIVATION OF MF^1Q FORMULAS WITH QUANTIFIERS

We are seeking for MF^1Q formulas in which may occur quantifiers with bound «case-variables» and with bound variables for individuals. In particular we try to prove such formulas obtained from an AF^1C formula by means of a S- or a s-transformation.

103.1 - If the formula is without any quantifier, it is a formula of APC and the case is trivial. If we use the method of §3, the axioms of APC are among the postulates. If we use the axioms of one of the systems from §4 on, which do not contain explicitely the axioms of APC, all formulas of APC can nevertheless be proved.

103.2 - If the formula is a formula with *t-quantifiers* only, then we use the axioms of §16 applied to *t*-quantifiers. We can prove this way formulas of MFQ for S5, and also for S4 and for S2′.

103.3 - To introduce quantifiers with variables for individuals, we state the axioms of § 16 as they are, and we can prove any formula of AF^1Q and also any formula from MPQ by a proper addition of quantifiers.

103.4 - But here there may be transformations involving *t*-variables and x-variables together. One axiom will suffice to take care of such transformations. This axiom is:

⊢ **E***t***E**x ax*t* → **E**x**E***t* ax*t*.

§ 104 - FORMULAS PECULIAR TO MF^1Q

The method sketched in the preceding number is only a tentative. To lead to general results, an extended Herbrand-theorem would have to be demonstrated for our formulas. But we try only to suggest roughly the kind of formulas to be expected in MF^1Q. Of course the formulas of APC (103.1), of MPC (103.2) and of AF^1C (103.3) are among the formulas of MF^1Q as presented here. But what of the **S**- and **s**-transforms (.1 below) and of other possible failures (.2 and .3 below) ?

104.1 - Let us consider the **S**-analogue of:

⊢ **A***x bx* → **A***x*(*ax*→*bx*) (0),

namely: **A***t* [**A**x bx*t* → **A**x**A***t*(ax*t*→bx*t*)] (1).

We cannot prove q*t* → **A***t*(p*t*→q*t*),

but only ⊢ **A***t* q*t* → **A***t*(p*t*→q*t*) (2).

By substitution we obtain:

⊢ **A***t* bx*t* → **A***t*(ax*t*→bx*t*) (3),

which leads to ⊢ **A**x**A***t* bx*t* → **A**x**A***t*(ax*t*→bx*t*) (4),

and to $\vdash$ **A***t*[**A**x**A***t* bx*t* → **A**x**A***t*(ax*t*→bx*t*)] (5),
which is a **S′**-analogue of the formula (0).

104.2 - But there are also formulas of MPQ depending on the two following ones:

104.21 - $\vdash$ **E***t***A**x ax*t* → **A**x**E***t* ax*t*,

104.22 - $\vdash$ **E**x**A***t* ax*t* → **A***t***E**x ax*t*,

whose inverses are not provable.

104.3 - Let us consider the formula (an equivalence):

$\vdash$ **E**x(*ax*→*bx*) ↔ (**A**x *ax*→**E**x *bx*) (1).

This is valid in AFC and it is equivalent to:

$\vdash$ **E**x(∼*ax*∨*bx*) ↔ (**E**x∼*ax*∨**E**x *bx*) (2).

But it may not be transformed into:

$\vdash$ **A***t*[(**E**x**A***t*(ax*t*→bx*t*) ↔ **A***t*(**A**x ax*t*→**E**x bx*t*)] (3).

We have indeed, by (1),

$\vdash$ **A***t***E**x(ax*t*→bx*t*) ↔ **A***t*(**A**x ax*t*→**E**x bx*t*) (4)

and (104.22):

$\vdash$ **E**x(**A***t*(ax*t*→bx*t*) →**A***t***E**x(ax*t*→bx*t*)

Hence we have only the implication:

$\vdash$ **E**x**A***t*(ax*t*→bx*t*) → **A***t*(**A**x ax*t*→**E**x bx*t*) (6),

leading also to:

103.4C $\vdash$ ◇**E**x *ax* → **E**x *ax*◇*ax*,

This is one of the few examples where 104.21 (or 104.22) leads to the failure of some **S**-transformations of AF^1C into MF^1Q.

§ 105 - SECOND ORDER MODAL FUNCTIONAL LOGIC AND IDENTITY

105.1 - A calculus MF^2Q might be derived from the axioms 103, plus axioms peculiar to predicates of second order.

105.2 - The theory of identity has been derived by Barcan, making use of the abstraction operation. A theory of this form will be outlined in section 11. But even without such an abstraction theory, a theory of strict identity might be derived from the following definition:

105.3 - '**I***xy*' for '**A**a**A***t*(ax*t*→ay*t*)'.

§ 106 - TRANSITION TO AN ABBREVIATED MFC CALCULUS

106.1 - To pass from MFQ to a notation equivalent to that used in MFC, we extend the correspondence introduced in §21, namely:

replace an atomic proposition 'p*t*', 'q*t*', ..., 'ax*t*', 'bx*t*', ..., by a proposition '*p*', '*q*', ..., '*ax*', '*bx*', ...;
and replace '**A***t*' by '□' and '**E***t*' by '◇'.

The relation between the variables 'a', 'b', 'c', ..., 'x', 'y', 'z', ... and the variables '*a*', '*b*', '*c*', ..., '*x*', '*y*', '*z*', ... will be discussed later (§117).

106.2 - If '*n*' is the number of a formula or rule of MFQ, then '*n*C' will be the number of the formula or rule corresponding to *n* by virtue of 106.1.

106.3 - The *n*C formulas or rules have just the form of the Barcan formulas and rules, if we apply the definitions 23.5 for '⇒' and '⇔'. Here are some examples:

103.4C	⊢	◇**E***x ax* → **E***x* ◇ *ax*,
104.1C	⊢	□**A***xbx* ⇒ **A***x*(*ax*⇒*bx*),
104.21C	⊢	◇**A***x ax* → **A***x*◇*ax*,
104.22C	⊢	**E***x*□*ax* → □**E***x ax*,
104.3C	⊢	**E***x*(*ax*⇒*bx*) ⇒ (**A***x ax*⇒**E***x bx*)

(but we do not have: **E***x*(*ax*⇒*bx*) ⇔ (**A***x ax*⇒**E***x bx*)).

105.3C '**I***yx*' for '**A***a*(*ax*⇒*ay*)'.

106.4 - The rules of notational transformation stated in this § do not introduce any confusion. But their correct interpretation is not possible if we forget that here (in Section 10 just as in Section 2) we have to do with abbreviations and the symbols omitted by virtue of an abbreviation do not become inexistent, but have to be restituted if we want to obtain the meaning results.

SECTION 11 - ABSTRACTS

As a preparation to a possible use of abstracts in MFC, it may be worth while to devote some pages to a theory of abstracts in MFQ. Such a theory may lead to a modal version of a theory of classes, and more generally to a modal version of set theory, and help to clear up the meaning of modal expressions of functional calculus.

§ 111 - ABSTRACTION

It may be expected that difficulties will be inherent in the consideration of elements of the modal proposition when these will be taken abstractly, since the characteristic of a modal proposition is just that it replaces the «abstract» mathematical assertions by some concrete modal forms of assertion. The operation of abstraction makes no difficulty of principle in MFQ, but it may create some difficulties of interpretations and some difficulties of translation in systems in which some «abstracted» variables would remain unwritten.

111.1 - Let us consider any proposition '*M*' of MFQ and variables 'x', 'y', 'z', ..., 'a', 'b', 'c', ..., 'r', 's', ... If 'α' represents one of these variables (occurring or not occurring in '*M*'), then '$\hat{\alpha}M$' is an abstract, and if 'α', 'β', 'γ' ... are different variables, then '$\hat{\alpha}\hat{\beta}\, M$', '$\hat{\alpha}\hat{\beta}\hat{\gamma}\, M$', ... are abstracts, which may be called *multiple abstracts*.

Abstracts, as just defined, are propositional functions. A propositional function is any lambda-function 'λαM', 'λαλβ*M*',... where '*M*' is a proposition.

When writing a propositional function under the form of an abstract, we replace each lambda before a variable by a circumflex above the variable.

111.2 - The rules of abstracts are those of lambda-functions.

111.3 - To state the *types* of the abstracts in MFQ, we start from the following primitive types:

υ is the type of a *proposition* in MFQ;

ι is the type of an *individual* in MFQ;

τ is the type of a *case*.

Derived denominations of types are formed according to the Church method.

E.g. '$\hat{x}$ ax*t*' is of type υι, '$\hat{x}\hat{t}$ ax*t*' is of type υιτ, '$\hat{t}$ p*t*' is of type υτ, '$\hat{a}\hat{t}$ ax*t*' is of type υ(υιτ)τ, '$\hat{x}\hat{y}$ rxy*t*' is of type υιι, '$\hat{x}\hat{y}\hat{t}$ rxy*t*' is of type υιιτ.

111.4 - An expression in which free *t*-variables are occurring is a *casual* one.

An expression in which quantified *t*-variables are occurring is a *modal* one.

An expression containing a circumflexed *t*-variable is *case-abstract*.

Expressions which are casual are not case-abstract, thus expressions which are case-abstract are non-casual.

But there may be case-abstract expressions which are modal.

Casual and modal expressions have this in common that they refer to cases; casual expressions refer to one case *t*, and modal ones refer to all or some cases.

Terms which may be applied to an expression may be extended to equivalent expressions or to entities designable by the expressions .

§ 112 - ABSTRACTS IN PROPOSITIONAL LOGIC

As a point of comparison with the more complicated abstracts of MFX, let us consider abstracts which may be built up in modal propositional logic, and which are equivalent to those used by von Wright in his *Essay in Modal Logic*.

112.1 - The abstract '$\hat{t}$ *pt*' is of the type υτ; it expresses the property of being a case *t* such that p*t*, or the class of cases where *p* is true; 'ɩ p*t*' is an event taken abstractly, what is common between the realizations of an event *p* in different cases.

112.11 - Instead of 'ɩ p*t*' we may simply write 'p', as '(ɩ p*t*)*t*' and 'p*t*' are the same.

'p' and 'ɩ p*t*' are non-casual designations, whereas 'p*t*' is casual.

112.2 - Let us define *general propositions*:

112.21 - 'p⊂q' for '**A***t*(p*t*→q*t*)'.

This is a strict implication.

It states that, regardless of cases, the presence of p entails the presence of q.

112.22 - 'p = q' for '**A***t*(p*t*↔q*t*)'.

This is a strict equivalence.

It states that, regardless of cases, the presence of p and that of q coïncide; hence that 'p' and 'q' may be substituted for each other.

112.23 - We may put:
'p≠q' for '∼(*p*=*q*)'.

112.3 - We may, by virtue of 112.01, write:

112.31 - '**A**p' for '**A**(ɩ p*t*) or '**A***t* p*t*' («*p* is necessary, happens necessarily»).

112.32 - '**E**p' for '**E**(ɩ p*t*)' or '**E***t* p*t*' («*p* is possible, happens possibly»).
Here '**A**' and '**E**' are of type υ(υτ).

112.4 - We define the *total* and the *empty* class of cases:
(Here we use subscripts.)

112.41 - '$U_{\upsilon\tau}$' for 'ɩ(p*t*∨∼p*t*)',

112.42 - '$O_{\upsilon\tau}$' for 'ɩ(p*t*∧∼p*t*)'.

112.5 - To define operations.

112.51 - '—p' for 'ɩ(∼p*t*)',

112.52 - 'p ∩ q' for 'ɩ(p*t*∧q*t*)',

112.53 - 'p ∪ q' for 'ɩ(p*t*∨q*t*)'.

We may add:

112.54 - 'p⊃q' for 'ɩ(p*t*→q*t*)',

112.55 - 'p⊃⊂q' for 'ɩ(p*t*↔q*t*)'.

112.6 - If we have an **a**-formula (a formula of APC), then, by 25.12, the corresponding **sa**-formula is valid in MPC, and we have a formula in terms of *p*-classes, which is the translation of the **a**-formula.

E.g. we have in APC: $\vdash \quad (p \wedge q) \rightarrow p,$
and in MPC: $\vdash \quad (\mathrm{p} \cap \mathrm{q}) \subset \mathrm{p}.$

112.7 - But it is not possible to replace '$\Rightarrow$' by '$\subset$', and any '$\Leftrightarrow$' by '=' in a formula of MPC with superposed modalities or with superposed symbols '$\Rightarrow$' or '$\Leftrightarrow$'.

E.g. we have in MPC: $\vdash (p \Rightarrow q) \Leftrightarrow (\sim q \Rightarrow \sim p).$
It is obvious that we can only write: $\vdash \hat{t}(\mathrm{p} \subset \mathrm{q}) = \hat{t}(-\mathrm{q} \subset -\mathrm{p}).$

112.8 - As our only purpose is to introduce the reader to MFC, we shall not discuss abstracts such as 'p p*t*', i.e. abstracts of type $\upsilon(\upsilon\tau)$, whose intuitive meaning is the content of a case. These might however be paralleled with abstracts '$\hat{a}$ *ax*' of AF²C.

§ 113 - ABSTRACTS $\hat{x}$M

113.0 - M being a proposition of MFQ, an abstract '$\hat{x}$ *M*' is of type $\upsilon\iota$.

113.01 - We use here 'α', 'β', 'γ', ... as variables of type $\upsilon\iota$. An expression such as 'αx' designates a proposition, because if 'α' is '$\hat{x}$ *M*', then 'αx' is '($\hat{x}$ *M*)x' or '*M*'.

113.1 - Abstracts of type $\upsilon\iota$ are not case-abstract.

There are two principal kinds of expressions of type $\upsilon\iota$, and which may be substituted to variables such as 'α'.

One kind are the expressions of the form '$\hat{x}$ ax*t*'. They designate a property in the precise case *t*. Hence they are casual expressions designating a casual property.

The other includes expressions with quantification upon *t*, such as '$\hat{x}$**E***t* ax*t*', '$\hat{x}$**A***t* ax*t*', which may be translated by «to be possibly an *a*», «to be necessarily an *a*»; hence they are modal expressions.

Both kinds of expressions may be made subject to the same definitions as the expressions for classes in AFC.

113.2 - Let us consider *general* propositions:

113.21 - '$\alpha \subset \beta$' for '**A**x(αx$\rightarrow\beta$x)'.

This is a «*general*» (or «*formal*») implication, but not a «*strict*» one.

113.22 - '$\alpha = \beta$' for '**A**x(αx$\leftrightarrow\beta$x)'.

This is a «*general*» (or «*formal*») equivalence, but not a «*strict*» one.

113.23 - '$\alpha \neq \beta$' for '$\sim(\alpha = \beta)$'.

113.3 - We may, by virtue of 113.01, write:

113.31 - '**A**α' for '**A**($\hat{x}$ ax)' or '**A**x αx',

113.32 - '**E**α' for '**E**($\hat{x}$ αx)' or '**E**x αx'.

Here '**A**' and '**E**' are of type $\upsilon(\upsilon\iota)$.

113.4 - For the *total* and the *empty* class:

113.41 - '$U_{\upsilon\iota}$' for '$\hat{x}(\alpha x \vee \sim\alpha x)$',

113.42 - '$O_{\upsilon\iota}$' for '$\hat{x}(\alpha x \wedge \sim\alpha x)$'.

Hence analogues of 112.43-46.

113.5 - For operations:

113.51 - '$-\alpha$' for '$\hat{x}(\sim\alpha x)$',

113.52 - '$\alpha \cap \beta$' for '$\hat{x}(\alpha x \wedge \beta x)$',

113.53 - '$\alpha \cup \beta$' for '$\hat{x}(\alpha x \vee \beta x)$;

similarly for '$\alpha \supset \beta$' and '$\alpha \supset\subset \beta$'.

§ 114 - *ABSTRACTS* $\hat{x}\hat{t}$M

114.0 - *M* being a proposition of MPQ, an abstract '$\hat{x}\hat{t}$ *M*' is of type $\upsilon\iota\tau$.

114.01 - 'a', 'b', 'c' are variables of type $\upsilon\iota\tau$, as 'ax*t*' is of type υ.

114.1 - There are two principal kinds of expressions of the type $\upsilon\iota\tau$, and which may be substituted to variables of that type. Both these kinds of expressions are non-casual.

One kind are the variables 'a', 'b', 'c' of the given type; they designate a property «abstractly» without reference to any case; they designate no-casual and non-modal properties.

The other kind may include abstracts with quantification upon t, such as '$\hat{x}\hat{t}$**E**t ax$t$'. These expressions are well-formed in MF¹Q. They designate modal properties, but they are realizable in cases.

Expressions of type $\upsilon\iota\tau$ can be made subject to the same kind of definitions as in § 113.

114.2 - *General* propositions.

114.21 - 'a$\subset$b' for '**AxA**t(ax$t$$\rightarrow$bx$t$)'.

This is a *general* and *strict* implication.

114.22 - 'a = b' for '**AxA**t(ax$t$$\leftrightarrow$bx$t$)'.

This is a *general* and *strict* equivalence. It expresses the identity of the two classes a and b in their abstraction, regardless of circumstances (of «cases»).

114.23 - 'a $\neq$ b' for '$\sim$(a=b)'.

114.3 - Let us introduce the definitions:

114.30 - '$\mathring{\mathbf{A}}$($\hat{x}\hat{t}$ M)' for '**AxA**t M',

'$\mathring{\mathbf{E}}$($\hat{x}\hat{t}$ M)' for '**ExE**t M'.

We have then, by virtue of 114.01:

114.31 - '$\mathring{\mathbf{A}}$a' for '**AxA**t ax$t$',

114.32 - '$\mathring{\mathbf{E}}$a' for '**ExE**t ax$t$'.

114.4 - For the *total* and the *empty* class:

114.41 - '$u_{\upsilon\iota\tau}$' for '$\hat{x}\hat{t}$(ax$t$$\vee$$\sim$ax$t$)',

114.42 - '$o_{\upsilon\iota\tau}$' for '$\hat{x}\hat{t}$(ax$t$$\wedge$$\sim$ax$t$)'.

Hence analogues of 112.41-42.

114.5 - For operations:

114.51 - '—a' for '$\hat{x}\hat{t}$$\sim$ax$t$',

114.52 - 'a $\cap$ b' for '$\hat{x}\hat{t}$(ax$t$$\wedge$bx$t$)',

114.53 - 'a $\cup$ b' for '$\hat{x}\hat{t}$(ax$t$$\vee$bx$t$)'.

Similarly, if wanted, for 'a$\supset$b' and 'a$\supset\subset$b'.

§ 115 - ABSTRACTS OF MF^2Q AND IDENTITY

Abstracts in which abstraction is made from a property are abstracts of second-order functional modal logic (MF^2Q). Such abstracts are '$\hat{\alpha}$ *M*', '$\hat{a}\hat{t}$ *M*' and '$\hat{a}$ *M*'. We shall confine ourselves in this section to abstracts '$\hat{\alpha}$ αx' and '$\hat{a}\hat{t}$ ax*t*', which occur in equivalents of the Barcan definitions of identity.

115.1 - In the abstract '$\hat{\alpha}$ αx', 'α' is a property of type υι, studied in §113, i.e. any property of x, casual or modal; '$\hat{\alpha}$ αx' is then «any property which may be asserted of x».

115.10 - Let us write 'ex α' for 'αx'. Then 'ex α' is «x is an α», and 'ex' is «$\hat{\alpha}$ exα» or «$\hat{\alpha}$ αx».

According to the terminology of Quine, 'ex' may be called «*the essence of* x» in MF^2Q.

115.2 - Let us pass to *general* propositions which may be considered as propositions about ex.

115.21 - 'ex⊂ey' for '**A**α(αx→αy)'.

This would be a formal implication enunciating the inclusion of ex in ey.

It may be proved that if **A**α(αx→αy), then **A**α(αy→αx) and **A**α(αx↔αy).

115.22 - 'ex = ey' for '**A**α(αx↔αy)'.

This is a general equivalence stating that the properties of x (in given cases) coïncide with those of y.

115.23 - 'ixy' for '**A**α(αx→αy)'.

This is the equivalent of the Barcan definition for the *material identity* ($\mathbf{I}_m$xy) of x and y. By what precedes, this definition states that the properties of x and of y (in given cases) coïncide.

115.3 - In the abstract '$\hat{a}\hat{t}$ ax*t*', abstraction is made, in the casual proposition ax*t*, from the property a and from the case *t*. Abstraction is thus made of all couples {a, *t*} of a property and a case, considered in a proposition ax*t*.

115.30 - Let us write 'e′xa*t*' for 'ax*t*'. Then 'e′ax*t*' is «x is an a in the case *t*». The expression 'e′x' may be interpreted, just as was done with 'ex', as being the essence of x, this essence being the class of couples {a, *t*} such that ax*t*.

115.4 - Let us pass to *general* propositions:
115.41 - 'e′x⊂e′y' for '**A**a**A***t*(ax*t*→ay*t*)'.
This is equivalent to '**A**a**A***t*(ax*t*↔ay*t*)'.
115.42 - 'e′x = e′y' for '**A**a**A***t*(ax*t*↔ay*t*)'.
This is a general equivalence stating that in all cases all properties of x and of y coïncide.
115.43 - '**I**xy' for '**A**a**A***t*(ax*t*→ay*t*)'.
This is the equivalent of the Barcan definition for the *strict identity* (**I**xy) of x and y. By what precedes, this definition states that e′x = e′y, i.e. that there is a coïncidence between all properties of the individuals x and y considered abstractly.

115.5 - One of the principal results of Barcan is that, in the modal functional calculus S4 (and hence in MFQ, which includes the modal functional calculus of S4), 'ixy' is equivalent to '**I**xy'. It may be seen that Barcan's demonstration is valid in MFQ.
The demonstration amounts to show that, if ixy, then (necessarily), if **I**xx, then **I**xy.
By the definition of 'ixy' (115.23), a consequence of ixy is that αx→αy. Let us take (ẑ **I**zx) for α; then (ẑ **I**xz)x → (ẑ **I**xz)y or **I**xx→**I**xy.

§ 116 - ABSTRACTS âM

The following abstracts, which do not correspond to notions needed in MFC, may however be mentioned here.

116.1 - The abstract â *M* is «to be a property a of MFQ, such that *M*». Such an abstract is of type υ(υιτ), as 'a' is of type υιτ.
116.10 - Let us write 'ξ', 'η', 'ζ', ..., for variables of type υ(υιτ). Then 'ξ a' is a proposition of MFQ.
A variable such as 'ξ' denotes the properties of an-individual-in-given-case.

116.2 - There are two ways of decomposing a proposition '*M*' of MFQ into a subject and a predicate. One is to decompose it into 'α x'. The other is to decompose it into 'ξ a'. The first one, not the second, follows the order «predicate-subject» of AFC, namely first 'α', then 'x'; of course it would be possible to restore the order in this case by defining '(a ξ′)' for 'ξ a'.

§ 117 - TRANSITION FROM MFQ TO MFC

The question left is how to motivate a translation of the expressions of MFQ, with *t*-variables, into a language without *t*-variables. We might, for more accuracy, call this language that of a 'MFQC' logic. We shall, in general ,simply call it 'MFC', since it may be proved that the system of MFQ is equivalent to that of the MPC of S5, and since its language is the same, with inessential modifications as the one of the various forms of MFC for S2, S4 and S5 as studied by Barcan and resumed in next sections.

117.0 - The principle of a translation from MFQ into MFC was: to use variables '*p*', '*q*', '*r*', '*s*', ... instead of 'p*t*', 'q*t*', 'r*t*', 's*t*', ...; to write '□' instead of '**A***t*', and '◇' instead of '**E***t*'.

117.1 - To translate the atomic propositions of MFQ, we have to introduce individual variables '*x*', '*y*', '*z*', ..., and predicate-variables '*a*', '*b*', '*c*', ... (we do not consider here notations for relations, except for identity). We write '*ax*', '*bx*', '*cx*', ..., '*ay*', '*by*', '*cy*' ... instead of 'ax*t*', 'bx*t*', 'cx*t*', ..., 'ay*t*', 'by*t*', 'cy*t*', ...

But to which kinds of variables of the MPQ will the '*x*', '*y*', '*z*', ..., '*a*', '*b*', '*c*' ... correspond ?

117.11 - We have just seen (116.2) that the correct and obvious translation is to put '*a*', '*b*', '*c*', ... for 'α', 'β', 'γ', ..., and then to identify the '*x*', '*y*', '*z*', ..., with the 'x', 'y', 'z', ... Of course the semantical interpretation of this translation involves difficulties, raised by Quine, Prior, and others. But we are not bound to an ontological interpretation of the x, y, z ... as permanent realities through possible worlds.

117.12 - Moreover we can introduce an alternative interpretation in which '*x*', '*y*', '*z*', ... are 'ξ′', 'η′', 'ζ′', ... and '*a*', '*b*', '*c*', ... are simply 'a', 'b', 'c', ... (However it must be underlined that in this interpretation no type is assigned to the 'ξ′', 'η′', 'ζ′', ...)

As the 'α', 'β', 'γ', ... and 'a', 'b', 'c', ... are of different types, it does not seem possible to introduce both interpretations concurrently for the variables '*a*', '*b*', '*c*', ..., unless a kind of stratifications theory could possibly be introduced.

Let us operate here with the interpretation 117.11 with 'α', 'β', 'γ', ...

117.2 - Since modalities are concerned, we translate, as in MPC, the '**A***t*' by '□' and the '**E***t*' by '◇'.

No abstracts with '*t*' are allowed, but these abstracts are not necessary.

117.3 - We shall, with Barcan, use abstracts with 'â', 'b̂', 'ĉ', ... which are the translations of abstracts with 'α̂', 'β̂', 'γ̂' ..., and abstracts with '*x̂*', '*ŷ*', '*ẑ*', ... which are the translations of abstracts with 'x̂', 'ŷ', 'ẑ' ... .

And we shall translate the quantifiers '**A**α', '**A**β', '**A**γ', ..., '**Ax**', '**Ay**', '**Az**. ..., by '**A***a*', '**A***b*', '**A***c*', ..., '**A***x*', '**A***y*', '**A***z*', ... And similarly with **E**-quantifiers.

117.4 - We may use the notations of §113 for class calculus, and introduce additional definitions, if desirable.

117.5 - We transfer the symbols 'i' (replacing the '$\mathbf{I}_m$' of Barcan) and '**I**' from MF^2Q to MF^2C.

SECTION 12 - FIRST-ORDER MODAL FUNCTIONAL CALCULUS

We give here, in accordance with Barcan, an outline of MF^1C, without deriving in detail some theorems which are obviously parallel to AFC and MF^1Q.

In her paper about the Deduction Theorem (JSL, XT, p. 116), Barcan uses systems obviously equivalent to the system given, but with deduction rules slightly modified.

§ 121 - POSTULATES

We choose our postulates in accordance with those of §103.

121.1 - First, postulates for some system in MFC.

We do not consider a system weaker than S2, which is the system used by Barcan. And if not mentioned otherwise, we do not make use of a system stronger than S2.

121.2 - Then, postulates proper to functional calculus.

We adopt with Barcan the following ones ,which are corresponding to those of Quine for APC, but with strict implication.

121.20 - If $\vdash P$, then $\vdash \mathbf{A}X\, P$.

121.21 - $\vdash \mathbf{A}X\, P \Rightarrow (Y/X)P$, with the usual restriction: no free occurrence of 'X' in '*P*' in a well-formed part of the form **A**Y Q.

121.22 - $\vdash$ $\mathbf{A}X(P \rightarrow Q) \Rightarrow (\mathbf{A}X\, P \rightarrow \mathbf{A}X\, Q)$.

121.23 - $\vdash$ $P \Rightarrow \mathbf{A}X\, P$, if 'X' is not free in '*P*'.

And the definition:

121.24 - '**E**X *P*' for '$\sim \mathbf{A}X \sim P$'.

121.3 - Then one postulate with modalities and quantifiers:

$\vdash$ $\Diamond \mathbf{E}X\, P \Rightarrow \mathbf{E}X \Diamond P$ (1).

(1) Prior has shown (1956) that, if one takes as underlying system S5 instead of S2, the postulate 121.3 becomes redundant since it may then be proved as a theorem. (JSL, XXI, 60). (The editor)

§ 122 - OBVIOUS DERIVED THEOREMS

122.1 - All derived theorems of §17 are valid in MF^1C.

122.2 - All derived theorems of §17 remain valid if we substitute '$\Box$**A**X' to '**A**X' and '$\Diamond$**E**X' to '**E**X'.

122.3 - All full transformations of **a**-theorems in §18 are valid in MF^1C.

122.4 - All full transformations of **a**-theorems remain valid if we substitute '$\Box$**A**X' to '**A**X' and '$\Diamond$**E**X' to '**E**X'.

§ 123 - MODALITIES WITH QUANTIFIERS

123.1 - $\vdash \mathbf{E}X\Diamond P \Rightarrow \Diamond\mathbf{E}X\, P$
(1) $\vdash P \Rightarrow \mathbf{E}X\, P$
(2) $\vdash \Diamond P \Rightarrow \Diamond\mathbf{E}X\, P$
(3) $\vdash \mathbf{E}X\Diamond P \Rightarrow \Diamond\mathbf{E}X\, P$.

123.2 - $\vdash \mathbf{E}X\Diamond P \Leftrightarrow \Diamond\mathbf{E}X\, P$

123.3 - $\vdash \mathbf{A}X\Box P \Leftrightarrow \Box\mathbf{A}X\, P$
(1) $\vdash \mathbf{E}X\Diamond\sim P \Leftrightarrow \Diamond\mathbf{E}X\sim P$
(2) $\vdash \sim\mathbf{E}X\Diamond\sim P \Leftrightarrow \sim\Diamond\mathbf{E}X\sim P$
(3) $\vdash \mathbf{A}X\sim\Diamond\sim P \Leftrightarrow \Box\sim\mathbf{E}X\sim P$
(4) $\vdash \mathbf{A}X\Box P \Leftrightarrow \Box\mathbf{A}X\, P$

123.4 - $\vdash \Diamond\mathbf{A}X\, P \Rightarrow \mathbf{A}X\Diamond P$
(1) $\vdash \mathbf{A}X\, P \Rightarrow P$
(2) $\vdash \Diamond\mathbf{A}X\, P \Rightarrow \Diamond P$
(3) $\vdash \Diamond\mathbf{A}X\, P \Rightarrow \mathbf{A}X\Diamond P$.

123.5 - $\vdash \mathbf{E}X\Box P \Rightarrow \Box\mathbf{E}X\, P$
(1) $\vdash \Diamond\mathbf{A}X\sim P \Rightarrow \mathbf{A}X\Diamond P$
(2) $\vdash \sim\mathbf{A}X\Diamond\sim P \Rightarrow \sim\Diamond\mathbf{A}X\sim P$

(3) $\vdash$ $\mathbf{EX}\sim\Diamond\sim P \Rightarrow \Box\sim\mathbf{AX}\sim P$
(4) $\vdash$ $\mathbf{EX}\Box P \Rightarrow \Box\mathbf{EX}\, P$

§ 124 - FUNCTIONAL PARALLELS OF WEAK TRANSFORMATIONS OF MPC

124.1 - $\vdash$ $\mathbf{AX}\Box\sim P \Rightarrow \mathbf{AX}(P\Rightarrow Q)$

124.2 - $\vdash \mathbf{AX}\, P \Rightarrow \mathbf{AX}(Q\Rightarrow P)$

124.3 - $\vdash$ $\Box\mathbf{AX}\sim(P\wedge Q) \Rightarrow \mathbf{AX}(P\Rightarrow\sim Q)$

124.4 - $\vdash$ $[\Box\mathbf{AX}\, P\wedge\Box\mathbf{AX}\, Q] \Rightarrow \mathbf{AX}(P\Leftrightarrow Q)$

124.5 - $\vdash$ $[\Box\mathbf{AX}\sim P\wedge\Box\mathbf{AX}\sim Q] \Rightarrow \mathbf{AX}(P\Leftrightarrow Q)$.

One example of a more complicated demonstration:

124.6 - $\vdash$ $\mathbf{AX}[P\Rightarrow(Q\vee M)] \Leftrightarrow \Box[Q\vee\mathbf{AX}(P\rightarrow M)]$, if '$X$' is not free in '$Q$'.
(1) $\vdash$ $(\sim P\vee Q\vee M) \Leftrightarrow [Q\vee(\sim P\vee M)]$
(2) $\vdash$ $[P\rightarrow(Q\vee M)] \Leftrightarrow [Q\vee(P\rightarrow M)]$
(3) $\vdash$ $\mathbf{AX}[P\rightarrow(Q\vee M)] \Leftrightarrow \mathbf{AX}[Q\vee(P\rightarrow M)]$
(4) $\vdash$ $\mathbf{AX}[P\rightarrow(Q\vee M)] \Leftrightarrow [Q\vee\mathbf{AX}(P\rightarrow M)]$
(5) $\vdash$ $\Box\mathbf{AX}[P\rightarrow(Q\vee M)] \Leftrightarrow \Box[Q\vee\mathbf{AX}(P\rightarrow M)]$
(6) $\vdash$ $\mathbf{AX}\Box[P\rightarrow(Q\vee M)] \Leftrightarrow \Box[Q\vee\mathbf{AX}(P\rightarrow M)]$
(7) $\vdash$ Th

§ 125 - THEOREMS RESTRICTED TO MF^1C

125.1 - $\vdash$ $\mathbf{EX}(P\Rightarrow Q) \Rightarrow (\mathbf{AX}\, P\Rightarrow\mathbf{EX}\, Q)$
(1) $\vdash$ $\mathbf{EX}\Box(P\rightarrow Q) \Rightarrow \mathbf{EX}(P\rightarrow Q)$
(2) $\vdash$ $\mathbf{EX}\Box(P\rightarrow Q) \Rightarrow \mathbf{EX}(\sim P\vee Q)$
(3) $\vdash$ $\mathbf{EX}\Box(P\rightarrow Q) \Rightarrow \mathbf{AX}(\mathbf{EX}\sim P\vee\mathbf{EX}\, Q)$
(4) $\vdash$ $\mathbf{EX}\Box(P\rightarrow Q) \Rightarrow \Box(\mathbf{AX}\, P\rightarrow\mathbf{EX}\, Q)$
(5) $\vdash$ $\mathbf{EX}\Box(P\rightarrow Q) \Rightarrow (\mathbf{AX}\, P\Rightarrow\mathbf{EX}\, Q)$

To prove the inverse, we should have:

$$\Box \mathbf{EX}\, P \Rightarrow \mathbf{EX}\Box P,$$

which is not the case.

As corollaries of 125.1:

125.11 - $\vdash$ $\mathbf{EX}(P \Rightarrow Q) \Rightarrow (P \Rightarrow \mathbf{EX}\, Q)$, if '$X$' is not free in '$P$'.

125.12 - $\vdash$ $\mathbf{EX}(P \Rightarrow Q) \Rightarrow (\mathbf{AX}\, P \Rightarrow Q)$, if '$X$' is not free in '$Q$'.

§ 126 - RULE OF REPLACEMENT

Barcan states a rule of replacement of equivalents as follows:

126.1 - If $\vdash \mathbf{A}x_1\mathbf{A}x_2 \ldots \mathbf{A}x_n(P \Leftrightarrow Q)$, then $\vdash R \Leftrightarrow (P/Q)R$.

126.2 - Hence

If $\vdash \Box^n \mathbf{A}x_1\mathbf{A}x_2 \ldots \mathbf{A}x_n(P \Leftrightarrow Q)$, then $\vdash R \Leftrightarrow (P/Q)R$.

126.3 - And in S4:

If $\vdash \Box \mathbf{A}x_1\mathbf{A}x_2 \ldots \mathbf{A}x_n(P \Leftrightarrow Q)$, then $\vdash R \Leftrightarrow (P/Q)R$.

§ 127 - DEDUCTION THEOREM

A deduction theorem has been proved by Barcan (JSL, XI, p. 115) for the system S4[1], equivalent to the system MF^1C for S4.

127.0 - The proof on hypotheses of $A_1, A_2, \ldots, A_n \vdash B$ is defined as usual in non-modal calculus as: «There is a finite list of formulas 'B_1', 'B_2',..., 'B_s' such that each B_i is one of the A_i's or is an axiom or results from preceding A_j's in the list by one of the rules of inference.»

127.1 - In S4:

If $A_1, A_2, \ldots, A_n \vdash B$, then $A_1, A_2, \ldots, A_{n-1} \vdash A \rightarrow B$.

The proof is a proof by cases, for the different cases considered in the definition.

127.2 - In S4:

If $A_1, A_2, \ldots, A_n \vdash B$, and if each A_i is of the form $\Box\Gamma_i$, then $A_1, A_2, \ldots, A_{n-1} \vdash A_n \Rightarrow B$.

The proof is of the same form as the preceding one, it is necessary to apply the rule of replacement of §126.

127.3 - The theorems 127.1 and 127.2 are not provable in system S2′. This is shown in 50.3 by means of the matrix 50.1.

SECTION 13 - IDENTITY

Like in first-order calculus we shall avoid a detailed proof of theorems obviously similar to theorems of assertoric logic.

For more perspicuousness we do not assert the theorems under the form of schemata.

§ 130 - POSTULATES FOR IDENTITY

We presuppose:

130.1 - The notation of abstracts with individual bound variables and the rules of such abstracts;

130.2 - The notation of abstracts with predicate variables and the rules of such abstracts;

130.3 - Postulates for quantification in MF^2C similar to postulates for quantification in MF^1C.

§ 131 - DEFINITIONS FOR BOTH FORMS OF IDENTITY

131.1 - 'ixy' for '$\mathbf{A}a(ax \rightarrow ay)$' (this is «*material identity*»).

131.2 - '$\mathbf{I}xy$' for '$\mathbf{A}a(ax \Rightarrow ay)$' (this is «*strict identity*»).

131.3 - $\vdash$ $\mathbf{I}xy \Leftrightarrow \Box ixy$

(1) $\vdash$ $\mathbf{I}xy \Leftrightarrow \mathbf{A}a(ax \Rightarrow ay)$

(2) $\vdash$ $\mathbf{I}xy \Leftrightarrow \Box\mathbf{A}a(ax \rightarrow ay)$ by 123.3

(3) $\vdash$ $\mathbf{I}xy \Leftrightarrow \Box ixy$ by df 131.1

131.4 - $\vdash$ $ixy \Leftrightarrow \mathbf{A}a(ax \leftrightarrow ay)$

131.5 - $\vdash$ $\mathbf{I}xy \Leftrightarrow \mathbf{A}a(ax \Leftrightarrow ay)$

§ 132 - IMMEDIATE CONSEQUENCES

132.1 - $\vdash$ $\mathrm{i}xx$

(1) $\vdash$ $ax \rightarrow ax$

(2) $\vdash$ $\mathbf{A}a(ax \rightarrow ax)$

(3) $\vdash$ Th

132.2 - $\vdash$ $\mathrm{i}xy \leftrightarrow \mathrm{i}yx$

132.3 - $\vdash$ $(\mathrm{i}xz \wedge \mathrm{i}zy) \rightarrow \mathrm{i}xy$

132.4 - $\vdash$ $\mathbf{I}xx$

132.5 - $\vdash$ $\mathbf{I}xy \Leftrightarrow \mathbf{I}yx$

132.6 - $\vdash$ $(\mathbf{I}xz \wedge \mathbf{I}zy) \Rightarrow \mathbf{I}xy$

§ 133 - IDENTITY EXPRESSED BY MEANS OF AN UNIVERSAL IMPLICATION

133.1 - $\vdash$ $\mathrm{i}xy \Rightarrow (ax \rightarrow ay)$

133.2 - $\vdash$ $ay \Rightarrow (\mathrm{i}xy \rightarrow ax)$

133.3 - $\vdash$ $ay \Leftrightarrow (\mathbf{A}x(\mathrm{i}xy \rightarrow ax)$

133.4 - $\vdash$ $\Box ay \Leftrightarrow \mathbf{A}x(\mathrm{i}xy \Rightarrow ax)$

133.5 - $\vdash$ $\Box ay \Leftrightarrow \mathbf{A}x(\mathbf{I}xy \Rightarrow ax)$ in S4

§ 134 - IDENTITY EXPRESSED BY MEANS OF AN EXISTENTIAL PROPOSITION

134.1 - $\vdash$ $(\mathrm{i}xy \wedge ax) \Rightarrow ay$

134.2 - $\vdash$ $ay \Leftrightarrow \mathbf{E}x(\mathrm{i}xy \wedge ax)$

(1) $\vdash$ $ay \Leftrightarrow \mathbf{E}x(\mathrm{i}yy \wedge ay)$

(2) $\vdash$ $ay \Rightarrow \mathbf{E}x(\mathrm{i}xy \wedge ax)$

(3) $\vdash$ $(\mathrm{i}xy \wedge ax) \Rightarrow ay$

(4) $\vdash$ $\mathbf{E}\hat{x}(\mathrm{i}xy \wedge ax) \Rightarrow ay$

(5) $\vdash$ Th

134.20 - $\vdash$ $\mathbf{E}x(\mathbf{I}xy \wedge ax) \Rightarrow ay$ from 134.1

134.21 - $\vdash$ $ay \rightarrow \mathbf{E}x(\mathbf{I}xy \wedge ax)$

(1) $\vdash$ $(\mathbf{I}yy \wedge ay) \Rightarrow \mathbf{E}x(\mathbf{I}xy \wedge ax)$

(2) $\vdash$ $\mathbf{I}yy \Rightarrow [ay \rightarrow \mathbf{E}x(\mathbf{I}xy \wedge ax)]$

(3) $\vdash$ Th

134.22 - If $\vdash AY$, then $\vdash \mathbf{E}X(\mathbf{I}XY \wedge AX)$.

But $\vdash ay \Rightarrow \mathbf{E}x(\mathbf{I}xy \wedge ax)$ is not valid in S2; the proof would require that $\vdash \Box\mathbf{I}yy$, which is only valid in S4 (see 134-31).

134.3 - $\vdash$ $\Box ay \Leftrightarrow \mathbf{E}x(\mathbf{I}xy \wedge \Box ax)$

(1) $\vdash$ $(\mathrm{i}xy \wedge ay) \Rightarrow ay$

(2) $\vdash$ $\Box(\mathrm{i}xy \wedge ax) \Rightarrow \Box ay$

(3) $\vdash$ $(\mathbf{I}xy \wedge \Box ax) \Rightarrow \Box ay$

(4) $\vdash$ $\mathbf{E}x(\mathbf{I}xy \wedge \Box ax) \Rightarrow \Box ay$

(5) $\vdash$ $\Box ay \Rightarrow (\mathbf{I}yy \wedge \Box ay)$

(6) $\vdash$ $\Box ay \Rightarrow \mathbf{E}x(\mathbf{I}xy \wedge \Box ax)$

(7) $\vdash$ Th

134.31 - $\vdash$ $ay \Rightarrow \mathbf{E}x(\mathbf{I}xy \wedge ax)$ In S4.

(1) $\vdash$ $(\Box\mathbf{I}yy \wedge ay) \Rightarrow (\mathbf{I}yy \wedge ay)$

(2) $\vdash$ $(\Box\mathbf{I}yy \wedge ay) \Rightarrow \mathbf{E}x(\mathbf{I}xy \wedge ax)$

(3) $\vdash$ $\Box\mathbf{I}yy$

(4) $\vdash$ Th

134.32 - $\vdash$ $ay \Leftrightarrow \mathbf{E}x(\mathbf{I}xy \wedge ax)$

§ 135 - EQUIVALENCES BETWEEN i AND I

135.1 - $\vdash$ $ixy \leftrightarrow \mathbf{I}xy$
(1) $\vdash$ $ixy \Rightarrow (\mathbf{I}xx \rightarrow \mathbf{I}xy)$
(2) $\vdash$ $\mathbf{I}xx$
(3) $\vdash$ $ixy \rightarrow \mathbf{I}xy$
(4) $\vdash$ $\mathbf{I}xy \Rightarrow ixy$
(5) $\vdash$ Th

135.2 - $\vdash$ $\Box \mathbf{I}xy \Leftrightarrow \mathbf{I}xy$ (Lemma valid in S4)
(1) $\vdash$ $\Box\Box ixy \Leftrightarrow \Box ixy$
(2) $\vdash$ Th by df

135.3 - $\vdash$ $ixy \Leftrightarrow \mathbf{I}xy$ in S4
(1) $\vdash$ $(ixy \wedge \mathbf{I}xx) \Rightarrow \mathbf{I}xy$
(2) $\vdash$ $\Box \mathbf{I}xx$
(3) $\vdash$ $ixy \Rightarrow \mathbf{I}xy$ (1), (2), by 33.4
(4) $\vdash$ $\mathbf{I}xy \Rightarrow ixy$
(5) $\vdash$ Th

§ 136 - NON-IDENTITY

136.1 - $\vdash$ $\bar{i}xy \Leftrightarrow \mathbf{A}a \sim (ax \rightarrow ay)$

136.2 - $\vdash$ $\bar{\mathbf{I}}xy \Leftrightarrow \mathbf{A}a \sim (ax \Rightarrow ay)$

136.3 - $\vdash$ $\bar{i}xy \Leftrightarrow \mathbf{E}a(ax \wedge \sim ay)$

136.4 - $\vdash$ $\bar{\mathbf{I}}xy \Leftrightarrow \mathbf{E}a\Diamond(ax \wedge \sim ay)$.

§ 137 - THEOREMS UPON NON-IDENTITY

137.1 - $\vdash$ $\mathbf{A}x(ax \Rightarrow \bar{i}xy) \Leftrightarrow \Box \sim ay$
(1) $\vdash$ $\sim ay \Leftrightarrow \mathbf{A}x(ax \rightarrow \sim ixy)$ from 134.2
(2) $\vdash$ $\Box \sim ay \Leftrightarrow \mathbf{A}x(ax \Rightarrow \sim ixy)$

137.2 - $\vdash$ $\Box\sim ay \Rightarrow \mathbf{A}x(ax \Rightarrow \sim \mathbf{I}xy)$
(1) $\vdash$ $\sim ay \Rightarrow \mathbf{A}y(ax \Rightarrow \sim \mathbf{I}xy)$ 124.20
(2) $\vdash$ $\Box\sim \mathbf{A}y(ax \Rightarrow \sim \mathbf{I}xy)$
(3) $\vdash$ Th

The converse is not provable, no more than the converse of 134.20.

137.3 - $\vdash$ $\Box\sim ay \Leftrightarrow \mathbf{A}x(ax \Rightarrow \sim \mathbf{I}xy)$ in S4
(1) $\vdash$ $\Box\sim ay \Leftrightarrow \mathbf{A}x(\mathbf{I}xy \Rightarrow \sim ax)$ 133.5 in S4
(2) $\vdash$ Th

* APPENDIX

SECTION *14 - L-FORMULATIONS OF MODAL PROPOSITIONAL LOGICS, GIVING DECISION PROCEDURES FOR THE SYSTEMS S2, S3, S4, S5 and S2′

§ *141 - SYSTEMS OF OHNISHI AND MATSUMOTO, RELATED TO S2, S3, S4, S5 AND S2′

Ohnishi and Matsumoto (1957-1959) licked a decision method for the systems S2, S4, S5 and S2′ into shape. Matsumoto (1960) also solved the problem for the system S3.

***141.1** - *For the system S2.*

One elaborates a modal system called 'Q2'.

First one supposes a L-formulation of the APC, using schemata of natural deduction for consequence-statements (Sequenzen) in the way of the LK-systems of Gentzen, where the consequence-statements may contain an arbitrary number (eventually zero) of antecedents and of consequents. The general *rules of structure* are:

1° the rules for *weakening* a consequence-statement, by adding an arbitrary antecedent or consequent;

2° the rules allowing to *permute* various antecedents or various consequents;

3° the rules allowing to *eliminate* an iterated antecedent or iterated consequent.

There is also the schema, called «*Cut*» (Schnitt). (In certain particular systems, this schema will be shown redundant.)

To this system, one adds the following *syntax rule* and *definitions*:

If '*P*' is a well-formed proposition of the APC, then 'P' and '$\Box P$' are well-formed propositions of Q2.

Definition: '$\Diamond P$' for '$\sim \Box \sim P$'.

System Q2 contains also two *derivation-schemata*, by which one can introduce a '$\Box$' respectively in an antecedent and in a consequent. To formulate these schemata, we shall represent by '$\mathfrak{X}$' a non-empty series of propositions (with an arbitrary number of them), and we represent by '$\Box\mathfrak{X}$' the series obtained by prefixing a '$\Box$' to each proposition of the series '$\mathfrak{X}$'.

By the signs '$\mathfrak{Y}$', '$\mathfrak{Z}$', we also represent series of propositions, but these, unlike '$\mathfrak{X}$', may be empty series.

The schemata then are formulated as follows:

For an antecedent:

$$\text{Q2}(\Box\vdash) \qquad \frac{P, \mathfrak{Y} \vdash \mathfrak{Z}}{\Box P, \mathfrak{Y} \vdash \mathfrak{Z}} \quad ;$$

For a consequent:

$$\text{Q2}(\vdash\Box) \qquad \frac{\mathfrak{X} \vdash P}{\Box\mathfrak{X} \vdash \Box P} \quad .$$

(One shall notice that the latter schema is never applicable to a consequence-statement with multiple consequents, nor to a consequence-statement without antecedent.)

Notice also that in Q2 one cannot demonstrate any consequence-statement of the form $\vdash \Box P$, since schema Q2($\vdash\Box$), by virtue of the convention adopted for the sign '$\mathfrak{X}$', does not permit to introduce a '$\Box$' in a consequent if there is no antecedent.

Ohnishi and Matsumoto proved the following meta-theorem: P is a theorem of S2 if and only if $\Box(q \rightarrow q) \vdash P$ is demonstrable in Q2 (the q-variable is an arbitrary propositional variable, which must not necessarily occur in 'P').

Since one can demonstrate that the cut-schema is redundant in Q2, this meta-theorem furnishes a very simple method of decision for S2.

Let us show with an example how to apply this decision procedure.

For instance, the expression $[p \Rightarrow (q \Rightarrow r)] \Rightarrow [(p \wedge q) \Rightarrow r]$.

First we replace the strict connectors '$\Rightarrow$' by their definition in terms of '$\Box$' and of '$\rightarrow$'. This gives the expression:

$$\Box\{\Box[p \rightarrow \Box(q \rightarrow r)] \rightarrow \Box[(p \wedge q) \rightarrow r)]\}.$$

We try then to demonstrate the consequence-statement:

$$\Box(s\rightarrow s)\vdash\Box\{\Box[p\rightarrow\Box(q\rightarrow r)]\rightarrow\Box[(p\wedge q)\rightarrow r)]\}.$$

We set the following table, starting from below and looking at each stage which premise(s) would be necessary to demonstrate in Q2 the wanted consequence-statement .If that way we can go up to consequence-statements which are axioms of Q2, then the expression is demonstrable in S2. In case we cannot, although the expression contains no connectors neither '□' operators, then the expression is not demonstrable in S2.

In regard of the considered expression, we get to the following table, which shows that we have to do with a theorem of S2.

$$\begin{array}{cc}
 & q\vdash q\ ;\ p,\ r\vdash r \\ \cline{2-2}
p,\ q\vdash p & q\rightarrow r,\ p,\ q\vdash r \\ \cline{1-1}\cline{2-2}
p\wedge q\vdash p & q\rightarrow r,\ p\wedge q\vdash r \\ \cline{2-2}
 & \Box(q\rightarrow r),\ p\wedge q\vdash r \\ \hline
\multicolumn{2}{c}{p\wedge q,\ p\rightarrow\Box(q\rightarrow r),\ p\wedge q\vdash r} \\ \hline
\multicolumn{2}{c}{p\rightarrow\Box(q\rightarrow r)\vdash(p\wedge q)\rightarrow r} \\ \hline
\multicolumn{2}{c}{\Box[p\rightarrow\Box(q\rightarrow r)]\ \vdash\ \Box[(p\wedge q)\rightarrow r]} \\ \hline
\multicolumn{2}{c}{s\rightarrow s,\ \Box[p\rightarrow\Box(q\rightarrow r)]\ \vdash\ \Box[(p\wedge q)\rightarrow r]} \\ \hline
\multicolumn{2}{c}{s\rightarrow s\ \vdash\ \Box[p\supset\Box(q\supset r)]\ \rightarrow\ \Box[(p\wedge q)\rightarrow r]} \\ \hline
\multicolumn{2}{c}{\Box(s\rightarrow s)\ \vdash\ \Box\{\Box[p\rightarrow\Box(q\rightarrow r)]\rightarrow\Box[(p\wedge q)\rightarrow r]\}}
\end{array}$$

***141.2** - *For system S3.*

We elaborate a modal system called 'Q3'.

It is formed exactly in the same way as Q2, with the only difference that the derivation schema Q2(⊢□) is replaced by the following:

$$\text{Q3}(\vdash\Box):\quad \frac{\mathfrak{X}\vdash\Box(q\rightarrow q),\ P\quad ;\quad \Box\mathfrak{X}\vdash P}{\Box\mathfrak{X}\ \vdash\ \Box\ P}\ .$$

One shall notice that this schema is not applicable if the consequence-statement which is taken as the second premisse has multiple consequents.

Likely we have the following meta-theorem:

P is a theorem of S3 if and only if $\Box(q \to q) \vdash P$ is demonstrable in Q3.

Since the cut-schema can also be shown as redundant in Q3, this gives an easy decision method for S3.

***141.3** - *For system S4.*

We elaborate a modal system called 'S4*'.

It is formed exactly like Q2 and Q3, but here the schema Q2($\vdash\Box$) is replaced by the following:

$$\text{S4*}(\vdash\Box): \quad \frac{\Box\mathfrak{Y} \vdash P}{\Box\mathfrak{Y} \vdash \Box P} .$$

(Remember that '$\mathfrak{Y}$' may be the empty series.)

We have the following meta-theorem:

P is a theorem of S4 if and only if $\vdash P$ is demonstrable in S4*.

Here also, since one can demonstrate the redundance of the cut-schema, we have a simple decision-method for S4.

***141.4** - *For system S5.*

We elaborate a modal system called 'S5*'.

It is formed in the same way as Q2, but here the schema Q2($\vdash\Box$) is replaced by the following:

$$\text{S5*}(\vdash\Box): \quad \frac{\Box\mathfrak{Y} \vdash \Box\mathfrak{Z}, P}{\Box\mathfrak{Y} \vdash \Box\mathfrak{Z}, \Box P} .$$

On shall notice that the schema may be applied to a consequence-statement with multiple consequents, but all the antecedents and consequents, different from the one on which modalization must be operated, have to start already with a '□'.

We have the following meta-theorem:

P is a theorem of S5 if and only if $\vdash P$ is demonstrable in S5*.

The redundance of the cut-schema is not provable for S5, but a decision procedure for S5 will still result from a meta-theorem connecting S5 with S4 (see further § *141.6).

***141.5** - *For system S2′* (T of Feys, M of von Wright).

We elaborate a modal system called 'M*'.

It is formed in the same way as system Q2, but here the schema Q2($\vdash \Box$) is replaced by the following:

$$\text{M*}(\vdash \Box): \qquad \frac{\mathfrak{Y} \vdash P}{\Box\mathfrak{Y} \vdash \Box P}\ .$$

One shall notice that the schema is applicable to a consequence-statement without antecedent, but not to a consequence-statement with multiple consequents.

We have the following meta-theorem:

P is a theorem of S2′ if and only if $\vdash P$ is demonstrable in M*.

Since one can show that the cut-schema is redundant in S2′, this furnishes a decision procedure for system S2′.

***141.6** - *Relations between S2, S3, S4 and S5.*

Matsumoto (1955) also established the following relations between the systems S3, S4 and S5.

We represent here by '$\text{SX} \vdash P$' a meta-theorem stating that the expression '$\vdash P$' is a theorem in the system denoted by 'SX'.

We dispose in one same column the meta-theorems connected in this sense that the truth of one entails the truth of the other and conversely.

The meta-theorems of one of the columns entail the ones of the next column, but the inverse relation does not hold.

$$\text{S3} \vdash \text{P} \rightarrow \left\{ \begin{array}{l} \text{S4} \vdash P \\ \text{S4} \vdash \Box P \end{array} \right. \rightarrow \left\{ \begin{array}{l} \text{S5} \vdash \Box P \\ \text{S4} \vdash \Diamond\Box P \\ \text{S4} \vdash \Box\Diamond\Box P \\ \text{S5} \vdash P \\ \text{S3} \vdash \Diamond\Diamond\Box P \end{array} \right. \rightarrow \left\{ \begin{array}{l} \text{S5} \vdash \Diamond P \\ \text{S4} \vdash \Diamond P \\ \text{S4} \vdash \Box\Diamond P \\ \text{S4} \vdash \Diamond\Box\Diamond P \\ \text{S3} \vdash \Diamond\Diamond P \\ \text{S3} \vdash \Diamond\Diamond\Box\Diamond P \end{array} \right.$$

The relation, stated in the third column, between S5 and S4 gives an easy decision procedure for S5, derived from the one proposed for S4.

§ *142 - SYSTEMS OF KANGER, RELATED TO S4, S5 AND S2′

Kanger (1957) on his side elaborated a decision method for S4, S5 and S2′.

***142.1** - *For system S4.*

Kanger elaborates a modal system, called 'S4*', which is formed from an L-formulation for the APC presented in the way of a natural deduction system according to Gentzen, authorizing consequence-statements with multiple consequents (or with an empty consequent).

The fundamental *axiom-schema* is of the form

$$\mathfrak{Y}_1, P, \mathfrak{Y}_2 \vdash \mathfrak{Z}_1, P, \mathfrak{Z}_2$$

where '$\mathfrak{Y}_1$', '$\mathfrak{Y}_2$', ..., '$\mathfrak{Z}_1$', '$\mathfrak{Z}_2$' represent suites of propositions which may be eventually the empty suite.

The system does not adopt any so-called general structure rules, but the derivation schemata are ingeniously arranged so as to supply this deficiency.

The *derivation-schemata* permitting the introduction of an APC connector are formulated so as to dispense with any general structure-rule. We present them here under a form usefull for a system S5* which will be treated under §*14.22. Here, for system S4*, the numerical index '*m*' appearing in the following schemata may simply be neglected.

Derivation schemata for the introduction of the connectors of the APC.

(⊢ →)
$$\frac{\mathfrak{Y}_1,\ \mathfrak{Y}_2,\ P^m,\ \mathfrak{Y}_3 \vdash \mathfrak{Z}_1,\ \mathfrak{Z}_2,\ Q^m,\ \mathfrak{Z}_3}{\mathfrak{Y}_1,\ \mathfrak{Y}_2,\ \mathfrak{Y}_3 \vdash \mathfrak{Z}_1,\ P^m \rightarrow Q^m,\ \mathfrak{Z}_2,\ \mathfrak{Z}_3}$$

(→ ⊢)
$$\frac{\mathfrak{Y}_1,\ \mathfrak{Y}_2,\ \mathfrak{Y}_3 \vdash \mathfrak{Z}_1,\ \mathfrak{Z}_2,\ P^m,\ \mathfrak{Z}_3 \quad ; \quad \mathfrak{Y}_1,\ \mathfrak{Y}_2,\ Q^m,\ \mathfrak{Y}_3 \vdash \mathfrak{Z}_1,\ \mathfrak{Z}_2,\ \mathfrak{Z}_3}{\mathfrak{Y}_1,\ P^m \rightarrow Q^m,\ \mathfrak{Y}_2,\ \mathfrak{Y}_3 \vdash \mathfrak{Z}_1,\ \mathfrak{Z}_2,\ \mathfrak{Z}_3}$$

(⊢ ∧)
$$\frac{\mathfrak{Y} \vdash \mathfrak{Z}_1,\ \mathfrak{Z}_2,\ P^m,\ \mathfrak{Z}_3 \quad ; \quad \mathfrak{Y} \vdash \mathfrak{Z}_1,\ \mathfrak{Z}_2,\ Q^m,\ \mathfrak{Z}_3}{\mathfrak{Y} \vdash \mathfrak{Z}_1,\ P^m \wedge Q^m,\ \mathfrak{Z}_2,\ \mathfrak{Z}_3}$$

(∧ ⊢)
$$\frac{\mathfrak{Y}_1,\ \mathfrak{Y}_2,\ P^m,\ Q^m,\ \mathfrak{Y}_3 \vdash \mathfrak{Z}}{\mathfrak{Y}_1,\ P^m \wedge Q^m,\ \mathfrak{Y}_2,\ \mathfrak{Y}_3 \vdash \mathfrak{Z}}$$

(⊢ ∨)
$$\frac{\mathfrak{Y} \vdash \mathfrak{Z}_2,\ \mathfrak{Z}_2,\ P^m,\ Q^m,\ \mathfrak{Z}_3}{\mathfrak{Y} \vdash \mathfrak{Z}_1,\ P^m \vee Q^m,\ \mathfrak{Z}_2,\ \mathfrak{Z}_3}$$

(∨ ⊢)
$$\frac{\mathfrak{Y}_1,\ \mathfrak{Y}_2,\ P^m,\ \mathfrak{Y}_3 \vdash \mathfrak{Z} \quad ; \quad \mathfrak{Y}_1,\ \mathfrak{Y}_2,\ Q^m,\ \mathfrak{Y}_3 \vdash \mathfrak{Z}}{\mathfrak{Y}_1,\ P^m \vee Q^m,\ \mathfrak{Y}_2,\ \mathfrak{Y}_3 \vdash \mathfrak{Z}}$$

(⊢ ~)
$$\frac{\mathfrak{Y}_1,\ \mathfrak{Y}_2,\ P^m,\ \mathfrak{Y}_3 \vdash \mathfrak{Z}_1,\ \mathfrak{Z}_2}{\mathfrak{Y}_1,\ \mathfrak{Y}_2,\ \mathfrak{Y}_3 \vdash \mathfrak{Z}_1,\ \sim P^m,\ \mathfrak{Z}_2}$$

(~ ⊢)
$$\frac{\mathfrak{Y}_1,\ \mathfrak{Y}_2 \vdash \mathfrak{Z}_1,\ \mathfrak{Z}_2,\ P^m,\ \mathfrak{Z}_3}{\mathfrak{Y}_1,\ \sim P^m,\ \mathfrak{Y}_2 \vdash \mathfrak{Z}_1,\ \mathfrak{Z}_2,\ \mathfrak{Z}_3}$$

The derivation schemata permitting the introduction of the □-sign are the following:

For the antecedent:

S4*(□⊢)
$$\frac{\mathfrak{Y}_1, \mathfrak{Y}_2, P, \Box P, \mathfrak{Y}_3 \vdash \mathfrak{Z}}{\mathfrak{Y}_1, \Box P, \mathfrak{Y}_2, \mathfrak{Y}_3 \vdash \mathfrak{Z}} .$$

One shall notice that this schema does not really introduce a □-sign in the antecedent; it does operate the elimination of an antecedent-proposition provided that another antecedent of the premise reproduces the same proposition but prefixed by a □-sign. As the antecedent of form '□P' could always be introduced in one of the axioms, the result of the schema is well the introduction of a '□' in front of an antecedent unprovided with it.

One shall notice, incidentally, the permutation of the suites $\mathfrak{Y}_2$ and $\mathfrak{Y}_3$. It is one of the artifices which allow the system to neglect a general structure rule authorizing the permutation of antecedents. An analogue artifice is introduced in the schemata relating to a consequent.

For the consequent, the derivation schema is as follows:

Let us represent by '$\mathfrak{Y}^*$' the suite containing all the propositions of form '□Q' which are a member of the suite denoted by '$\mathfrak{Y}$', and containing no other proposition. (The suite $\mathfrak{Y}^*$ must be void if the suite $\mathfrak{Y}$ does not contain any member beginning with '□'.)

S4*(⊢ □)
$$\frac{\mathfrak{Y}^* \vdash P}{\mathfrak{Y} \vdash \mathfrak{Z}_1, \Box P, \mathfrak{Z}_2} .$$

One shall notice that the schema can only be applied to a consequence-statement with just *one* consequent. In addition, the premise must count between its antecedents all the antecedents of form '□Q' present in the conclusion, and no other antecedent.

But one can introduce among the antecedents of the conclusion each proposition not starting with a '□', and one can also introduce arbitrary consequents, represented here by the symbols '$\mathfrak{Z}_1$' and '$\mathfrak{Z}_2$'. The supplementary consequents of form '$\Box Q$' are not prohibited. This last faculty is necessary because the presence of these supplementary consequents in the premise would made the schema unapplicable and because these supplementary consequents may be necessary for the further steps of a demonstration.

Kanger demonstrated the following meta-theorem:
On expression P is demonstrable in system S4 if and only if the consequence-statement $\vdash P$ is demonstrable in system S4* just described.

*142.2 - *For system S5.*

Kanger elaborates a modal system which he calls 'S5*'.

This one is also formed, in the same way as S4*, from an L-formulation for the APC, but this time the schemata comprise new conditions, which compel the particular notation of the indices.

Each propositional variable, figuring either in an antecedent or in a consequent of a consequence-statement, must be bearing a numerical index, which we simply represent by a number placed as exponent behind the variable. (Of course, the indices have nothing in common with the exponential function.)

Two the same propositional variables bearing different indices will be treated as different variables.

As ***variables for the indices***, we shall use the signs 'n', 'm', being understood that two different indices-variables can represent different indices, but also one and the same index.

Let us represent by the sign 'P^n' a propositional expression (eventually complex, i.e. formed by connectors) in which each of the propositional variables is bearing the same index n. Let us represent by '$\mathfrak{Y}^n$', '$\mathfrak{Z}^n$', suites of similar propositions, where all the propositional variables present in the suite in question are affected by the same index n. The signs '$\mathfrak{Y}$', '$\mathfrak{Z}$', without index, will represent suites of propositions whose propositional variables are bearing one and the same arbitrary index.

The axiom-schema for system S5* is then formulated as follows:

$$\mathfrak{Y}_1, P^n, \mathfrak{Y}_2 \vdash \mathfrak{Z}_1, P^n, \mathfrak{Z}_2 .$$

One shall notice that the consequent which has to be identical to one of the antecedents must have all its variables bearing the same index as the ones of the antecedent.

The schemata for the connectors of the APC are the same as in §14.21, but here the indices are necessary.

The schema for sign '□' in the antecedent is formulated as follows:

S5*(□ ⊢)
$$\frac{\mathfrak{Y}_1,\ \mathfrak{Y}_2,\ P^m,\ \Box P^n,\ \mathfrak{Y}_3 \vdash \mathfrak{Z}}{\mathfrak{Y}_1,\ \Box P^n,\ \mathfrak{Y}_2,\ \mathfrak{Y}_3 \vdash \mathfrak{Z}}\ .$$

One shall notice that the indices present in the antecedent 'P^m' must not be the same as the ones present in the antecedent '$\Box P^n$'; the antecedent 'P^m' is simply canceled out of the conclusion.

The schema for sign '□' in a consequent is formulated as follows:
Under the condition that the index 'n' does not affect any propositional variable □-free in '$\mathfrak{Y}$', '$\mathfrak{Z}_1$', '$\mathfrak{Z}_2$' or '$\mathfrak{Z}_3$', then:

S5*(⊢ □)
$$\frac{\mathfrak{Y} \vdash \mathfrak{Z}_1,\ \mathfrak{Z}_2,\ P^n,\ \mathfrak{Z}_3}{\mathfrak{Y} \vdash \mathfrak{Z}_1,\ \Box P^m,\ \mathfrak{Z}_2,\ \mathfrak{Z}_3}$$

(A variable is called «□-free» if it is not placed in the scope of any □-sign, nor, of course, of any ◇-sign, this sign being here an abbreviation for '∼□∼'.)
As consequence of the condition, when an index 'n' affects a □-free variable present in '$\mathfrak{Y}$', '$\mathfrak{Z}_1$', '$\mathfrak{Z}_2$' or '$\mathfrak{Z}_3$', then, in the conclusion, all the indices 'n' present in P must be changed into a new numerical index 'm', not beared by any □-free variable in '$\mathfrak{Y}$', '$\mathfrak{Z}_1$', '$\mathfrak{Z}_2$' nor '$\mathfrak{Z}_3$'. (This new index 'm' may already occur in □-bound parts of this conclusion.)

The meta-theorem demonstrated by Kanger is the following:
An expression P is a theorem of S5 if and only if one can demonstrate in S5* the consequence statement $\vdash P^1$ (where all the propositional variables are bearing the same index 1).

Here a few examples of the decision procedure for S5.
1. For instance decide of the sequence $\vdash p \vee \Box \sim \Box p$.

We affect first all the variables with the index '1'. Then we look from which premises on we could derive this expression in S5*. In that manner we go up, stage by stage, to see if likely we might get to axioms. The enquiry proceeds backwards, starting from below the table. We obtain ,in fact, following demonstration:

$$\begin{array}{c} p^1,\ \Box p^2 \vdash p^1 \\ \hline \Box p^2 \vdash p^1 \\ \hline \vdash\ \sim \Box p^2,\ p^1 \\ \hline \vdash p^1,\ \Box \sim \Box p^1 \\ \hline \vdash p^1 \vee \Box \sim \Box p^1 \end{array}$$

2. For the expression: $[(p \rightarrow q) \Rightarrow p] \Rightarrow p$.

We first replace the strict '$\Rightarrow$' connectors by their definition in terms of '$\Box$' and of '$\rightarrow$'. We affect all the variables with the index '1' and we proceed as above. We obtain following demonstration:

$$\begin{array}{c} \Box[(p^1 \rightarrow q^1) \rightarrow p^1],\ p^1 \vdash q^1,\ p^1 \\ \hline \Box[(p^1 \rightarrow q^1) \rightarrow p^1] \vdash p^1 \rightarrow q^1,\ p^1 \quad ; \quad p^1 \vdash p^1 \\ \hline (p^1 \rightarrow q^1) \rightarrow p^1,\ \Box[(p^1 \rightarrow q^1) \rightarrow p^1] \vdash p^1 \\ \hline \Box[(p^1 \rightarrow q^1) \rightarrow p^1] \vdash p^1 \\ \hline \vdash \Box[(p^1 \rightarrow q^1) \rightarrow p^1] \rightarrow p^1 \\ \hline \vdash \Box\{\Box[(p^1 \rightarrow q^1) \rightarrow p^1] \rightarrow p^1\} \end{array}$$

3. For the expression: $[(p \Rightarrow q) \rightarrow p] \Rightarrow p$.

We find out it is not possible to go up to axioms. Indeed we can only propose following table, which should start with a unprovable consequence-statement:

$$\begin{array}{c} p^2 \vdash q^2,\ p^1 \quad (?) \\ \hline \vdash p^2 \rightarrow q^2,\ p^1 \\ \hline \vdash \Box(p^1 \rightarrow q^1),\ p^1 \quad ; \quad p^1 \vdash p^1 \\ \hline \Box(p^1 \rightarrow q^1) \rightarrow p^1 \vdash p^1 \\ \hline \vdash [\Box(p^1 \rightarrow q^1) \rightarrow p^1] \rightarrow p^1 \\ \hline \vdash \Box\{[\Box(p^1 \rightarrow q^1) \rightarrow p^1] \rightarrow p^1\} \end{array}$$

4. For the expression: $[(p \Rightarrow q) \rightarrow p] \Rightarrow p$.
We shall see it is not demonstrable.

$$\begin{array}{c} p^2, p^3 \vdash q^2, q^3, p^1 \quad (?) \\ \hline p^2 \vdash p^3 \rightarrow q^3, q^2, p^1 \\ \hline \vdash p^2 \rightarrow q^2,\ p^3 \rightarrow q^3, p^1 \\ \hline \vdash \Box (p^1 \rightarrow q^1), p^2 \rightarrow q^2, p^1 \end{array} \qquad \begin{array}{c} \\ \hline p^2 \vdash q^2, p^1, p^1 \quad (?) \\ \hline \vdash p^2 \rightarrow q^2, p^1, p^1 \\ \hline \vdash \Box (p^1 \rightarrow q^1), p^1, p^1 \ ; p^1 \vdash p^1, p^1 \end{array}$$

$$\begin{array}{c} \hline \vdash \Box (p^1 \rightarrow q^1), \Box (p^1 \rightarrow q^1), p^1 \ ; \ p^1 \vdash \Box (p^1 \rightarrow p^1), p^1 \end{array} \qquad \begin{array}{c} \hline \Box (p^1 \rightarrow q^1) \rightarrow p^1 \vdash p^1, p \end{array}$$

$$\begin{array}{c} \hline \Box (p^1 \rightarrow q^1) \rightarrow p^1 \vdash \Box (p^1 \rightarrow q^1), p^1 \quad ; \quad \Box[\Box (p^1 \rightarrow q^1) \rightarrow p^1] \vdash p^1, p^1 \\ \hline \Box (p^1 \rightarrow q^1) \rightarrow p^1, \Box[\Box (p^1 \rightarrow q^1) \rightarrow p^1] \vdash p^1 \\ \hline \Box[\Box (p^1 \rightarrow q^1) \rightarrow p^1] \vdash p^1 \\ \hline \vdash \Box[\Box (p^1 \rightarrow q^1) \rightarrow p^1] \rightarrow p^1 \\ \hline \vdash \Box\{\Box[\Box (p^1 \rightarrow q^1) \rightarrow p^1] \rightarrow p^1\} \end{array}$$

5. Likewise the expression $[(p \Rightarrow q) \Rightarrow p] \rightarrow p$ is not demonstrable, as the preceding table shows if we cut off the last line from below.

6. Likewise the expression $[(p \Rightarrow q) \rightarrow \Box p)] \rightarrow \Box p$ is not demonstrable, as the following table shows:

$$\begin{array}{c} p^2 \vdash q^2, p^1 \quad (?) \\ \hline \vdash p^1, p^2 \rightarrow q^2 \\ \hline \vdash \Box (p^1 \rightarrow q^1)\ , p^1 \end{array} \quad ; \quad \begin{array}{c} \\ \hline p^1 \vdash p^1 \\ \hline \Box p^1 \vdash p^1 \end{array}$$

$$\begin{array}{c} \hline \Box (p^1 \rightarrow q^1) \rightarrow \Box p^1 \vdash p^1 \\ \hline \Box (p^1 \rightarrow q^1) \rightarrow \Box p^1 \vdash \Box p^1 \\ \hline \vdash [\Box (p^1 \rightarrow q^1) \rightarrow \Box p^1] \rightarrow \Box p^1 \end{array}$$

***142.3** - For system S2′ (or M, or T).
Kanger elaborates a modal system called 't*'.
This system is formed in the same way as system S4*, but the

schema for the □-sign in the consequent is modified as follows:

Let us here represent by the sign '$\mathfrak{Y}^*$' the suite made of all the propositions '*P*' such that the suite '$\mathfrak{Y}$' contains the corresponding propositions '□*P*' and formed only with these propositions.

The schema is formulated as follows:

$$\text{t}^*(\vdash \Box) \qquad \frac{\mathfrak{Y}^* \vdash P}{\mathfrak{Y} \vdash \mathfrak{Z}_1, \Box P, \mathfrak{Z}_2} \; .$$

In other terms, the antecedent $\mathfrak{Y}$ of the conclusion must take over all the antecedents of the premise but must prefixe an '□' to each of them. More, '$\mathfrak{Y}$' might contain supplementary antecedents, not starting with a '□' when they are not present in the premise.

Kanger demonstrated the following meta-theorem:

An expression *P* is demonstrable in system S2′ if and only if the sequence $\vdash P$ is demonstrable in his system t*.

BIBLIOGRAPHY

Abraham, Leo

Implication, modality and intension in symbolic logic; *The Monist,* **43** (1923), 119-133.

Ackermann, Wilhelm

Über die Beziehung zwischen strikten und strenger Implikation; in *Logica Studia Paul Bernays Dedicata,* Neuchâtel, 1959, pp. 9-18.
(Also in *Dialectica,* **12** (1958), pp. 213-222.)

— Begründung einer strengen Implikation; *J. Symb. Logic,* **21** (1956), pp. 113-128.

Alban, M. J.

Independence of the primitive symbols of Lewis's calculi of propositions; *J. Symb. Logic,* **8** (1943), pp. 24-26.

Anderson, Alan Ross

Improved decision procedures for Lewis's calculus S4 and von Wright's calculus M (Extract for the XVth meeting of the Assoc. for Symb. Logic, Washington 1952); *J. Symb. Logic,* **18** (1953), pp. 187-189.

— Improved decision procedures for Lewis's calculus S4 and von Wright's calculus M; *J. Symb. Logic,* **19** (1954), pp. 201-214.

— On the interpretation of a modal system of Łukasiewicz; *The Journal of Computing Systems,* **1** (1954), pp. 209-210.

— On alternative formulations of a modal system of Feys-von Wright; *ibidem,* **1** (1954), pp. 211-212.

— Correction to a paper on modal logic; *J. Symb. Logic,* **20** (1955), p. 150.

— Independent axiom schemata for S5; *J. Symb. Logic,* **21** (1956), pp. 255-256.

— Reduction of deontic logic to alethic modal logic (Abstract); *J. Symb. Log,* **22** (1957), p. 105.
— *The formal analysis of normative systems,* Technical report n° 2 prepared under contract SAR/Nonr-609 (16), New-Haven, Interaction Laboratory. Sociology department, Yale University, November 15, 1956, 99 pp.
— Independent axiom schemata for von Wright's M; *J. Symb. Logic,* **22** (1957), pp. 241-244.
— A reduction of deontic logic to alethic modal logic; *Mind,* n. s. **67** (1958), pp. 100-103.
— *Completeness theorems for the system E of entailment and EQ of entailment with quantification.* Technical report n° 6 SAR/Nonr-609 (16), New-Haven 1959.
(Also to appear in *Zeitschrift f. math. Logic und Grundlagen der Mathematik.)*
— Entailment schorn of modality (Abstract for the XXVIth meeting of the Assoc. for Symb. Logic of 1961); *J. Symb. Logic,* **25** (1960), p. 388.
— Logik, Normen und Rollen; *Ratio,* **1** (1962), pp. 32-43.
— Modal logics II: Toward a formal analysis of cultural objects; in *Boston Studies in the Philosophy of Science,* Proceedings of the colloquium of 1961/62, Dordrecht, Reidel, 1963, pp. 117-143.
— Some open problems concerning the system E of entailment; *Acta Philosophica Fennica,* fasc. **16** (1963), pp. 7-18.

Anderson, Alan Ross, and **Belnap,** Nuel Dinsmore, Jr.
A modification of Ackermann's «rigorous implication» (abstract); *J. Symb. Logic,* **23** (1958), pp. 457-458.
— Modalities in Ackermann's «rigorous implication»; *J. Symb. Logic,* **24** (1959), pp. 107-111.
— The pure calculus of entailment (*J. Symb. Logic,* **27** (1962), pp. 19-52.

Anderson, Alan Ross, **Belnap,** Nuel D., Jr., and **Wallace,** John Roy
Independent axiom schemata for the pure theory of entailment; *Zeitschr. f. math. Logik und Grundl. der Math,* **6** (1960), pp. 93-95.

Apostel, Leo

Modalités physiques et techniques; *Actes du XI Congrès Internat. de Philos.* Bruxelles 1953, vol. 14, Amsterdam, North-Holland Publ. Cy, 1953, pp. 97-104.

Åqvist, Lennart

Postulate sets and decision procedure for some systems of deontic logic; *Theoria,* **19** (1963), pp. 154-175.

— On Dawson-models for deontic logic; *Logique et Analyse,* **7,** n° 25-26 (1964), pp. 14-21.

— Results concerning some modal systems that contain S2; *J. Symb. Logic,* **29** (1964), pp. 79-87. (*)

Back, Kurt W.

A nerve net system in modal logics; *Logique et Analyse,* **7,** n° 25-26 (1964), pp. 22-31.

Barcan, Ruth C. (later Mrs. J. A. **Marcus**)

A functional calculus of first order based on strict implication; *J. Symb. Logic,* **11** (1946), pp. 1-16.

— The deduction theorem in a functional calculus of first order based on strict implication; *J. Symb. Logic,* **11** (1946), pp. 115-118.

— The identity of individuals in a strict functional calculus of second order; *J. Symb. Logic,* **12** (1947), pp. 12-15.

Barcan-Marcus, Ruth

The elimination of contextually defined predicates in a modal system; *J. Symb. Logic,* **15** (1950), p. 92.

— Strict implication, deducibility, and the deduction theorem; *J. Symb. Logic,* **18** (1953), pp. 234-236.

— Interpreting quantification; *Inquiry,* **5** (1962) p. 252-259.

— Modal Logics I: Modalities and intensional languages; in *Boston Studies in the Philosophy of Science,* Proceedings of the colloquium of 1961/62, Dordrecht, Reidel, 1963, pp. 97-104. (Discussion with **Follesdal** D., **Kripke** S., **McCarthy** J. and **Quine** W., *ibidem,* pp. 105-116.)

— Classes and attributes in extended modal systems; *Acta Philosophica Fennica,* fasc. **16** (1963), pp. 123-136.

(*) Added in proof.

Bayart, Arnould

La correction de la logique modale du premier et second ordre S5; *Logique et Analyse,* **1** (1958), pp. 28-44.

— Quasi-adéquation de la logique modale de second ordre S5 et adéquation de la logique modale de premier ordre S5; *Logique et Analyse,* **2** (1959), pp. 99-121.

Becker-Freyseng, Albrecht

Die Aristotelische Theorie der Möglichkeitsschlüsse, eine logisch-philologische Untersuchung der Kapitel **13-22** *von Aristoteles'* Analytica priora I. (Dissertation Münster in West. 1932). Berlin, 1933, 98 pp.

Becker, Oskar

Zur Logik der Modalitäten; *Jahrb. f. Philos. und phenomenol. Forschung,* **11** (1930), pp. 496-548.

— Das formale System der ontologischen Modalitäten; *Blätter für deutsche philosophie,* **16** (1942), pp. 287-422.

— Ein «natürliches» formales System der logisch-ontologischen Modalitäten; *ibidem,* **18** (1944), pp. 82-93.

— *Einführung in die Logistik, verzüglich in den Modalitäten,* Meisenheim am Glan, Anton Heim, 1941, 92 pp.

— *Untersuchungen über den Modalkalkül,* Meisenheim am Glan, Anton Heim, 1952, 87 pp.

Behmann, Heinrich

Die typenfreie Logik und die Modalität; *Actes du XI Congrès Internat. de Philosophie, Bruxelles* (Colloque de Logique), Amsterdam, North-Holland Publ. Cy, 1953, vol. **14**, pp. 88-96.

Belnap, Nuel Dinsmore. See at **Anderson**, A. R.

Bennett, Jonathan Francis

Meaning and implication; *Mind,* n.s. **63** (1954), pp. 451-463.

Bergmann, Gustav

Contextual definitions in non-extensional languages; *J. Symb. Logic,* **13** (1948), p. 140.

— The finite representations of S5; *Methodos* (Milan), **1** (1949), pp. 217-219.

— A syntactical characterization of S5; *J. Symb. Logic* **14** (1949), pp. 173-174.

— The representations of S5; *J. Symb. Logic,* **21** (1956), pp. 257-260.

— The philosophical significance of modal logic; *Mind,* n.s. **69** (1960), pp. 466-485.

Beth, Evert Willem

Le système S4 et la topologie; *Rapport CETIS n° 26* (août 1961), Rapport n° 13, contract 010-60-12, 15, novembre 1961, pp. 143-147.

— See also **Nieland**.

Blanché, Robert

Quantity, modality and other kindred systems of categories; *Mind,* n.s. **61** (1952), pp. 369-375.

Bochenski, Innocentius M.

Notes historiques sur les propositions modales; *Revue des Sciences Philosophiques et Théologiques,* **26** (1937), pp. 673-692.

— Sancti Thomae Aquinatis de modalibus opusculum et doctrina; *Angelicum,* **17** (1940), pp. 180-218.

Boll, Marcel, et **Reinhardt,** Jacques

A propos des logiques polyvalentes: les modalités et la vraisemblance; *Revue Philos. de la France et de l'Étranger,* **140** (1950), pp. 143-179.

— Une interprétation des modalités aristotéliciennes; *Congrès International de Philosophie des Sciences, Paris 1949,* vol. **2** (1951), pp. 15-18.

Borkowski, L.

O terminach modalnych (On modal terms); *Studia Logica,* **7** (1958), pp. 7-37 (English summary, pp. 40-42).

Bradley, R. D.

Must the future be what it is going to be ?; *Mind,* n. s. **68** (1959), pp. 193-208.

Bronstein, D. J.

Necessity, implication and definition, in *Harvard University, Graduate School of Arts and Sciences, Summaries of theses accepted in partial fulfillment of the requirements for the degree of Doctor in Philosophy 1933* (1934), pp. 320-324.

Bronstein, D. J., and **Tarter,** Harry

Review of Lewis and Langford's «*Symbolic Logic*»; *The Philosophical Review,* **43** (1934), pp. 305-309.

— Possibility and implication; a reply; *ibidem,* **44** (1935), pp. 69-71.

Brugger, Walter

Die Modalität einfacher Aussage-Verbindungen; *Scholastik,* **47** (1942), pp. 217-235.

Bull, R. A.

Modal logics with intuitionist propositional fragments, (abstract); *J. Symb. Logic,* **28** (1963), pp. 262-263 (*).

Carnap, Rudolf

Review of **Lewis** and **Langford's** «*Symbolic Logic*»; *Erkenntnis,* **4** (1934), pp. 65-66.

— Modalities and quantifications; *J .Symb. Logic,* **11** (1946), pp. 33-64.

— *Meaning and necessity, a study in semantics and modal logic,* Chicago, The University of Chicago Press, 1947, VII-210 pp.

Castañeda, Hector Neri

Imperatives and deontic logic; *Analysis,* **19** (1958), pp. 42-48.

— The logic of obligation; *Philosophical Studies,* **10** (1959), pp. 17-22.

— Obligation and modal logic; *Logique et Analyse,* **3** (1960), pp. 40-48.

Caton, Charles E.

A stipulation of a modal propositional calculus in terms of modalized truth-values; *Notre Dame Journal of Formal Logic,* **4** (1963), pp. 224-226 (*).

Cauchy, Venant

Notes on the modal syllogism; *The Modern Schoolman,* **34** (1957), pp. 121-130.

Church, Alonzo

A formulation of the logic of sense and denotation; in *Structure, Method and Meaning*; *Essays in Honor of H. M.*

(*) Added in proof.

Sheffer, ed. **Henle** P, **Kallen**, H. M. and **Langer**, S. K., New York, 1951, pp. 3-24.

Churchman, C. West

On finite and infinite modal systems; *J. Symb. Logic,* **3** (1938), pp. 77-82.

Curry, Haskell Brooks

A theory of formal deducibility (Notre Dame Mathematical Lectures, n° 6). Notre Dame (Indiana), 1950, VII-126 pp.

— The elimination theorem when modality is present; *J. Symb. Logic,* **17** (1952), pp. 249-265.

— *Foundations of mathematical logic.* New York, McGraw-Hill Book Cy, 1963, XII-408 pp.

Darbon, André

Les catégories de la modalité (édition posthume d'un cours donné en 1940-41). Paris, Presses Universitaires de France, 1956, VIII-165 pp.

Davis, Chandler

Lattices and modal operators; Harvard Doctoral Thesis, 1950.

— Modal operators, equivalence relations, and projective algebras; *American Journal of Mathematics,* **76** (1954), pp. 747-762.

Dawson, Edward E.

A model for deontic logic; *Analysis,* **19** (1958-59), pp. 73-78.

Destouches, Jean-Louis

Intervention d'une logique de modalité dans une théorie physique; *Synthese* (Bussum), *7* (1948-9), pp. 411-417.

Diamond, A. H., and **McKinsey,** J. C.C.

Algebras and their subalgebras; *Bullet. of the American Mathematical Society,* **53** (1947), pp. 959-962.

Drake, Frank R.

'Model inference' in modal systems (Abstract), *J. Symb. Logic,* **27** (1962), p. 377.

— A decision procedure for Prior's system D (Abstract); *ibidem,* **27** (1962), pp. 377-378.

— On McKinsey's syntactical characterizations of systems of modal logic; *ibidem,* **27** (1962), pp. 400-406.

Dugundji, James

Note on a property of matrices for Lewis and Langford's calculi of propositions; *J. Symb. Logic,* **5** (1940), pp. 150-151.

Dummett, Michael Anthony Eardly, and **Lemmon,** Edward John

Modal logics between S4 and S5; *Zeitsch. f. mathemat. Logik and Grundlagen der Mathematik,* **3** (1959), pp. 250-264.

Ducan-Jones, A. E.

Is strict implication the same as entailment ?; *Analysis,* **2** (1934-5), pp. 70-78.

Emch, A. F.

Implication and deducibility; *J. Symb. Logic,* **1** (1936), pp. 26-35 and p. 58.

— Deducibility with respect to necessary and impossible propositions; *J. Symb. Logic,* **2** (1937), pp. 78-81.

Emde, G.

Kriterien für die Herleitbarkeit in Modalitätenstrukturen; *Archiv f. math. Logik und Grundlagenforschung,* **3** (1958), pp. 79-111.

Février-Destouches, Paulette

Applications des logiques modales en physique quantique; *Theoria* (Madrid), **1** (1952), pp. 167-169.

Feys, Robert

— Les logiques nouvelles des modalités; *Revue Néoscolastique de Philosophie,* **40** (1937), pp. 517-553 and **41** (1938), pp. 217-252.

— Les systèmes formalisés des modalités aristotéliciennes; *Revue Philosophique de Louvain,* **48** (1950), pp. 478-509.

— Oudere en nieuwe modaliteitenlogica; *Handelingen van the XIXe Vlaamse Filologencongres,* Brussel, 1951, pp. 284-289.

— Les logiques modales (Thèmes de discussion); *Theoria* (Madrid), **1** (1952), pp. 163-166.

— A simplified proof of the reduction of all modalities to

42 in S3; *Boletin de la Soc. Matematica Mexicana,* **10** (1953), pp. 53-57.
— Una demonstración simplificada de la reducción de todas les modalidades a 42 en S3 (Spanish translation ot the preceding): *Memoria del Congresso Cientifico Mexicano, I, Ciencias fisicas y matematicas,* Universidad Nacional Autónomo de Mexico, Mexico, 1953, pp. 81-89.
— Expression modale du «devoir-être» (Abstract from the Amsterdam Meeting of the Assoc. f. Symb. Logic); *J. Symb. Logic,* **20** (1955), pp. 91-92.
— Modèles à variables de différentes sortes pour les logiques modales M″ ou S5; in «*The Concept and the Role of the Model in Mathematics and Natural and Social Sciences*», ed. by B. K. **Kazemier** and D. **Vuysje**. (Proc. of the Colloquium organ. at Utrecht, jan. 1960), Dordrecht, Reidel, 1961, pp. 58-72.

Fisher, Mark
A system of deontic-alethic modal logic; *Mind,* n.s. **71** (1962), pp. 231-236.

Fitch, Frederic Brenton
Note on Leo Abraham's «transformations» of strict implication; *The Monist,* **13** (1933), pp. 297-298.
— Modal functions in two-valued logic; *J. Symb. Logic,* **2** (1937), pp. 125-128.
— Note on modal functions; *ibidem,* 4 (1939), pp. 115-116.
— Corrections to two papers on modal logic (concern the foregoing); *ibidem,* **13** (1948), pp. 38-39.
— Intuitionistic modal logic with quantifiers; *Portugaliae Mathematica,* **7** (1948, ed. 1949), pp. 113-118.
— The problem of the Morning Star and the Evening Star; *Philosophy of Science,* **16** (1949), pp. 137-141.

Freudenthal, Hans
Zur intuitionistischen Deutung logischer Formeln; *Composito Mathematica,* **4** (1936), pp. 112-116.

Geach, Peter Thomas
Imperative and deontic logic; *Analysis,* **18** (1958), pp. 49-56.

Goedel, Kurt

Eine Interpretation des intuitionistischer Aussagenkalküls; *Ergebnisse eines mathematisches Kolloquiums,* **4** (1933), pp. 34-40.

Goetlind, E.

A system of postulates for Lewis's calculus S1; *Norsk Matematisk Tidsskrift,* **32** (1950), pp. 89-92.

Guillaume, Marcel

Rapports entre calculs propositionnels modaux et topologie impliqués par certaines extensions de la méthode des tableaux sémantiques. Système de Feys-von Wright; *Comptes rendus des Séances de l'Académie des Sciences* (Paris), vol. **246** (1958), pp. 1140-1142.

— Rapports entre calculs propositionnels modaux et topologie impliqués par certaines extensions de la méthode des tableaux sémantiques. Système S4 de Lewis; *ibidem,* **246** (1958), pp. 2207-2210.

— Rapports entre calculs propositionnels modaux et topologie impliqués par certaines extensions de la méthode des tableaux sémantiques. Système S5 de Lewis; *ibidem,* **247** (1958), pp. 1282-1283.

Hacking, Jan

What is strict implication ? *J. Symb. Logic,* **28** (1963), pp. 51-71 (1).

Halldén, Sören

A note concerning the paradoxes of strict implication and Lewis's system S1; *J. Symb. Logic,* **13** (1948), pp. 138-139.

— A question concerning a logical calculus related to Lewis's system of strict implication, which is of special interest for the study of entailment; *Theoria,* **14** (1948), pp. 265-269.

— Results concerning the decision problem of Lewis's calsuli S3 and S6; *J. Symb. Logic,* **14** (1949), pp. 230-236.

— On the decision problem of Lewis's calculus S5; *Norsk Matematisk Tidsskrift,* **31** (1949), pp. 89-94.

— *Nägra resultat i modal logic* [Some results in modal lo-

(1) Added in proof.

gic] (Dissertation). Uppsala, Almquist & Wiksells boktryckeri A.B., 1950, 34 pp.

— A reduction fo the primitive symbols of the Lewis's calculi; *Portugaliae Mathematica,* **8** (1949, publ. 1950), pp. 85-88.

— On the semantic non-completeness of certain Lewis calculi; *J .Symb. Logic,* **16** (1951), pp. 127-129.

— A pragmatic approach to modal theory; *Acta Philosophica Fennica,* fasc. **16** (1963), pp. 53-64.

Hamblin, C. L.

Review of **Prior**'s «*Time and Modality*»; *Australasian Journal of Philosophy,* **36** (1958), pp. 232-234.

Hanson, Norwood Russell

It's actual, so it's possible; *Philosophical Studies,* **10** (1959), pp. 69-80.

Harre, R.

Modal expressions in ordinary and technical language; *Australasian Journal of Philosophy,* **37** (1959), pp. 41-56.

Heath, A. E.

Review of **Lewis**'s «*A Survey of Symbolic Logic*»; *Scientia,* **27** (1929), pp. 399-400.

Hempel, Carl G.

Review of Oskar **Becker**'s «*Zur Logik der Modalitäten*»; *Jahrb. Fortschr. Math.,* **50** (for 1930, publ. 1932-33), pp. 37-39.

Henderson, G. P.

Is there only one correct system of modal logic ?; *Aristotelian Society Suppl.,* vol. **33** (1959), pp. 41-56.

Hintikka, Kaarlo Jaakko Juhani

An application of logic to algebra, *Mathematica Scandinavica,* **2** (1954), pp. 243-246.

— Modality as referential multiplicity; *Ajatus* (Helsinki), **20** (1957), pp. 49-64.

— Necessity, universality and time in Aristotle; *ibidem,* **20** (1957), pp. 65-90.

— Quantifiers in deontic logic; *Societas Scientiarum Fennica, Commentationes Humanarum Litterarum,* **23** (1957), pp. 2-23.

— An Aristotelian Dilemma; *Ajatus,* **21** (1959), pp. 87-92.

— Modality and quantification; *Theoria* (Lund), **27** (1961), pp. 110-128.

— The Modes of modality; *Acta Philosophica Fennica* fasc. **16** (1963), pp. 65-82.

Huntington, E. V.

Independent postulates relates to C. I. Lewis's theory of strict implication; *Mind,* n.s. **43** (1934), pp. 181-198.

— Postulates for assertion, conjunction, negation and equality; *Proc. of the Americ. Acad. of Arts and Sciences,* **72** (1937), pp. 1-44.

Ishimoto, Arata

A set of axioms of the modal propositional calculus equivalent to S3; *The Science of Thought* (Tokyo), **1** (1954), pp. 1-11.

— A note on the paper «A set of axioms of the modal propositional calculus equivalent to S3»; *ibidem,* **2** (1956), pp. 69-72.

— A formulation of the modal propositional calculus equivalent to S4; *ibidem,* **2** (1956), pp. 73-82.

Itoh, Makoto

Yoso ronrigaku no kenkyu [A study of modal logic]; *Kisokagaku,* vol. 3, n° 7 (1949), pp. 434-440.

— A lattice-theoretic research on modal propositional calculus and monadic predicate calculus (in Japanese), *Kagaku-Kisoron-Kenkyu,* vol. **1** (1955), pp. 142-125 and 162-167 and vol. **2** (1956), pp. 258-265.

— On the relation between the modal sentential logic and the monadic predicate calculus (in Japanese); *Journal of the Japanese Association for Philosophy of Science,* **3** (1954), pp. 142-145, **4** (1955), pp. 162-167, and **6** (1956), pp. 258-265.

Jaskowski, Stanislaw

On the modal and causal functions in symbolic logic; *Studia Philosophica* (Poznan), **4** (1949-50), pp. 71-92.

Jónsson, Bjarni, and **Tarski,** Alfred

Boolean Algebras with operators; *American Journal of*

Mathematics, **73** (1951), pp. 891-939 and **74** (1952), pp. 127-162.

Juhos, Béla
Ein- und zweistellige Modalitäten; *Methodos,* **6** (1954), pp. 69-83.

Kalinowski, Jerzy
Teoria zdan normatywnych. - Théorie des propositions normatives (French translation); *Studia Logica* (Warsaw), **1** (1953), pp. 113-146 and 147-182.
— Errata, *ibidem,* pp. 299-300.

Kanger, Stig Gustav
Provability in logic (*Acta Universitatis Stockholmiensis, Stockholm Studies in Philosophy,* **1**); Stockholm, Almqvist & Wiksell, 1957, 47 pp.
— The Morning Star paradox; *Theoria (*Lund), **23** (1957), pp. 1-11.
— A note on quantification and modalities; *ibidem,* **23** (1957), pp. 133-134.
— On the characterization of modalities; *ibidem,* **23** (1957), pp. 152-155.

Katsoff, Louis O.
Modality and probability; *The Philosophical Review,* **46** (1937), pp. 78-85.

Kneale, William Calvert
Modality de dicto and de re; in *Logic, Methodology and Philosophy of Science,* Proceedings of the 1960 International Congress Stanford, 1960, pp. 622-633.

Kripke, Saul Aaron
A completeness theorem in modal logic; *J. Symb. Logic,* **24** (1959), pp. 1-14.
— Semantic analysis of modal logic (Abstract for the 24-th Meeting of the Association for Symb. Logic 1959), *ibidem* **24** (1959), pp. 323-324.
— The problem of entailment (Abstract); *ibidem,* **24** (1959), p. 324.
— The undecidability of monadic modal quantification theory; *Zeitschr. f. mathematische Logik und Grundlagen der Mathematik,* **8** (1962), pp. 113-116.

— Semantical analysis of modal logic I. Normal propositional calculi; *Ibidem,* **9** (1963), pp. 67-96.
— Semantical considerations on modal logics *Acta Philosophica Fennica*; fasc. **16** (1963), pp. 83-94.

Kubinski, Tadeusz
O pewnej metodzie tworzenia logic modalnyk (On a method of constructing modal logics). (Polish, with English and Russian summaries); *Studia Logica* (Warsaw), **4** (1946), pp. 212-240.

Langford, Cooper Harold. See at **Lewis,** I. C.

Lemmon, Edward John
Alternative postulate sets for Lewis's S5; *J. Symb. Logic,* **21** (1946), pp. 347-349.
— New Foundations for Lewis modal systems; *ibidem,* **22** (1957), pp. 176-186.
— Quantifiers and modal operators; *Proceedings of the Aristotelian Society,* **58** (1947-58), pp. 244-268.
— Is there only correct system of modal logic ? *Aristotelian Society Suppl.* **33** (1959), pp. 23-40.
— Quantified S4 and the Barcan formula (Abstract for the XXVI-th Meeting of the Association for Symbolic Logic 1961); *J. Symb. Logic,* **24** (1960), pp. 391-392.
— An extension algebra and the modal system T; *Notre Dame Journal of Formal Logic,* **1** (1960), pp. 2-12.
— A theory of attributes based on modal logic; *Acta Philosophica Fennica,* fasc. **16** (1963), pp. 95-122.
— See also at **Dummett,** M. A. E.

Lemmon, E. J., **Meredith,** C. A., **Meredith,** D., **Prior,** A. N., and **Thomas,** I.
Calculi of pure strict implication (roneotyped), 1957, 22 p.

Leonard, Henry S.
Two-valued truth-tables for modal functions; in *Structure, Method and Meaning. Essays in honor of Henry M. Sheffer,* New York, Liberal Arts, 1949, pp. 42-67.

Lewis, Clarence Irving
Implication and the algebra of logic; *Mind,* n.s. **21** (1912), pp. 522-531.

— Interesting theorems in symbolic logic; *Journal of Philosophy,* **10** (1913), pp. 239-242.
— A new algebra of strict implication; *Mind,* n.s. **23** (1914), pp. 240-247.
— The matrix algebra for implication; *Journal of Philosophy,* **11** (1914), pp. 589-600.
— *A Survey of symbolic logic.* Berkeley, University of California Press, 1918, VI-409 pp.
— Strict implication. An emendation; *Journal of Philosophy,* **17** (1920), pp. 300-202.
— Emch's calculus and strict implication; *J. Symb. Logic,* **1** (1936), pp. 77-86.
— Notes on the logic of intension; in *Structure, Method and Meaning. Essays in honor of Henry M. Sheffer,* New-York, Liberal Arts, 1941, pp. 25-34.

Lewis, Clarence Irving, and **Langford,** Cooper Harold
Symbolic Logic, New York, 1932, XI-506 pp.
— *Id.,* Second edition, New York, Dover Publications, 1959 (with Appendix incorporating some results of Parry). XI-506 pp.

Löb, M. H.
Extensional interpretation of modality (Abstract); *J. Symb. Logic,* **27** (1962), pp. 381-382.

Lorenzen, Paul
Zur Begründung der Modallogik; *Archiv. f. Mathematische Logik und Grundlagenforschung,* **2** (1954), pp.15-28 (Also in *Archiv für Philosophie,* **5** (1954), pp.95-108.)

Lukasiewicz, Jan
A system of modal logic; *The Journal of Computing Systems,* **1** (1953), pp. 111-149.
— A system of modal logic; *Actes du XIe Congrès International de Philosophie, Bruxelles 1953,* (Colloque de Logique), Amsterdam, North-Holland, 1953, vol. **14**, pp. 82-87.
— Arithmetic and modal logic; *The Journal of Computing Systems,* **1** (1953), pp. 213-219.
— On a controversial problem of Aristotle's modal syllogistic; *Dominican Studies,* **7** (1954), pp. 114-123.

— *Aristotle's syllogistic from the standpoint of modern formal logic. Second edition enlarged.* Oxford, Clarendon Press, 1957, XV-222 pp.

McCall, Storrs

Aristotle's modal syllogisms. Amsterdam, North-Holland Publ. Cy, 1963, 100 pp.

McKinsey, John Charles Chinoweth

A note on Bronstein's and Tarter's definition of strict implication; The *Philosophical Review,* **43** (1934), pp. 518-520.

— A solution of the decision problem for the Lewis calculus S2 (Extract for the 6th Meeting of the Ass. for Symb. Logic, Philadelphia, 1940), *J. Symb. Logic,* **5** (1940), p. 39.

— Proof that there are infinitely many modalities in Lewis's system S2; *ibidem,* **5** (1940), pp. 110-112.

— A correction to **Lewis** and **Langford**'s *Symbolic Logic*; *ibidem,* **5** (1940), p. 149.

— A solution of the decision problem for the Lewis system S2 and S4 with an application to topology; *ibidem,* **6** (1941), pp. 117-134.

— On the number of complete extensions of the Lewis systems of sentential calculus; *ibidem,* **9** (1944), pp. 41-45.

— On the syntactical construction of systems of modal logic; *ibidem,* **10** (1945), pp. 83-96.

— Construction of modal logic; *Proceedings of the Tenth International Congress of Philosophy, Amsterdam 1948,* Amsterdam, North-Holland, 1953, p. 740.

— Systems of modal logic which are not unreasonable in the sense of Halldén; *J .Symb. Logic,* **18** (1953), pp. 109-113.

— See also at **Diamond**, A. H.

McKinsey, J. C. C., and **Tarski,** Alfred

The algebra of topology; *Annuals of Mathematics,* **45** (1944), pp. 141-191.

— Some theorems about sentential calculi of Lewis and Heyting; *J. Symb. Logic,* **13** (1948), pp. 1-15.

Margenau, Henry
Probability, many-valued logics, and physics; *Philosophy of Science,* **6** (1939), pp. 65-87.
Matsumoto, Kazuo
Sur la structure concernant la logique moderne; *Journal of the Osaka Institute of Science and Technology, The Kinki University, Part I, Math. and Phys.,* **2** (1950), pp. 67-78.
— On a lattice relating to the intuitionistic logic; *ibidem,* **2** (1950), pp. 97-107.
— Reduction theorem in Lewis's sentential calculi; *Mathematica Japonicae,* **3** (1955), pp. 133-135.
— Decision procedure for modal sentential calculus S3; *Osaka Mathematical Journal,* **12** (1960), pp. 167-175.
Matsumoto, Kazuo, **Ohnishi,** M., und **Ridder,** J.
Die Gentzenschen Schlussverfahren in modalen Aussagenlogiken. I*; *Koninklijke Nederlandsche Akademie van Wetenschappen, Proceedings of the Section of Sciences,* **58**.
(Also *Indagationes Mathematica,* **17** (1955), pp. 481-491.
— See also at **Ohnishi,** M.
Meredith, Carew Arthur
Contributions to the investigation of pure strict implication (roneotyped). 1956, 26 pp.
— *Interpretations of different modal logics in the «property calculus»*; August 1956, recorded and expanded by A. N. Prior, mimeographed, Dept. of Philosophy, University of Canterbury.
— See also at **Lemmon,** E. J.
Meredith, D. See at **Lemmon,** E. J.
Moisil, Grigore Constantin
Sur la théorie classique de la modalité des jugements; *Annales Scientifiques de l'Université de Jassy,* **40** (1938), pp. 235-240.
— Remarques sur la logique modale du concept, *Annales de l'Académie Roumaine, Mémoires de la section scientifique,* sér. 3, **16** (1941), pp. 975-1012.

— Logique modale; *Disquisitiones mathematicae et physicae* (Bucharest), **2** (1942), pp. 3-98.

— Les logiques non-Chrysippiennes et leur applications, *Acta Philosophica Fennica,* **16** (1963), pp. 137-152.

Montague, Richard

Syntactical treatments of modality with corollaries on reflexion principles and finite axiomatizability; *Acta Philosophica Fennica,* fasc. **16** (1963), pp. 153-168.

Monteiro, Antonio

Normalidad en los algebras de Heyting monadicas, *Actas de las X Jornadas Matemáticas Argentinas,* 1957, pp. 50-51.

— Algebras monádicas, *Atas do Secundo Colóquio Brasiliero de Matematica,* 1960, pp. 33-52.

More, Trenchard, Jr.

Negated implicational lattice A′3; *J. Symb. Logic,* **24** (1959), p. 320.

Myhill, John R.

On the interpretation of the sign '⊃'; *J. Symb. Logic,* **18** (1953), pp. 60-62.

— Problems arising in the formalization of intensional logic; *Logique et Analyse,* **1** (1958), pp. 74-83.

Nakumura, A.

On the infinitely many-valued treshold logics and on Wright's system M″; *Zeitsch. f. Math. Logik u. Grundlag.,* **8** (1962), pp. 147-164.

Nelson, Everett J.

Intentional relations; *Mind,* n.s. **39** (1940), pp. 440-453.

Nieland, J. J. F.

Construction sémantique du système S5. Implication stricte; *Rapport* CETIS, n° 26, août 1961, rapport n° 7, contrat 010-60-12, 1 octobre 1961, pp. 75-77.

Nieland, J. J. F. et **Beth,** E. W.

Construction sémantique du système S4; *ibidem,* rapport n° 6, pp. 66-74.

— Construction sémantique du système S5. Implication et nécessité; *ibidem,* rapport n° 2, pp. 21-30.

Ohnishi, Masao.
Gentzen decision procedures for Lewis's systems S2 and S3; *Osaka Mathematical Journal,* **13** (1961), pp.125-137 (*).

Ohnishi, Masao, and **Matsumoto,** Kazuo.
Gentzen method in modal calculi, I; *Osaka Mathematical Journal,* **9** (1957), pp. 113-130.
— Gentzen method in modal calculi, II; *ibidem,* **11** (1959), pp. 115-120.
— A system for strict implication; *Annals of the Japan Association for Philosophy of Science,* **2** (1964), pp. 183-188 (*).
— See also at **Matsumoto,** K.

Pap, Arthur
Strict implication, entailment, and modal iteration; *The Philosophical Review,* **64** (1955), pp. 604-613.

Parry, William Tuthill
Ein Axiomensystem für eine neue Art von Implikationen; *Ergebnisse eines mathematisches Kolloquium,* Heft **4** (1931-2, publ. 1933), pp. 5-6.
— Zum Lewisschen Aussagenkalkül; *ibidem,* pp. 15-16.
— Implication; *Harvard University, Graduate School of Arts and Sciences, Summaries of theses accepted in partial fulfilment of the requirements of Doctor in Philosophy, 1932* (pp. 332-335).
— The postulates for «strict implication»; *Mind,* n.s. **43** (1934), pp. 78-80.
— Modalities in the Survey system of strict implication; *J. Symb. Logic,* **4** (1959), pp. 137-154.

Pogorzhelski, W., and **Slupecki,** Jerzy
Podstawowe wlasnosci systemow dedukeyjlych dedukeyinych logikach. I. (Basic properties of deductive systems based on non-classical logics); *Studia Logica* (Poznan), **9** (1960), pp. 163-176.

Poirier, René
Logique et modalité du point de vue organique et physique. (*Actualités scientifiques et industrielles,* n° 1163). Paris, Hermann & Cie, 1952, 113 pp.

(*) Added in proof.

Poliferno, Mario J.

Decision algorithm for some functional calculi with modality; *Logique et Analyse,* **4** (1961), pp. 138-153.

— Correction to a paper on modal logic; *Logique et Analyse,* **7**, n° 25-26 (1964), pp. 32-33.

Porte, Jean

Recherches sur les logiques modales; in *Le raisonnement en mathématiques et en sciences expérimentales, Colloques internationaux de la Recherche Scientifique, n° 70.* Paris, Éditions du Centre National de la Recherche Scientifique, 1958, pp. 117-126.

— The Ω-system and the Ł-system of modal logics (Forthcoming in *Acta Philosophica Fennica*).

Prior, Arthur Norman

In what sense is modal logic many-valued ?; *Analysis* (Oxford), **12** (1952), pp. 138-143.

— Modality de dicto and modality de re; *Theoria* (Lund), **18** (1952), pp. 174-180.

— On propositions neither necessary nor impossible; *J. Symb. Logic,* **18** (1953), pp. 105-108.

— Three-valued logic and future contingents; *The philosophical Quarterly* (St Andrews), **3** (1953), pp. 317-326.

— The paradoxes of derived obligation; *Mind,* n.s. **63** (1954), pp. 64-65.

— Many-valued and modal systems. An intuitive approach; *The Philosophical Review,* **63** (1954), pp. 626-630.

— The interpretation of two systems of modal logic, *The Journal of Computing Systems,* **4** (1954), pp. 201-208.

— Diodorian modalities, *The Philosophical Quarterly* (St Andrews), **5** (1955), pp. 205-213.

— Modality and quantification in S5, *J. Symb. Logic,* **21** (1955), pp. 60-62.

— *Time and modality* (Being the John Locke lectures for 1955-6 delivered in the University of Oxford). London, Oxford University Press, 1957, IX-148 pp.

— The necessary and the possible. The first of three talks on «The Logic game»; *The Listener,* **57** (1957), pp. 627-628.

— Diodorus and modal logic. A correction; *The Philosophical Quarterly* (St Andrews), **8** (1958), pp. 226-230. (A correction to «Diodoran modalities», 1955.)
— The syntax of time-distinctions; *Franciscan Studies,* **18** (1958), pp. 105-120.
— Notes on a group of modal systems; *Logique et Analyse,* **2** (1959), pp. 122-127.
— Some axiom-pairs for material and strict implication, *Zeitsch. f. math. Logik u. Grundlagen d. Math.,* **7** (1961), pp. 61-65.
— Quantification and Ł-modality; *Notre Dame Journal of Formal Logic,* **3** (1962), pp. 142-147.
— Possible worlds; *The Philosophical Quarterly* (St Andrews), **12** (1962), pp. 36-43.
— Tense-logic and the continuity of time; *Studia Logica* (Poznan), **13** (1962), pp. 133-151.
— The formalities of Omniscience; *Philosophy,* **37** (1962), pp. 114-129.
— The theory of implication; *Zeitsch. f. math. Logik und Grundlagen der Math.,* **9** (1963), pp. 1-6.
— See also at **Lemmon,** E. J.

Quine, William van Orman
Notes on existence and necessity; *Journal of Philosophy,* **40** (1943), pp. 113-127.
— The problem of interpreting modal logic; *J. Symb. Logic,* **12** (1947), pp. 43-48.
— Three grades of modal involvement; *Actes du XIe Congrès International de Philosophie, Bruxelles 1953,* Amsterdam, 1953, vol. **14**, pp. 65-81.
— Reference and modality. In author's book: *From a Logical Point of View,* Cambridge (Mass.), Harvard University Press, 1953, pp. 139-159.
— Comment on the paper of **Barcan-Marcus** R., Modal Logics I: Modalities and intensional languages; in *Boston Studies in the Philosophy of Science,* Dordrecht, Reidel, 1963, pp. 97-104.

Rasiowa, Helena
Algebraic treatment of the functional calculi of Heyting

and Lewis; *Fundamenta mathematicae,* **38** (1951, publ. 1952), pp. 99-126.
— On modal theories; *Acta Philosophica Fennica,* fasc. 16 (1963), pp. 201-214.

Reinhardt, Jacques. See at **Boll,** M.

Rescher, Nicholas
A contribution to modal logic; *The Review of Metaphysics,* **12** (1958), pp. 186-189.
— An axiom system for deontic logic; *Philosophical Studies,* **9** (1958), pp. 24-30.
— On the formalization of two modal theses; *Notre Dame Journal of Formal Logic,* **1** (1961), pp. 154-157.
— A probabilistic approach to modal logic; *Acta Philosophica Fennica,* fasc. **16** (1963), pp. 215-226.
— A quantificational treatment of modality; *Logique et Analyse,* **7**, n° 25-26 (1964), pp. 34-42.
— Aristotle's theory of modal syllogisms and its interpretation; in *The Critical Approach to Science and Philosophy; Essays in honor of Karl Popper,* ed. M. **Bunge**, Glencoe (Ill.) 1964, pp. 152-177 (*).

Ridder, J.
Formalistische Betrachtungen über intuitionistische und verwandte logische Systeme; *Koninklijke Nederlandsche Akademie van Wetenschappen. Proceedings of the Section of Sciences,* **53** (1950), pp. 327-336; 446-455; 787-799; 1375-1389; and **54** (1951), pp. 94-105; 169-177; 226-236. (Also in *Indagationes Mathematicae,* **12** (1950), pp. 75-84; 98-107; 231-243; 445-459; and **13** (1951), pp. 94-105; 169-177; 226-236).
— Ueber modale Aussagenlogiken und ihren Zusammenhang mit Strukturen; *ibidem,* 55 (1952) or *Indagationes Mathematicae,* **14** (1952), and **56** (1953), pp. 213-223; 459-467; **15** (1953), pp. 1-11; 99-110, and **16** (1954), pp. 117-128, 389-396.
— Die Gentzensschen Schlussverfahren in modalen Aussagenlogiken, I; *Indagationes Mathematicae,* **17** (1955), pp. 163-276.

(*) Added in proof.

— Sie also at M. **Matsumoto,** G.

Robinson, Abraham

Introduction to Modal Theory and to the Metamathematics of Algebra, Amsterdam, North-Holland Publishing Company, 1963, 300 pp. *

Rose, Alan

Self-dual primitives for modal logic; *Mathematische Annalen,* **125** (1952-3), pp. 284-286.

— A simplified self *m*-al set of primitive functors for the *m*-valued propositional calculus; *Zeitsch. f. math. Logik u. Grundl. d. Math.,* **8** (1962), pp. 257-266.

Ross, James F.

Does «*x* is possible» ever yield «*x* exists» ?; *Theoria* (Lund), **28** (1962), pp. 173-195.

Rubin, Jean E.

Remarks about a closure algebra in which closed elements are open; *Proceedings of the Americ. Math. Soc.,* **7** (1956), pp. 30-34.

— Bi-modal logic, double-closure algebras, and Hilbert space; *Zeitsch. f. math. Log. u. Grundl. d. Math.;* **8** (1962), pp. 305-322.

Sanchez-Mazas, Miguel

Un intento de expressión matematica de la lógica modal clásica: El grupo de matrices modales y el sistema de coordenadas modales; *Theoria* (Madrid), **1** (1952), pp. 188-192.

Schmidt, Arnold

Systematische Basisreduktion der Modalitäten bei Idempotenz der positiven Grundmodalitäten; *Mathematische Annalen,* **122** (1950), pp. 71-89.

— Idempotente implikative Modalitätenstrukturen (Abstract for the Amsterdam Meeting of the Assoc. f. Symb. Logic, Sept. 1954); *J. Symb. Logic,* **20** (1955), p. 92.

— Ein aussagenlogischer Zugang den Modalitäten der strikten Logik; *Proceedings of the International Congress of Mathematicians, Amsterdam 1954,* **2,** pp. 407-408.

(*) Added in proof.

— Das fundamentale Implikationensystem einer implikativen Modalitätenstruktur mit idempotenter Möglichkeit; *Archiv f. math. Logik und Grundlagenforschung,* **2** (1956), pp. 33-54.

— Die Gesamtheit der idempotenten implikativen Modalitätenstrukturen; *ibidem,* **3** (1957), pp. 29-49.

— Ueber einige neuere Untersuchungen zur Modalitätenlogik; in *Logica Studia Paul Bernays Dedicata,* Neuchâtel, 1959, pp. 204-217.
(Also in *Dialectica,* **12** (1958), pp. 408-421).

Scholz, Heinrich

Review of L. **Baudry's** «*La querelle des futurs contingents (Louvain 1465-1475)*»; Paris, 1950, *Deutsche Literaturzeitung,* **74** (1953), pp. 67-72.

Scroggs, Schiller Joe

Extensions of the Lewis system S 5; *J. Symb. Logic,* **16** (1951), pp. 112-120.

Shaw-Kwei, Moh

The deduction theorems and two new logical systems; *Methodes,* **2** (1950), pp. 56-75.

— Chü-yow yow-ch'ung koh moh-t'ai-tzu ti moh-t'ai hsi-t'ung. (Modal systems with a finite number of modalities); *Acta Mathematica Sinica,* **7** (1957), pp. 1-27 (English summary reprinted in *Mathematical Review,* **21** (1960), p. 2).

— Modal systems with a finite number of modalities (Revised English translation of the preceding); *Scientia Sinica,* **7** (1958), pp. 388-412.

Simons, Leo

New axiomatizations of S3 and S4; *J. Symb. Logic,* **18** (1953), pp. 309-316.

— A reduction in the number of independent axiom schemata for S4; *Notre Dame Journal of Formal Logic,* **3** (1962), pp. 256-258.

Slupecki, Jersy. See at **Pogorzhelski,** W.

Smiley, Timothy John

Natural systems of logic, Ph. D. Thesis, University of Cambridge (1956). (Refered to by Drake, in *J. Symb. Logic,* **27** (1962), p. 406.)

— On Łukasiewicz Ł-modal systems; *Notre Dame Journal of Formal Logic,* **2** (1961), pp. 149-153.
— Entailment and deducibility; *Proc. of the Aristotelian Society,* **59** (1959), pp. 223-254.
— Relative necessity (Forthcoming in *J. Symb. Logic*).

Smith, H. B.
Review of **Lewis** and **Langford**'s «*Symbolic Logic*»; *Journal of Philosophy,* **30** (1933), pp. 302-360.
— Review of **Lewis** and **Langford**'s «*Symbolic Logic*»; *Philosophy of Science,* **1** (1934), pp. 239-246.
— Abstract logic or the science of modality; *ibidem,* **1** (1934), pp. 369-397.
— The algebra of propositions; *ibidem,* **3** (1936), pp. 551-578.
— Modal logic — a revision; *ibidem,* **4** (1937), pp. 383-384.

Smullyan, Arthur F.
Entailment-schemata and modal function (Extract for the 6-th Meeting of the Assoc. f. Symb. Logic, Philadelphia, 1940); *J. Symb. Logic,* **5** (1940), p. 40.
— Modality and description; *ibidem,* **13** (1948), pp. 31-37.

Sobocinski, Bolesław
Note on a modal system of Feys-von Wright; *The Journal of Computing Systems,* **1** (1953), pp. 171-178.
— A contribution to the axiomatization of Lewis's System S5; *The Notre Dame Journal of Formal Logic*; **3** (1962), pp. 59-60.
— A note on the regular and irregular modal systems of Lewis; *ibidem,* **3** (1962), pp. 109-113.
— On the generalized Brouwerian axioms; *ibidem,* **3** (1962). pp. 123-128.
— An axiom-system for {K,N}-propositional calculus related to Simons's axiomatization of S3; *ibidem,* **3** (1962), pp. 206-208.
— A note on modal systems; *ibidem,* **4** (1963), pp. 155-157. (*)

Sugihara, Takeo
The axiomatization of the Aristotelian modal logic; *Memoirs of the Liberal Arts College, Fukui University,* **2** (1953), pp. 53-60.

(*) Added in proof.

— Strict implication free from implicational paradoxes; *ibidem,* **4** (1955), pp. 55-59.

— Four-valued propositional calculus with one designated truth value; *Memoirs of the Liberal Arts College, Fukui University,* **5** (1956), pp. 41-48.

— Necessity and possibility in Aristotelian syllogistic; *ibidem,* **6** (1957), pp. 75-87, and **7** (1957), pp. 15-22.

— The number of modalities in T supplemented by the axiom $CL^2p\ L^3p$; *J. Symb. Log.,* **27** (1962), pp. 407-408 (*).

Sweet, Albert M.

Toward a pragmatical explication of epistemic modalities, *Notre Dame Journal of Formal Logic,* **4** (1963), pp. 145-150. (*)

Tang, Tsao-Chen

Algebraic postulates and a geometric interpretation for the Lewis calculus of strict implication; *Bulletin of the American Mathematical Society,* **44** (1938), pp. 737-744.

Tarski, Alfred. See at **Jónsson,** B., and at **McKinsey,** J. J. C.

Tarter, Harry. See at **Bronstein,** J. D.

Thomas, Ivo

Note on a modal system of Łukasiewicz; *Dominican Studies,* **9** (1953), pp. 167-170.

— Solutions of five modal problems of Sobocinski; *The Notre Dame Journal of Formal Logic,* **3** (1962), pp. 199-200.

— S 1° and Brouwerian axioms; *ibidem,* **4** (1963), pp. 151-152. (*)

— S 1° and generalized S5-axioms; *ibidem,* **4** (1963), pp. 153-154. (*)

— A final note on S 1° and the Brouwerian axioms; *ibidem,* **4** (1963), pp. 231-232 (*).

— See also at **Lemmon,** E. J.

Toernebohn, Håkan

Notes on modal operators; *Theoria* (Lund), **24** (1958), pp. 130-135.

— A study in modal logic, *ibidem,* **27** (1961), pp. 151-164.

(*) Added in proof.

Tsao-Chen, Tang
A paradox of Lewis's strict implication; *Bullet. of the American Mathematical Society,* **42** (1936), pp. 707-709.
— The theorem «p⥽q. = .pq = q» and Huntington's relation between Lewis's strict implication and Boolean algebra; *ibidem,* **42** (1936), pp. 713-746.
— Algebraic postulates and a geometric interpretation for the Lewis calculus of strict implication; *ibidem,* **44** (1938), pp. 737-744.

Turquette, Atwell R.
Many-valued logics and systems of strict implication; *The Philosophical Review,* **63** (1951), pp. 365-379.
— Modality, minimality and many-valuedness; *Acta Philosophica Fennica,* fasc. **16** (1963), pp. 261-276.

Ushenko, A.
Review of **Lewis** and **Langford**'s «*Symbolic Logic*»; *The Monist,* **42** (1932), p. 309.

Vasiliev, N. A.
Imaginary (non-Aristotelian) logic; *Atti del V. Congresso internazionale di Filosofia,* Napoli, 1924, Naples, 1925, pp. 107-109.

von Wright, Georg Hendrik
Ueber Wahrscheinlichkeit. Eine logische und philosophische Untersuchung. (Acta Societatis Scientiarum Fennicae, n.s. A, vol. **3** n° 11). Helsingfors, 1945, 66 pp.
— *An Essay in Modal Logic.* Amsterdam, North-Holland Publ. Cy, 1951, VII-90 pp.
— Deontic logic; *Mind,* **60** (1951), pp. 1-15.
— Interpretations of modal logic; *ibidem,* **61** (1952), pp. 165-177.
— On the logic of some axiological and epistemological concepts; *Ajatus* (Helsinki), **17** (1952), pp. 213-234.
— A new system of modal logic; *Actes du XIe Congrès International de Philosophie, Bruxelles 1953,* Amsterdam, 1953, vol. **5**, pp. 59-63.
— Review of **Becker**'s «Untersuchungen über den Modalkalkül»; *J. Symb. Logic,* **18** (1953), p. 327.
— *On the logic of negation.* (*Societas Scientiarum Fennica*

Commentationes Physico-Mathematicae, XXII, 4). Kopenhavn, Ejnar Munksgaards Forlag, 1959, 30 pp.

Vredenduin, P. G. J.

A system of strict implication; *J .Symb. Logic,* **4** (1939), pp. 73-76.

Wajsberg, Mordchaj

Ein erweiterter Klassenkalkül; *Monatshefte f. Math. und Phys.,* **40** (1933), pp. 113-126.

Wallace, John Roy. See at **Anderson,** A. R.

Ward, Morgan

A determination of all possible systems of strict implication; *American Journal of Mathematics,* **57** (1935), pp. 261-266.

Weyl, Hermann

The ghost of modality; in *Philosophical Essays in Memory of Edmund Husserl,* ed. by M. **Farber**, 1940, pp. 278-303.

Wiener, Norbert

Mr. Lewis and implication; *Journal of Philosophy,* **13** (1916), pp. 656-662.

Wisdom, John

Review of **Lewis** and **Langford**'s «*Symbolic Logic*»; *Mind,* n.s. **43** (1934), pp. 99-109 and 279.

Wolff, P.

Truth, futurity and contingency; *Mind,* n.s. **69** (1960), pp. 398-402.

Yonemotsu, Naoto.

On systems of strict implication; *Tõhoku Mathematical Journal,* ser. 2, **3** (1951), pp. 48-58.

— A decision method and a topological interpretation for systems of logical implication; *Memoirs of the Osaka University of the Liberal Arts and Education*; *B. Natural Science,* n⁰ **3** (1954), pp. 6-20.

— A note on systems of logical implication; *ibidem,* n⁰ **3** (1954), pp. 21-24.

— A note on modal systems, von Wright's and Lewis's S1; *ibidem,* n⁰ **4** (1955), p. 45.

— A note on modal systems (II), *ibidem,* n⁰ **6** (1957), pp. 9-10.

— Systems of weak implication; *ibidem*, n° **9** (1960), pp. 137-158.

Zeman, J. Jay

Bases for S4 and S4.2 without added axioms; *Notre Dame Journal of Formal Logic*, **4** (1963), pp. 227-230 (*).

(*) Added in proof.

INDICES

I. *Symbols denoting the several modal systems.*

II. *The several calculi*

III. *Various symbols*

IV. *Some peculiar technical words*

V. *Some matrices*

Imprimé en Belgique (523)
par l'Imprimerie Nauwelaerts, Louvain

[illegible]